PLAYS for LIVING and LEARNING

Plays for Living and Learning

Twenty-five dramatic programs
for classroom and assembly

by

HELEN LOUISE MILLER

Publishers   **PLAYS, INC.**   *Boston*

MANUFACTURED IN THE UNITED STATES OF AMERICA

FOREWORD

Children in today's elementary schools are learning how to deal effectively with real problems. Because modern educators believe that effective learning takes place in a functional setting, the school day is built around experiences that make constant demands on the child's skills and abilities. This book of plays and programs reflects this point of view.

The situations in the plays correspond to learning situations in the classroom. The purpose of the book is to furnish the teacher with dramatizations which can be incorporated into units of instruction. For example, "The Polka Dot Pup," read or produced in class, might stimulate interest in fire prevention and inspire the development of a unit on this topic. Or, the same play might well be included in an already established unit as a vehicle for displaying charts, exhibits, posters, reports and other aids to fire prevention actually developed in the classroom. Such a program, produced for a school assembly or parent groups, provides the class with a real learning situation and, at the same time, interprets modern techniques to parents and others interested in the "how's" of present-day teaching.

The subject matter used in PLAYS FOR LIVING AND LEARNING follows general topics usually included in the elementary curriculum. Sixth-graders, discovering basic ideas about money and its use, for instance, will recognize their own experiences in "The Bar-None Trading Post," as they trace the story of money from barter to banking.

All of the plays and programs have been written with a

v

view to supplementing classroom instruction as well as providing scope and opportunity for actual learning. Children reading or producing the plays will see themselves and their classroom activities reproduced and dramatized. Teachers using the book may find ideas or suggestions in the plays which may be incorporated into their own teaching. A production of "Right of Adoption" might lead to a class project of adopting trees in the school neighborhood for intensive study and observation.

It is suggested that the production of these plays be made as authentic as possible. Wherever practical, the pupils' own work should be used as demonstration material. When the classroom teacher plays the part of the teacher in the play, when a real parent steps into the role of a stage parent, when actual experiences are duplicated by stage experiences, the production becomes a living dramatic creation, and the children have shared a meaningful experience in "living and learning."

Helen Louise Miller

TABLE OF CONTENTS

PLAYS for LIVING and LEARNING

The Curious Quest

(Citizenship)

Characters

LARRY HAMILTON
MARIE HAMILTON
RICHARD BRISTOW
BOB NAYLOR
DON BENTLEY
PAMELA BENTLEY
MR. BENTLEY
SALLY
BADGER

SETTING: *The Bentley living room.*

AT RISE: PAMELA BENTLEY *is directing a rehearsal of a school play. Two chairs have been pushed together center stage as a throne for the* KING *and* QUEEN, *played by* LARRY *and* MARIE. *Each monarch wears a newspaper crown and* LARRY *holds a folded newspaper as a scepter.* LARRY *sits with one leg thrown over the arm of his chair, and* MARIE *is slumped down in hers. She steals a look at her script which is in her lap. Other members of the cast stand about, awaiting instructions.*

PAMELA: For goodness' sake! That's no way for a king to sit, Larry Hamilton. A King should be more regal.

LARRY: I don't know how to be legal.

3

PAMELA: *Regal* . . . not *legal!* It's what kings are when they sit on their thrones.

LARRY: Then it means *uncomfortable*. This chair seems to have lumps and bumps all over it.

PAMELA: Now sit up straight, both of you. Marie, stop peeking at your lines. I'll tell you if you get stuck. Now let's start again.

LARRY: O.K., O.K. (*In a deep voice*) What ho, my love, where is our beauteous daughter this morning?

MARIE (*Speaking in a stilted, unnatural voice*): She is in the garden, my liege. Shall I summon her?

LARRY: Nope. I . . . er . . . mean . . . *No*, my love. Let her enjoy the beauty she cannot see.

MARIE: Alas, our poor child is blind. Sob! Sob! Sob!

PAMELA (*In great disgust*): No! No! No! (*Grabs script from* MARIE *and points to it.*) You don't read "Sob, sob, sob." Those are the stage directions. You are supposed to sob because your daughter is blind.

MARIE: Oh, I get it. Shall I try again?

PAMELA: No, I can't bear it. Just go on from there.

LARRY: From where she says, "Sob, sob, sob?"

PAMELA (*Outraged*): She doesn't say, "Sob, sob, sob!" She just dabs at her eyes with a lace handkerchief or something.

MARIE: I don't have a lace handkerchief.

PAMELA: Never mind. Go on. Take your next line, King.

LARRY (*Throwing his leg over chair arm again*): It's not my turn. This is where the Grand Chambermaid comes in.

PAMELA: Chamberlain, silly! Not Chambermaid! (*To* DICK) That's where you enter, Dick. Now remember, try to talk real loud.

DICK (*Entering stiffly and shouting*): Sire, the suitors are without.

LARRY: I think that's dumb. It makes me feel as if I should say . . . "without what?"

PAMELA: It doesn't mean without anything! It means outside.

LARRY: Then why doesn't he say "outside"?

PAMELA: Because it isn't old-fashioned. This is an old-fashioned play so the people must talk old-fashioned talk. You can't expect kings and queens to talk the way we do.

LARRY: O.K., so the suitors are without. How many are there, Lord Chamberlain?

DICK: Only three, my lord.

LARRY: Show them in.

MARIE: I hope they are young and handsome, my lord.

LARRY (*To* PAMELA): Now there's another silly line. What difference does it make if the suitors are handsome or not. The Princess can't see 'em anyhow. She's blind.

PAMELA (*Angrily*): But she doesn't *stay* blind, you idiot. That's part of the plot. When the Prince fulfils his quest, the bandage falls from her eyes and she can see. Now let's have the three suitors.

BOB: I'm the only one here. Don and Badger went downstairs to look at television.

LARRY: That's a good idea. What's on?

PAMELA: Never you mind what's on. We've got to get this play in shape for tomorrow and it won't be fit for anything at this rate. (*To* SALLY) Sally, you go down and drag them up here. (SALLY *exits as* PAM *wipes her forehead and fans herself with her script.*) This is a terrible job. I'll never write another play as long as I live.

MARIE (*In a comforting voice*): I think it's a lovely play, Pam. It's just these horrible boys. They never take anything seriously. (MR. BENTLEY *enters.*)

MR. BENTLEY: Oh, hello, children. Has anyone seen the evening paper?

PAMELA: It must be here some place, Daddy. But would you *please* go somewhere else to read it? We're having our play rehearsal here.

MR. BENTLEY: So I see. How's it going?

PAMELA (*Almost in tears*): Terrible. Just terrible.

MR. BENTLEY: Well, don't worry, Pam. They always say the worst rehearsals turn out the best performances. Now, if I can just find the evening paper. . . . (*Looks around for it*)

LARRY: Maybe this is part of it on my head, Mr. Bentley.

MR. BENTLEY: What's that, Larry?

LARRY (*Taking off his crown and inspecting it*): Yes. Here's the sports section all right; and I think Marie is wearing the front page. (*Unrolling scepter*) And this seems to be the business and financial section.

MR. BENTLEY: Bless my soul! Pamela, how many times have I told you not to monkey with the evening paper!

PAMELA: I'm sorry, Daddy. I thought it was last night's paper.

MR. BENTLEY: This isn't fit for anything now. You youngsters might as well keep it.

LARRY: I told her we didn't need any old crowns, but she said it would create atmosphere.

PAMELA: Well, you needed something to make you feel like a king.

LARRY: A newspaper crown didn't make me feel like anything. I guess I'm just no actor.

PAMELA: I'll say you're not.

MR. BENTLEY: What is the purpose of this production anyhow, Pam?

PAMELA: It's for our social studies class. We're having open house and I wrote an original play.

MR. BENTLEY: You wrote it?

PAMELA: Well, I got some of my ideas out of a fairy tale but I put it together and now we're rehearsing.

MARIE: It's really a lovely play, Mr. Bentley, if only these boys would act their parts right. (SALLY *enters with* DON *and* BADGER.)

SALLY: Here they are, Pam, but I practically had to drag them by the hair.

BADGER: It was right at the best part.

DON: They were going to catch the killer almost any minute. Oh, hello, Dad. Did you come to see the play?

MR. BENTLEY: No, I came to get the evening paper, but since I'm here, I might as well stay, if I'm not in the way. I used to do a bit of acting now and then when I was in school. Maybe I can help. (*Sits down*) What's it all about?

SALLY: It's about a King and Queen who have a beautiful blind daughter. That's me. (*Holds up bandage*) See, here's the bandage I wear when I'm on stage. Three suitors come to the palace to ask for my hand, but the King. . . .

PAMELA: Don't tell any more, Sally. That's just where we are now. Enter the three suitors. (BOB, DON *and* BADGER *approach the throne.*)

BOB: Hail, mighty King.

DON *and* BADGER: Hail, mighty King.

SALLY: I think they should say something to the Queen, too, Pam.

PAMELA: O.K. All three can say, "Hail, gracious Queen."

BOB, DON, *and* BADGER: Hail, gracious Queen.

LARRY: You three princes desire to marry my daughter.

PAMELA: You're supposed to say that as if it's a question. Make your voice go up at the end like this. (*Repeating with rising inflection*) You three princes desire to marry my daughter?

LARRY: O.K. I'll say it that way the next time.

BOB, DON, *and* BADGER: We do, your Majesty.

LARRY: Then I have a quest for you. Go forth into my kingdom. Search in every town and village, in every forest and every valley until you have found the most precious gift for the Princess. The one who brings the most priceless object in my kingdom shall have the hand of the lovely Princess Imogene.

PAMELA: And that's the end of the first act. How do you like it, Daddy?

MR. BENTLEY: Well, I can hardly say at this point. What do the suitors bring back?

BOB: I bring back a piece of gold.

DON: I bring a piece of lead.

BADGER: And I bring a lump of coal.

MR. BENTLEY: Ummm! And which one gets the Princess?

SALLY: There's the part I don't like, Mr. Bentley. When Badger holds up the lump of coal, the bandage falls from my eyes and the King gives him my hand in marriage. I don't think a lump of coal is very romantic.

PAMELA: But that's the whole point of the play. Coal is the most precious thing in the kingdom. Without it the other metals would be worthless.

SALLY: I still don't think it's romantic. Ugly old coal!

PAMELA: What do you think, Daddy?

MR. BENTLEY: You say this is a play for your social studies class?

ALL: Yes.

MR BENTLEY: Then why don't you write about something you know and understand?

PAMELA: We understand about coal, Daddy.

MR. BENTLEY: Yes, but all this fairy tale nonsense! Why not write about America, your own country?

PAMELA: But we don't have kings and queens and princes and princesses in America.

LARRY: No, and I think it's a good thing. I like your idea, Mr. Bentley.

PAMELA: I don't think it would be very dramatic.

MR. BENTLEY: You could make it dramatic. Living in America is the most dramatic thing I know.

PAMELA: But how could we make a story out of it?

MR. BENTLEY: Go ahead with your quest idea, only transfer it to America. Let Larry be Uncle Sam instead of a king.

LARRY: I'd like that. Then I could talk like a real American and not have to say "What ho, my love," and all that slush!

MARIE: If Larry's going to be Uncle Sam, I could be Miss Liberty. We went to a party one time as Uncle Sam and Miss Liberty, and we still have the costumes at home, don't we, Larry?

LARRY: Mom will know where they are.

SALLY: What could I be, Mr. Bentley?

MR. BENTLEY: Maybe you would like to be the figure of Justice.

SALLY: That's a great idea. All the statues and pictures of Justice represent her as wearing a blindfold.

MR. BENTLEY: And I'll make you a pair of scales out of two pie pans and some chain we have down cellar.

PAMELA: I still don't see how we can work it out. What sort of quest would we have?

MR. BENTLEY: Well, suppose Uncle Sam and Miss Liberty decide to have a quest for citizenship. Ask your citizens to bring in whatever they consider most important to Americans.

PAMELA: That sounds too hard.

MR. BENTLEY: Nonsense. There are many things right in this room that should be precious to Americans. Your job is to decide what is the most precious of all.

DICK: Could we try it right now? I see something I could bring.

MR. BENTLEY: That might be a good idea. I'll go downstairs and make a pair of scales for our lady Justice. That should give the rest of you time to decide what to bring. Remember, it should be something no American could do without, something that is most precious to a good citizen.

PAMELA: You make it sound like a game.

MR. BENTLEY: It *is* a game in a way, but Justice will have to decide who is the best citizen. Come along, Sally, you can help me make the scales. (SALLY *and* MR. BENTLEY *exit.*)

MARIE: Come on, Larry, let's run home and dig out those costumes.

LARRY: O.K. I'd much rather wear an Uncle Sam suit than that silly old crown and a long bathrobe. (*Exit* MARIE *and* LARRY.)

BOB: What do we do now? Just take anything we want out of this room?

DON: Yes. That seems to be the idea. Anything that would be important to an American citizen.

BADGER: This is almost like a treasure hunt.

DICK: It's easier than being Lord Chamberlain. I'm always afraid I'll forget my lines. (*The boys wander around the room, peering at objects, choosing and then rejecting them as they go.*)

PAMELA: Well, I guess I'd better write little speeches for Uncle Sam and Miss Liberty to explain the idea of the quest. (*Sits at table and begins to write.*) I'll have to make them short or they'll never be able to learn them.

BOB: It's a good thing we've been studying about citizenship in school or I wouldn't be able to think of a thing.

BADGER: That doesn't help me much. I wish I had that little book we were reading, *Keys to Citizenship.*

DON (*At desk*): Here, take mine. Let's look at it together. Maybe we'll both get some ideas.

DICK (*Smugly*): I have mine already picked out.

BOB: You're too smart. Golly, I'm like the prince in the play. All I can think of is money.

BADGER: That won't do. Money is no proof that you're a good citizen or a bad one.

Don (*Seizing book*): Oh boy! Oh boy! This picture gives me an idea. I know what I'm bringing.

Badger (*Snatching book*): Let me see. Let me see. Aw, I don't see any bright idea in *that* picture. Let's look at the next page, Bob.

Bob: Ummmm. I know what it means to be a good citizen all right, but I don't know how to demonstrate it.

Badger: The Liberty Bell! There's an idea. No American would want to give up the Liberty Bell.

Bob: Dry up! Where would we get a liberty bell in this room? Mr. Bentley says we can find everything we need right here. We can't get a liberty bell.

Badger: Yeah, I guess you're right.

Bob: Democracy. No American would want to give up democracy, but that's another thing you can't pick up in your hands and carry around with you. It's just a word. . . .

Badger: If it's a word, then it should be in a dictionary. There's an idea for you. Bring a dictionary and open it to the word *democracy*.

Pamela: Miss Reed says democracy is more than a word. It's an idea . . . a way of life. I don't think a dictionary's any good.

Badger: If you're so smart, why don't you get into this play?

Pamela: Maybe I will, now that I have those speeches written. I think I know what to bring.

Bob: And so do I now. Badger, you gave me an idea after all.

Badger: I did? Boy, that's funny. I give everybody else ideas and can't get any myself. Oh well, I'll keep on trying. (*Studies book industriously as* Larry *and* Marie *enter in costume.*)

Marie: How do we look?

Larry: I didn't bother with the long hair and whiskers just for practice.

PAMELA: You look wonderful, and here are your speeches. Better read them over.

DON (*At door*): Hey, Dad and Sally, we're ready up here.

MR. BENTLEY (*Offstage*): So are we. We'll be there in a minute.

BOB: How are the ideas perkin', Badger?

BADGER: Give me time, boy. I'll crash through with something.

DICK: At least you'll get an "A" in your citizenship quiz. I never saw you study so hard before. (*Enter* SALLY *and* MR. BENTLEY. *He has a pair of scales. She adjusts her blindfold as* UNCLE SAM *and* MISS LIBERTY *take their places center stage.* JUSTICE *stands to one side.*)

LARRY (*As* UNCLE SAM): Ladies and gentlemen, you are all citizens of the United States, but what does that citizenship mean to you?

MARIE (*As* LIBERTY): Does it mean that you are truly a citizen or just an inhabitant of this great nation?

LARRY: Today we are going to conduct a quest for citizenship. We have asked each member of our cast to bring in something that he considers priceless to an American citizen.

MARIE: What will they bring? What would *you* bring if you were in their place?

LARRY: Each young citizen will place his offering on the scales of Justice. The article which tips the scales the most will be judged the most precious possession of a citizen of these United States.

MARIE: Our first young citizen is Richard Bristow. (RICH-ARD *picks up a page of the newspaper and advances toward* JUSTICE.)

RICHARD: I think the most precious right of an American Citizen is freedom of speech and freedom of the press. I, therefore, offer this newspaper in which are printed the news, the daily programs of radio and television, as well as editorials and articles criticizing our government and public officials, as an example of this freedom. I feel sure no American would want to part with this right of citizenship. (*Places the newspaper on scales which move to some degree.* JUSTICE *must control the movement of the scales according to the play.*)

LARRY (*As* UNCLE SAM): You have seen the presentation of Freedom of Speech and Freedom of the Press by Richard Bristow. Our next young citizen is Pamela Bentley. (PAMELA *goes quickly to a table and picks up a small Bible.*)

PAMELA: I think the most precious right of every American citizen is the freedom to worship according to his own conscience. I, therefore, place this Bible on the scales of Justice. (*Scales tip considerably.*)

MARIE (*As* LIBERTY): Surely no American citizen would wish to give up this precious freedom. We now call on young citizen Bob Naylor.

BOB (*Approaching* JUSTICE, *pulls his report card out of his pocket and places it on the scales*): I think the greatest right of an American citizen is the right to a free education. As a symbol of this right to go to school and develop my own talents, I place this report card on the scales. I am sorry that it is not a better one, but I think it expresses the idea of every citizen's right to education. As some great man once said: "America fears no enemy but ignorance." (*Scales tip*)

LARRY (*As* UNCLE SAM): I guess none of us would want to give up his right to an education, even though school does get some of us down at times; and you can all see that the scales of Justice are tipped heavily by Bob's offering. Our next contributor is Donald Bentley.

DON (*Advancing with a set of car keys*): These are the keys to my father's car. I'm not yet old enough to drive, but it is a real privilege of American citizenship. Not so much the driving itself, but the right to travel from place to place, across state boundaries without bothering about passports or permission slips. Americans can travel where they wish, when they wish, and I think that is something no American citizen would willingly give up. (*Places car keys on scales.*)

MARIE (*As* LIBERTY): America is a big country with many kinds of people, but it has never been necessary to set up rules or barriers separating one group from another. I guess Americans are like one big family and we like to go visiting. The right to free travel and free trade is pretty important.

LARRY (*As* UNCLE SAM): And now, our last young citizen, Badger . . . er . . . excuse me, Bartholdi Mendoza.

BADGER (*Approaches* JUSTICE *with one hand in his pocket*): I guess you all know I am not the brightest student in our school, and it took me quite a while to decide what would be most precious to an American citizen. I was looking through my school textbook on citizenship, when suddenly I remembered this. (*Takes sample ballot out of his pocket*) It is a sample ballot for the coming election. I got it at school, and I was taking it home for my father. He will show it and explain it to my uncle who has just come to this country. My father says the greatest and most precious thing to him, as a citizen, is his right to vote, so I place this ballot on the scales of Justice. (*Scales go way, way down.*)

MR. BENTLEY (*Applauding loud and long*): Bravo, bravo, my boy. You really hit the nail on the head. Without the ballot, the other rights and privileges of citizenship could disappear almost overnight. Sally, let me congratulate you. You tipped the scales at exactly the right place.

SALLY: I hardly had any control over them, Mr. Bentley. They just seemed to tip themselves.

MR. BENTLEY: And no wonder! The ballot of a free man is the most precious thing any citizen can have. Your right to vote in secret and have your vote counted is your greatest right. Furthermore, it is your greatest responsibility. Never forget it, boys and girls. Vote every time you have the chance. Remember, your vote is your voice in the government.

LARRY: We already vote, Mr. Bentley, in class and in our school elections.

BOB: And in our outside clubs and organizations.

DON: We could even vote right here, couldn't we, Dad?

MR. BENTLEY: Vote on what?

DON: On whether we want to produce the King and Queen play or the one we have just created for ourselves.

LARRY: All in favor of *this* play?

ALL: Aye.

LARRY: The aye's have it!

PAMELA: But it isn't finished.

LARRY: Why isn't it finished? The ballot was pronounced the most precious possession of any American Citizen.

PAMELA: But it needs something else, just as the curtain comes down. Maybe we should say or do something all together.

MARIE: We could pledge allegiance to the flag.

SALLY: Or sing "The Star-Spangled Banner."

DON: What about the Freedom Pledge we learned last week?

PAMELA: That's the very thing, Don. We'll say it together as the curtain closes:

ALL: We are Americans . . . free Americans.
   Free to speak without fear,
   Free to worship God in our own way,
   Free to stand for what we think is right,
   Free to oppose what we believe is wrong,
   Free to choose those who govern our country.
   This heritage of freedom we pledge to uphold
   For ourselves and all mankind.*

THE END

* This pledge is from an official Freedom Train Publication of The American Heritage Foundation.

The Bar-None Trading Post

(Money)

Characters

Cowboy Pete ⎫
Rangler Joe ⎬ *custodians of trading post*
Sunbonnet Sally ⎪
Buckaroo Betsy ⎭
Miss Fulton, *the teacher*
Mr. Farrel, *bank president*
Kathie
Tom
George
Stuart
Virginia
Lucy
Sam

Setting: *The Bar-None Trading Post. The center of the stage is occupied by a long counter, well-stocked with toys, comic books, games, puzzles, and odds and ends such as would appeal to youthful traders.*

At Rise: Cowboy Pete *is standing on a chair adjusting the sign above the counter*, bar-none trading post, *as* Rangler Joe, Sunbonnet Sally *and* Buckaroo Betsy *boss the job.*

16

SUNBONNET SALLY: A little more to the left! Now to the right! Up a little higher! No! Just a teeny-tiny bit lower. There! Hold it! That's exactly right.

COWBOY PETE (*Descending from chair*): How does it look?

SUNBONNET SALLY: Fine. How does our stock look?

COWBOY PETE: Swell. I only hope we have enough to go around.

BUCKAROO BETSY: Just look at those picture puzzles! I'd like to have some of those myself.

RANGLER JOE: Yeah! And there's a neat space helmet I could use. Maybe I could trade a Hopalong hat and a Roy Rogers gun.

BUCKAROO BETSY: Nothing doing. We're supposed to run this trading post. We're not in business to swap things for ourselves.

RANGLER JOE: You win. Shall I ring the bell?

SUNBONNET SALLY: Maybe we'd better wait till Miss Fulton makes a final inspection before we admit the customers.

COWBOY PETE: Where is Miss Fulton?

BUCKAROO BETSY: Out in the hall, keeping the rest of the class from coming in here until we're ready.

RANGLER JOE: I saw her talking to some man a while ago.

BUCKAROO BETSY: Oh, I know who that was. That was Mr. Farrel. He's the president of the First National Bank. I often see him when I go to the bank with Daddy.

COWBOY PETE: I wonder if he's coming to the trading post. Golly! What if he'd bring along a million dollars he'd like to trade!

SUNBONNET SALLY: Don't be silly! You know we aren't to use any money at all at the trading post. And anyhow, not even bankers go around with a million dollars.

COWBOY PETE: Miss Fulton *said* she might bring an important guest to the trading post—someone who could give us a lot of help with our money unit.

MISS FULTON (*Entering with* MR. FARREL): Well, it looks as if you're ready to start business. Mr. Farrel, here are Sunbonnet Sally, Buckaroo Betsy, Cowboy Pete, and Rangler Joe. They're in charge of our trading post.

CHILDREN: Good afternoon, Mr. Farrel.

MR. FARREL: Hello, folks. Looks like an interesting setup you have here.

MISS FULTON: I've just been telling Mr. Farrel how you boys and girls decided you wanted to have some real experience with barter, so you created this trading post.

MR. FARREL: Even a banker can see the fascination of barter as a means of exchange, but I think, after you've had your fun, you'll be glad to go back to the more modern custom of using dollars and cents.

MISS FULTON: Cowboy Pete, suppose you ring the bell. Your customers are getting pretty impatient. Mr. Farrel and I will be a pair of interested bystanders.

COWBOY PETE (*Ringing bell*): Right this way, folks, right this way to the Bar-None Trading Post.

RANGLER JOE: See what you want and swap for it! Absolutely nothing for sale.

COWBOY PETE: Your money's no good today, folks. Fair trade's the order of the day. (*Children enter laden with objects they wish to trade as* COWBOY PETE, RANGLER JOE, SUNBONNET SALLY *and* BUCKAROO BETSY *sing to the tune of "Old MacDonald Had a Farm."*)

Welcome to our trading post, E-I-E-I-O.

The sharpest trader gets the most, E-I-E-I-O.

With a swap, swap here and a swap, swap there,

Here a swap, there a swap, everywhere a swap, swap,

Welcome to our trading post, E-I-E-I-O! (*As the song ends,* CHILDREN *crowd around the trading post.*)

KATHIE: I have a doll I'd like to trade for some puzzles.

BUCKAROO BETSY: Very well. I'll give you three puzzles for the doll.

KATHIE: Oh dear! That's not nearly enough. This was a very expensive doll and those puzzles can't be worth more than ten cents apiece.

BUCKAROO BETSY: But this doll is at least five years old; and look—her wig is coming off. The puzzles are in good shape and none of the pieces is missing.

KATHIE: I still think I should get at least five puzzles.

BUCKAROO BETSY: How about three puzzles and we'll throw in this game of checkers. Some of the checkers are missing but you can use something else. (*They make the exchange.*)

KATHIE: O.K. I'll give the checker set to my little brother.

TOM (*Holding up comic books*): How about giving me ten comic books in exchange for these?

COWBOY PETE: How many do you have there?

TOM: Ten, of course.

COWBOY PETE: Sorry, pal! Ours are more recent. Some of yours are pretty beat up! We'll give you seven for your ten.

TOM: Only seven!

COWBOY PETE: Take it or leave it, chum.

TOM: O.K., I'll take it. (*They make the exchange.*)

GEORGE: Got any baseball gloves?

RANGLER JOE: Sure. Here's a catcher's mitt that should be just your size.

GEORGE: What do you want for it?

RANGLER JOE: What do you have to trade?

GEORGE: I've got a mouth organ. (*Waves it in the air*)

RANGLER JOE: Nope! Too risky! Mouth organs aren't sanitary. (GEORGE *looks disappointed and puts mouth organ back in his pocket.*) What else do you have to offer?

GEORGE: How about a tool kit? (*Opens it up*) The hammer

handle's broken and the screw driver's not much good, but outside of that, it's O.K.

RANGLER JOE: I guess we could let you have it for a tool kit. What do you think, Pete?

COWBOY PETE: It's O.K. by me. We might have a demand for tool kits.

GEORGE: Thanks, fellas! (*Handing over tool kit and putting on mitt.*) This looks like a bargain.

RANGLER JOE: Some bargain! A ten-dollar tool kit for a three-dollar baseball glove!

COWBOY PETE: How many times must I tell you not to place a money value on these things? We're trading . . . not buying and selling.

RANGLER JOE: But gee whiz! These things cost money.

COWBOY PETE: We determine our price by supply and demand . . . not by how much things cost. If we were exchanging goods for money, then we'd have to decide how much they were worth in dollars and cents.

MISS FULTON: I'm afraid he's right, Joe. Only money measures value by a common standard. The price of any article is its value expressed in money.

COWBOY PETE: Since we aren't using any money, we have no definite standards, so we make them up as we go.

VIRGINIA: Will someone please wait on me? I've been standing here for ages and these flatirons are as heavy as lead. (*VIRGINIA has a pair of decorated flatirons used as book ends.*)

SUNBONNET SALLY: They're very pretty, Virginia. What do you want in a trade?

VIRGINIA: I'm not sure. I think I'd like a new picture for my room. Do you have any pictures?

SUNBONNET SALLY: How do you like this one? (*Displays picture*)

VIRGINIA: Oh, I like that a lot. But I don't think it's worth a pair of book ends. Suppose I give you one book end, and keep the other one. Maybe something will come in later that I would like to have.

SUNBONNET SALLY: In the meantime what would we do with *one* book end? Sorry, we'll have to have the pair in exchange for the picture.

VIRGINIA: Oh, dear! I don't think I'd like to use this method of doing business all the time. If my flatirons were money, I could spend part of it now and save the rest till later.

MR. FARREL: And you would be sure that your money would have just the same value tomorrow as it has today.

VIRGINIA: That's right. But this way, I have to spend both my flatirons at one time. But never mind. Give me the picture. At least it will be easier to carry than these heavy flatirons. (*They make the exchange.*)

MR. FARREL: The people of ancient times made the same discovery about weight, Virginia, when they attempted to adopt some standard for money. It had to be something indestructible, yet light enough to carry around.

MISS FULTON: They soon found out that bars of copper and bronze were entirely too heavy when large sums were involved.

VIRGINIA: I can easily understand that, Miss Fulton. I'd hate to buy something that cost five hundred flatirons.

SUNBONNET SUE: I don't blame you. Enjoy your picture, Virginia. If one comes in later that you like better, maybe you can trade it back again.

LUCY: I guess it's my turn now. Look what I have. (*Holding up box*) I should get something perfectly wonderful for this.

BUCKAROO BETSY: What in the world is it?

LUCY: It's my collection of sea shells. I've stopped collecting and I want to start a new hobby. Got any suggestions?

BUCKAROO BETSY: Here's a small collection of butterflies we can offer you and a half-filled stamp album. (*Holds them up*)

LUCY: No, I don't think I'd be interested. Besides, my sea shell collection is much bigger. I have almost nine hundred shells. They should be worth a lot.

BUCKAROO BETSY: I guess they were worth a lot at one time, Lucy. Remember, Miss Fulton told us about some early tribes of people who used shells for money. Maybe you're a *shellionaire!*

LUCY: I don't think sea shells would make very good money. They're all shapes and sizes, and some of them are so thin and delicate they would wear away with constant use.

BUCKAROO BETSY: It's lucky for us the United States uses gold instead of sea shells for its standard coin.

LUCY: I have a five-dollar gold piece. But I'd never spend it. (*Displays gold piece on chain around her neck*) It was given to me when I was a baby and I wear it as a little locket.

MISS FULTON: When you see the size of a five-dollar gold piece, you can easily understand why we couldn't use gold quarters, dimes and pennies. They would be entirely too small to handle.

MR. FARREL: Actually our smaller coins, our silver, nickel and copper coins, are only tokens issued by the government for our convenience.

LUCY: But what about my shells? What will you give me in exchange?

COWBOY PETE (*Pointing*): Here's a nice little music box. How would you like that?

LUCY: Does it play?

COWBOY PETE: Sure it plays. I'll wind it for you. (*Demonstrates music box*)

LUCY: That's sweet. Do you have any more?

COWBOY PETE: Nope, that's our one and only.

LUCY: I'll take it, and from now on, I'm going to collect music boxes instead of sea shells. (*They make the exchange.*)

COWBOY PETE: It's a deal. You can be our biggest music box customer. Next. Who's next?

SAM: I guess I am. (*Holding up alarm clock*) How about trading an alarm clock for a wrist watch?

COWBOY PETE: We don't carry anything as valuable as a wrist watch, Sam. (*Holding up pocket watch*) But here's a pretty good pocket watch I could let you have.

SAM: Sold. (*They make the exchange.*) Now here's something else. What will you give me for these? (*Holds up several Confederate Greenbacks*)

RANGLER JOE: No money accepted at this trading post, partner.

COWBOY PETE: You heard what the man said, Sam. Nothing at this counter is for sale.

SAM: But I'm not trying to buy anything.

RANGLER JOE: That's money, isn't it?

SAM: It's money all right, but it's not the kind of money the United States Government endorses. Take a good look at it.

RANGLER JOE (*Reading*): Confederate States of America . . . One hundred dollars. Why this is Civil War money. Where did you get it?

SAM: It was in an old trunk up in our attic. Mom said I could have it. If this were 1865, I'd be rich.

MR. FARREL: I'm afraid not, sonny. You see, Confederate money was never United States legal tender.

SAM: Wasn't it legal in the South?

MR. FARREL: It was legal all right. But you see, the gold and silver in southern banks was soon used up and the Confederate Government printed great quantities of this paper money. It was hardly worth the paper it was printed on.

SAM: You mean my hundred-dollar bill was never any good?

MR. FARREL: All I can tell you is that about the time of the end of the Civil War, Confederate paper notes were worth about a cent on the dollar.

SAM: Jiminy Crickets! Then my hundred dollars would be worth only about a dollar. Even if I had a thousand of these things I wouldn't be rich.

MR. FARREL (*Shaking his head*): No, Sam, you would be poor . . . very poor. In fact, everybody in the South was poor right after the Civil War because of the worthless Confederate money and the terrible rise in prices. A bushel of corn meal cost eighty dollars in Richmond, Virginia. Flour cost a thousand dollars a barrel, and even a newspaper cost a dollar.

SUNBONNET SALLY: Isn't that what you call *inflation?*

MR. FARREL: I can see somebody has been doing some studying about coinage and currency in this class. Yes, Sally, *inflation* is the correct word. You see, paper money is merely a written promise on the part of the government to pay a definite sum in gold, on demand.

SUNBONNET SALLY: That's why we say our paper money is as good as gold.

MR. FARREL: It's as good as gold as long as the country in question has enough gold to back up the paper bills it prints. However, when a country runs out of gold and floods the market with paper money, prices rise as the value drops. As each new batch of worthless money is printed, the prices hit a new high.

BUCKAROO BETSY: Imagine paying a hundred dollars for a loaf of bread.

MR. FARREL: That could happen if our American dollar should drop in value. In fact, that same thing did happen in many countries after World War I and World War II.

BUCKAROO BETSY: I hope we never have inflation here in the United States.

MR. FARREL: I hope so, too, Betsy, but right now you have your customer to take care of. You never did decide what you'll trade Sam for his Confederate money.

SAM: Don't bother about me. I've decided to keep my Confederate money. Maybe I'll find some more in that old trunk of ours.

MR. FARREL: That would make an interesting hobby. Perhaps you could even find some *shinplasters*.

SAM: Shinplasters? What are they?

MR. FARREL: During the Civil War period in both North and South, gold and silver coins were out of circulation. For months the only small change was sticky little postage stamps, until Congress decided to issue fractional currency.

SAM: That sounds important. But what does it mean?

MR. FARREL: You know what fractions are, don't you? Fractional currency was paper money worth less than a dollar. People took to calling this kind of paper money "shinplasters," because the bills were worth so little . . . some only five and ten cents.

MISS FULTON: It's almost closing time, girls and boys, but I see you have another customer.

STUART (*Rushing in, out of breath*): I was afraid the trading post would close before I got here. Do you have any tool chests?

RANGLER JOE: We sure do, Stuart. George Mayfield traded one in for a baseball glove. What do you have to offer?

STUART: Well, the fact is, I don't have anything with me. But I have a dandy model airplane at home complete with a motor. How about that?

RANGLER JOE: That would be fine, but it's no good unless you have it with you.

STUART: Couldn't I write a slip of paper and sign it as a guarantee that I'd bring the airplane in first thing tomorrow?

RANGLER JOE: What are you trying to do? Open a charge account?

STUART: No. But it would be almost the same as giving you a check, wouldn't it?

RANGLER JOE: Golly, I don't know. How about that, Mr. Farrel? Is that anything like paying for something by check?

MR. FARREL: It's not exactly the same thing, but I must say, it is very similar. After all, a check is just a piece of paper that promises to pay. A man can give a check to pay a debt when he knows he has at least that much money in the bank. Now Stuart really knows he has the model plane and the slip of paper is his promise to pay.

RANGLER JOE: Well, I guess if a bank could do business with checks, we could take Stuart's promise.

MR. FARREL: Of course, our bank would demand proof of Stuart's identity.

RANGLER JOE: Oh, we all know Stuart all right.

COWBOY PETE: And we even know he has the airplane. I've seen it. It's a dandy.

STUART: Then how about it, fellas? Do I get the tool kit?

RANGLER JOE: Is it all right with you girls?

GIRLS: It's all right with us. Stuart always keeps his promises.

STUART (*Reading as he writes on slip of paper*): I hereby promise to give the Bar-None Trading Post one model airplane complete with Midget Motor in exchange for one Power Boy Tool Kit. Signed . . . Stuart A. Martin.

RANGLER JOE: That sounds legal enough. Okay, Stuart. Here's your tool kit. (*Hands it over*) Hope you enjoy it.

COWBOY PETE: Any more customers?

MISS FULTON: It looks as if we're finished for the day. Now tell me, how do you like the barter system?

COWBOY PETE: It's all right, but it's a lot of work.

SUNBONNET SALLY: I think people would get into all sorts of

arguments if they had to trade furniture for clothing, or food for transportation or TV sets for automobiles.

RANGLER JOE: I'll take money any day in the week.

BUCKAROO BETSY: So will I. Imagine paying the gas bill with home-made pies or collecting your wages in produce instead of dollars.

MISS FULTON: Well, Mr. Farrel, as a banker, do you have anything more you could tell our class about money?

MR. FARREL: Yes, I have something very important to say to the class about money. But first, I have something to trade.

COWBOY PETE: Oh, boy! Here comes that million dollars!

MR. FARREL: It's nothing half so exciting, Pete. It's just the start of a small coin collection I thought might be of interest to you. (*Produces coin album as children crowd around.*)

RANGLER JOE: I'm afraid we don't have anything of equal value to trade, Mr. Farrel. Some of those coins really look interesting.

MR. FARREL: All coins are interesting to a numismatist.

ALL: To a what?

MR. FARREL: To a *numismatist*. That's what I am . . . a coin collector.

MISS FULTON: There's a new word for you, boys and girls. *Numismatics* means the study of coins.

MR. FARREL: Coin collecting is a fascinating hobby . . . instructive too, because you can read a country's history in its coins. Even the portraits of dead kings and queens, ancient emperors and royal princes are to be found on old coins.

BUCKAROO BETSY: What's this coin, Mr. Farrel? The design looks like a pine tree.

MR. FARREL: The name should speak for itself.

SUNBONNET SALLY: It must be a pine tree shilling.

MR. FARREL: Right. And the date is 1652. You can read about John Hull, the man who minted this coin, in your history books.

RANGLER JOE: Sure. I remember the story of the pine tree shillings. John Hull gave his daughter her weight in shillings when she was married.

MR. FARREL: And since daughter Hannah was no lightweight, it took twenty-six hundred dollars' worth of shillings to balance the scales.

COWBOY PETE: Wow!

MR. FARREL: Every one of these coins has a story. There are pirate coins, pieces of eight, Spanish doubloons; there are a few Roman coins, and some that are mentioned in the Bible.

RANGLER JOE: Golly! What can we give you for this collection, Mr. Farrel?

COWBOY PETE: Offer him all the rest of our stock. It's worth it.

MR. FARREL: I'll trade my coin collection, even up, for a day of your time.

ALL: A day of our time?

MR. FARREL: Yes. If Miss Fulton will bring your class down to the bank for a day, or even a half-day, so we can show you how to put your money to work, the coin collection is yours. Is it a bargain?

MISS FULTON: It's a bargain, Mr. Farrel. We've been hoping to arrange a school visit to a bank as our final experience with our money unit. We accept your invitation with pleasure.

MR. FARREL (*Handing coin collection to* COWBOY PETE): Then here you are, Pete. Here's the coin collection to be kept in your classroom as long as you care to have it.

COWBOY PETE: Gee! Thanks a million, Mr. Farrel. We surely do appreciate it. Maybe all of us will become . . . nu . . . numis . . . numis . . . what-ever-you-call-its!

MR. FARREL: Numismatists. Well, I really hope so, because it's a lot of fun.

RANGLER JOE: And what was that you said about putting our money to work, Mr. Farrel?

MR. FARREL: Oh yes, yes indeed. That's the most important thing to remember about money, you know. You can always make it work for you.

BUCKAROO BETSY: How? I never heard of putting money to work.

MR. FARREL: You'll hear plenty about that, Betsy, when you visit our bank. When you put your money to work you send it out to a bank to earn interest for you.

SUNBONNET SUE: We work interest problems in school, but I never thought of it that way before. We just called it *saving*.

MISS FULTON: And saving is another word for *thrift*. Before Mr. Farrel leaves the Bar-None Trading Post, let's sing our John Brown Thrift Song for him. It might give him some good ideas. (*Children sing to the tune of "John Brown Had a Little Indian." Half of the group sings the first stanza.*)

John Brown saved up every penny,
John Brown saved up every penny,
John Brown saved up every penny,
Saved up every penny did he.

(*The other half sings second stanza.*)

Ben Brown squandered every penny,
Ben Brown squandered every penny,
Ben Brown squandered every penny,
Squandered every penny did he.

(*All sing refrain*)

One little, two little, three little pennies,
Four little, five little, six little pennies,
Seven little, eight little, nine little pennies,
Ten little pennies—the score.
Ten little, nine little, eight little pennies,

Seven little, six little, five little pennies,
Four little, three little, two little pennies,
One little penny—no more!

(*First half*)
John Brown saved up every penny,
(*Second half*)
Ben Brown never did have any.
(*All*)
Think fast—thrifty John or Benny
Which would you like to be?

(*Repeat refrain if desired*)

THE END

The Petrified Prince

(Language)

Characters

KING OF GRAMMARIA
LORD CHANCELLOR
LESLIE AMES   } *visitors from America*
CARTER FINLEY
MODERATOR OF MODIFIERS
SUPERVISOR OF SUBJECTS AND PREDICATES
PRINCESS PARTICIPLE
BLUE PENCIL BRIGADE, *six*
PETRIFIED PRINCE

SETTING: *The main throne room of the court of the King of Grammaria. At one side of the stage is a large cabinet, similar to a cedar wardrobe, the opening of which is concealed by a draw curtain. The throne is center stage. On the other side of the stage is a large table laden with books, papers, and a typewriter.*

AT RISE: *The* KING *is seated at the typewriter, pecking away. After working laboriously for a few minutes, he removes his crown and wipes his forehead with his handkerchief, then leans forward and taps a small desk bell. His* CHANCELLOR *enters.*

CHANCELLOR: Your Majesty rang for me?
KING: Yes. This heavy crown is giving me a royal headache.

31

Please take it away and bring me my summer-weight diadem.

CHANCELLOR: At once, Your Majesty. (*Picks up crown and starts to leave.* KING *resumes typing.* CHANCELLOR *clears his throat.*) Your Majesty will pardon me, but I venture to suggest that the royal headache might be caused by too much work and too little sleep.

KING: Quite so, (*With a heavy sigh*) but we will not spare ourselves until our work is finished. This proclamation must go forth today.

CHANCELLOR: What number is this proclamation, Sire? And to what does it refer?

KING: This is Proclamation Number 2,298 and it deals strictly with Infinitive Splitters.

CHANCELLOR: Infinitive Splitters, Sire?

KING (*Positively*): Infinitive Splitters. (*Reading*) "Attention, citizens of Grammaria! From this day forth, Infinitive Splitting shall be considered a capital offense which shall be punished with extreme severity. Anyone known to have split an infinitive, or even suspected of splitting an infinitive, is subject to due process of law." Is that clear, Mr. Chancellor?

CHANCELLOR: Oh, quite clear, Sire. Quite clear. Only . . . well . . . I was . . . wondering, Sire, if you plan to post examples of Split Infinitives throughout the kingdom, er . . . just as . . . er . . . a warning to our . . . er . . . more ignorant subjects.

KING: An excellent suggestion! I will order the Royal Printer to print some horrible examples . . . such as, "He hopes to actually see the circus," instead of, "He actually hopes to see the circus," or "He decided to carefully study the matter," instead of, "He decided to study the matter carefully."

CHANCELLOR: Splendid, Sire! I am sure even the most stupid dolts in the country will now be sure to clearly . . . (KING *clears his throat as a warning.*) I . . . er . . . that is . . . I meant to say, Sire, that even the most stupid dolts in the country will be sure to understand the matter clearly.

KING: I am glad to hear that you corrected yourself just in time, Lord Chancellor. I should hate to break in a new man just as you are becoming of some use to me. And now, my crown, if you please.

CHANCELLOR (*Picking up crown*): Certainly, Sire. At once. Oh, by the way, Your Majesty, have you remembered that this is the day you have granted an audience with the two children from America?

KING (*Fumbling through some cards on his desk*): You mean those two little monsters from . . . (*Names town where play is being produced*)?

CHANCELLOR: Yes, Your Majesty. Their names are Leslie Ames and Carter Finley. They've been waiting in the anteroom for over an hour, Sire.

KING: Humph! I suppose I *must* see them. But they tell me the speech of American children is . . . well . . . peculiar, to say the least.

CHANCELLOR: I feel it my duty to remind you, Sire, that diplomatic relations with the United States would be seriously endangered if . . . er . . . if anything should happen to these two young visitors.

KING: I understand, Mr. Chancellor, and I promise you that I will keep a tight rein on my temper.

CHANCELLOR: But . . . oh dear . . . I do hope you will forgive my mentioning this, Sire, but . . . well . . . suppose one of them should, in the excitement of the moment, so far forget himself as to let slip a double negative?

KING: A DOUBLE NEGATIVE! Now by the stars above, you forget yourself, Lord Chancellor! Not even an American would dare utter a double negative in my presence.

CHANCELLOR: But, Sire, I have been reading about the manners and customs of these children, Sire. And oh, please forgive me for daring to say such a thing, Your Majesty, I have it on good authority that some American children in good social standing have been known to say, (*Clears his throat*) "I ain't got no pencil!"

KING (*Leaping to his feet as if he has been stabbed*): Enough! Enough! I will hear no more! Next thing you'll tell me that they might say, "I don't do nothing" or "I can't go no place."

CHANCELLOR: In some cases, it is as bad as that, Your Majesty.

KING: Then I won't see these barbarians!

CHANCELLOR: But you promised, Your Majesty.

KING: Then I won't answer for the consequences. I'm warning you, Chancellor, if one of those children so much as misplaces a modifier, I'll . . . I'll . . .

CHANCELLOR: Don't say it! Don't say it, Your Majesty! Someone might be listening. Now, please, Sire, sit down and calm yourself and I will bring your summer-weight diadem at once.

KING: Very well. But I'm warning you about those children for the last time. (CHANCELLOR *exits hurriedly with crown.* KING *seats himself on throne.*) Oh dear, oh dear! I must not let myself get so upset. (*Pulling book from pocket*) I will read from my "Pocketbook of Poetic Rules" to steady my nerves. (*Settles himself.* LESLIE *and* CARTER *enter as the* KING *reads*)

A NOUN can name a person, place, or object . . . like an ARM or FACE.

A PRONOUN can be used instead like SHE for SUE or HE for TED.

An ADJECTIVE tells shape and size, makes pictures for our inner eyes.

An ADVERB answers HOW? WHEN? WHERE? Like SLOWLY, QUICKLY, HERE and THERE.

A VERB . . . well, there you have a notion of how to put a thought in MOTION.

A VERB can make a sentence GO; puts ACTION in the Grammar Show.

In all these rules, there's one omission; it is the lowly PREPOSITION.

Beware of them! IN, AT and BY, ABOVE and YONDER, NEAR and NIGH.

These words, remember, Johnny Smith, you never end a sentence WITH. (*The two children burst out laughing. The* KING *starts up in anger.*)

KING (*Roaring with rage*): Who are you? Where did you come from?

CHILDREN (*Laughing in delight*): You did it again! You did it again!

KING: Did what?

CHILDREN: Ended a sentence with a preposition. You said, "Where did you come from?" FROM is a PREPOSITION.

LESLIE: You should have said: "From where did you come?"

CARTER: "Whence came you?" would sound more like a king. I always thought kings talked more like poets.

KING: You . . . you . . . whippersnappers you! You dare to criticize the King of Grammaria?

LESLIE: Oh, no, Sire. We weren't criticizing. We were just laughing.

KING: Laughing! But that's a thousand times worse than criticizing!

CARTER: Then we apologize, Your Majesty. We thought you were making a joke . . . the way our teacher does sometimes, about prepositions. You know, Leslie, like that funny sentence she's always quoting to us about not ending a sentence with a preposition?

LESLIE (*Laughing*): Oh yes! You mean, "What did you bring

me *that* book that I didn't want to be read to out of up for?"

KING (*Shouting*): Enough! Enough! Chancellor! Chancellor! Guards! Guards! Get these monsters out of here at once, before I forget myself and plunge this country into war with the United States. (*Enter* CHANCELLOR *with light-weight crown.*)

CHANCELLOR: Your Majesty! What is it? What is the matter?

KING (*Shaking with rage and pointing to children*): Get them out of here!

CHANCELLOR: But, Sire, these are your guests, your visitors from America.

KING: Get them out of here. They came in unannounced.

CHANCELLOR: I can't imagine how that happened, Your Majesty. I told them to wait in the anteroom.

LESLIE: We got tired of waiting. That marble bench was hard and cold.

CARTER: And we heard the King reading some funny poetry, so we came in. It sounded swell.

KING (*With a roar of rage*): Swell!

CHANCELLOR (*Clapping his hand over* CARTER's *mouth*): Don't ever say that! Excuse him, please, Your Majesty. I am sure he is ignorant of our customs.

KING: Silence! If you two MUST stay, I will give you a brief audience. (*To* CHANCELLOR) My summer diadem, please. (*Adjusts crown*) Now, what can we do for you?

CARTER: We just want to learn more about your country and your customs.

LESLIE: Maybe you'll think this a silly question, Your Majesty, but do you have a last name?

KING: What an impertinent question! Of course, I have a last name. I am King Syntax.

CARTER: Didn't we study something about *syntax* in school?

KING: I should hope so! I am called King Syntax because I have charge of the rules governing word relationships in a sentence.

LESLIE: That sounds like a terrific job. Do you have any helpers?

KING: Certainly. My Lord Chancellor here has charge of CASE. That's a very important job.

CARTER (*Blankly*): Case?

CHANCELLOR: Of course—Nominative, Possessive and Objective. I see to it that subjects are in the nominative case, and I have to deal with all sorts of stupid people who insist on saying, "This is him" and "Between you and I," and countless other ridiculous case errors. (*Tapping bell on desk*) Perhaps you would like to talk with the Moderator of the Modifiers and the General Supervisor of Subjects and Predicates.

LESLIE: That would be very nice!

KING (*Grabbing his head in his hands*): There's that word again! That dreadful, dreadful word!

LESLIE: Goodness! Did I say something wrong?

CHANCELLOR: Oh, not exactly wrong, my dear. But His Majesty is frantic with the misuse of the word NICE.

LESLIE: Oh, yes, I remember. Our teacher is always reminding us to use better and more accurate words than NICE. I should have said "That would be most agreeable, or very pleasant."

CHANCELLOR: I see that you understand.

LESLIE: And I'll try and remember.

KING (*More moaning sounds*): Get them out of here! Get them out of here!

CARTER: Now what? What did she say now?

CHANCELLOR: She said: "Try AND remember" instead of "Try TO remember."

LESLIE: Oh dear! I'm almost afraid to open my mouth.

CARTER: I wish he'd leave us talk in our own way. He makes me nervous.

KING (*In a frenzy*): That does it! That absolutely does it! Chancellor, did you hear what that miserable boy said?

CHANCELLOR: Yes, Your Majesty, I heard. But, please, Your Majesty . . .

KING: He said LEAVE instead of LET. That is a criminal offense. Call the Guards!

CHANCELLOR: You forget, Sire, that these children are under the protection of the United States government.

KING: Then let me get rid of them in my own way. I will take the usual precautions. No one will ever know.

CHANCELLOR: No! No, Your Majesty! For your own sake, you cannot do this terrible thing.

KING: Flesh and blood can stand no more. I will permit them to go unharmed if you get them out of here within the hour. But we cannot remain in the same room. I will retire.

CHANCELLOR: As you wish, Your Majesty. (KING *descends from throne and describes a wide circle around the two children as if he fears to contaminate himself by their presence.*)

KING (*At door*): Let me know when it is safe for me to return. (*Exit*)

LESLIE: My goodness! Is he always like that?

CARTER: What do you suppose is eating him?

CHANCELLOR: Children! Children! No slang, please! It would be as much as my life is worth to permit you to remain another instant in this palace if the King heard you use slang.

LESLIE: Why? What's the matter with slang?

CHANCELLOR: In Grammaria we speak only the purest and most correct English. No slang is permitted. No grammar rules are broken. (*Enter* MODERATOR OF THE MODIFIERS *and the* GENERAL SUPERVISOR OF SUBJECTS AND PREDICATES.)

MODERATOR: You rang for us, Lord Chancellor?

CHANCELLOR: Yes. His Majesty would like you to explain your duties to our visitors from the United States.

MODERATOR: I have full charge of adjectives and adverbs as well as adjective and adverbial phrases and clauses. I also supervise and eliminate dangling participles.

LESLIE: It sounds ever so important. But what exactly do you do?

MODERATOR: I see to it that adjectives and adverbs are not confused. Our people must learn to say, "They did their work *well*" instead of "They did their work *good*." They must learn to place adjective phrases and clauses close to the words they modify instead of making such ridiculous mistakes as the man who put this advertisement in the paper: (*Pulls paper from pocket, reading*) "Wanted: A piano by an elderly gentleman with square mahogany legs." (CHILDREN *laugh heartily*.)

LESLIE: Imagine an old gentleman with square mahogany legs! (*Laughs again*)

MODERATOR: That was no laughing matter for the gentleman who inserted the ad in the paper. He was executed.

CHILDREN: Executed?

CARTER: You mean he was really put to death?

MODERATOR (*Nods his head grimly*): At dawn.

CARTER (*Whistles in amazement*): I can't believe it.

MODERATOR: Our King does not tolerate anyone who makes Grammaria ridiculous.

LESLIE: But it was just a silly mistake.

MODERATOR: It was the gentleman's *last* mistake, young lady.

LESLIE: Carter, I'm scared. Let's get out of here before we say AIN'T or HAVE WENT or something terrible.

CHANCELLOR: Don't be alarmed, child. Listen to what the Department of Subjects and Predicates has to say.

GENERAL SUPERVISOR: My work is very important. I must see

that subjects and predicates agree at all times. Just yesterday I sent a whole family into exile because the parents had failed to teach their children the rule that *each, every, one, everyone, everybody, none, no one* and *nobody* take verbs in the singular.

CARTER: Wasn't that a very harsh punishment?

GENERAL SUPERVISOR: Harsh? My dear boy, you should see what we do to people in Grammaria who make mistakes with irregular verbs. Have you spoken with the Major-Domo of Irregular Verbs? We can call him at once.

LESLIE: Oh, no. That won't be necessary, thank you, sir. Carter and I are frightened of irregular verbs. We might be hung for making a mistake ourselves.

CHANCELLOR: Careful, careful, my child! A person is never HUNG, not even in Grammaria. The correct word is HANGED, you know.

CARTER: Well, I'll be hanged if I can understand such severe rules and regulations. Don't the people ever rebel?

CHANCELLOR: We have no revolutions in Grammaria, young man. Everybody respects and honors their . . . (*Clears throat, almost choking over his words*) I . . . er . . . mean to say . . . everybody respects and honors HIS King, our beloved Syntax, the Second.

LESLIE: Syntax, the Second? Was there ever a Syntax the First? (CHANCELLOR *and courtiers exchange meaningful glances.*)

CHANCELLOR: We do not speak of any other king of Grammaria, my friends. (*Bell sounds offstage*) And now, if you will excuse me, I must attend his Gracious Majesty. You gentlemen may return to your posts. (*To children*) I will send Princess Participle to conduct you on a tour of the palace. (*Exit all except* LESLIE *and* CARTER.)

LESLIE: Let's go home, Carter. This place gives me the creeps.

CARTER: It *is* a queer place, but I'd like to see the rest of the joint.

LESLIE: Sh! Please, Carter, don't use any more slang. They might lock us up or something.

CARTER: Look at all these books and papers. The King must do a lot of writing.

LESLIE: And look at that closet or cabinet. (*Pointing to curtained wardrobe.*) What do you suppose is in there?

CARTER: Probably more grammar rules.

LESLIE: I think I'll take a peek. (*As she touches the curtain, PRINCESS PARTICIPLE enters and screams a warning.*)

PRINCESS: No! No! Please! You mustn't touch that!

LESLIE (*Drawing back*): Oh, excuse me. I know I shouldn't have been so snoopy. But I'm like the Elephant's Child in Mr. Kipling's story. I have "a 'satiable curiosity!"

CARTER: Is there something terrible in the closet?

PRINCESS (*Starting to cry*): Oh yes! Something terrible indeed.

LESLIE: What in the world is it?

PRINCESS (*Looking around fearfully*): It's . . . it's . . . oh dear! Please don't tell anyone I told you. It's my brother.

BOTH CHILDREN: Your brother?

CARTER: You mean your brother is shut up in that closet?

PRINCESS (*Crying harder*): Yes. He's been there for years and years.

LESLIE: But he'll starve to death. He'll die. Why doesn't someone let him out?

CARTER: Why doesn't he come out himself? There's only a curtain on the door.

PRINCESS: He can't! He's turned to stone!

BOTH CHILDREN: Turned to stone!

PRINCESS: Yes. They call him the Petrified Prince!

LESLIE: How perfectly dreadful. How did it happen?

PRINCESS: It was my wicked uncle, King Syntax, the Second. He couldn't stand the way my brother talked. After my father died, my uncle seized control of the Kingdom. He was so very strict about enforcing all the rules of Grammaria that my poor brother said he was petrified to open his mouth. I think that is what gave my uncle the idea. At any rate, one day when my brother was making a speech in this room, he unfortunately said "I seen my duty and I done it!" Oh it was terrible! My uncle went into a perfect frenzy and before anyone could stop him, he had turned my brother to stone. Ever since that day he has been standing in that cabinet. I see to it that he is dusted regularly, and on his birthday the King lets me hang a wreath of flowers on his curtain. Oh dear! Oh dear! I can't bear to think of him.

CARTER: Then your brother is really the rightful king of the country.

PRINCESS: Yes. But how can a petrified prince ever become king?

LESLIE: Isn't there some way to break the King's spell? (*The* PRINCESS *shakes her head.*)

CARTER: Couldn't we force your uncle to restore him to life?

PRINCESS: No one can force my uncle to do anything against his will.

CARTER: But suppose we could catch him in some grammatical errors!

PRINCESS: Never! He knows every rule and every exception to the rule.

LESLIE: We caught him ending a sentence with a preposition.

PRINCESS: That is not serious. In fact, it is acceptable in many sections of the country.

CARTER: But surely he makes *some* mistakes. No one is perfect.

LESLIE: I wish Miss (*Names teacher*) were here. She can always find mistakes. Why, my compositions are always covered with blue pencil marks!

CARTER: Hurrah! That gives me an idea. (*Rummages through papers on the* KING'S *desk*) Some people who speak perfect English do not know the first thing about the mechanics of writing. Maybe the King's written work does not measure up to his spoken English.

LESLIE (*Pointing to a paper in* CARTER'S *hand*): Look! Look! He has written *Grammaria* with a small *G*.

CARTER: And there's a period where he should have used a question mark.

LESLIE (*Shaking her head*): Oh my! This is terrible. Miss (*Names teacher*) would say the King has no sentence sense at all. Here's a whole paragraph just strung together with dots and dashes.

PRINCESS: Do you really mean it?

CARTER: See for yourself.

PRINCESS: Oh this is wonderful! Simply wonderful. I am going to send for the Blue Pencil Brigade.

LESLIE: The Blue Pencil Brigade? What's that?

PRINCESS: That is what we call the staff of teachers who teach the palace children. Three taps of the bell will summon them. (*Taps bell three times*)

CARTER: If we can prove that the King's state papers wouldn't rate a passing mark in English, he might be willing to come to terms about your brother.

PRINCESS: It's certainly worth trying. (BLUE PENCIL BRIGADE *enters. There are six girls, each armed with a gigantic blue pencil.*)

CAPTAIN: You sent for us, Your Highness?

PRINCESS: Yes, Captain. I want to ask your brigade to go over these papers and mark them, just as you would mark the compositions in your classrooms.

CAPTAIN: At once, Your Highness. (*To* TEACHERS.) Be seated, ladies. (*Girls begin to mark papers at desk. All make clucking noises of disapproval.*)

PRINCESS (*Hopefully*): Are they very bad?

CAPTAIN: Atrocious! Simply atrocious! I have found six spelling errors in the first paragraph.

SECOND TEACHER: Three run-on sentences on the first page! This person has no idea of end punctuation.

THIRD TEACHER: This is unbelievable. Apostrophes everywhere you look! He must have shaken them out of a salt shaker!

FOURTH TEACHER: No commas! Absolutely no commas! Not a comma in a carload! Who could this ignorant person be?

FIFTH TEACHER: Disgusting! Absolutely disgusting! You should see what this ignoramus has done with quotation marks!

SIXTH TEACHER: Here are the same old spelling demons, *too* for *two*, *their* for *there*, *stoped* for *stopped*, *hopping* for *hoping!* (*She spells out words.*) Really this is almost too painful for me to correct.

CAPTAIN (*With a shriek*): And look, look, ladies! Look at this. The pronoun "I," written as a small letter! (*They all collapse in their chairs.*)

PRINCESS: What would you recommend for the person who has written these papers, ladies?

CAPTAIN: He should be sent back to the first grade.

SECOND: He should be exiled from Grammaria.

THIRD: He should be executed.

FOURTH: He should be exposed to the public.

FIFTH: He should be imprisoned.

SIXTH: He should be denied the rights of citizenship. (KING *and* CHANCELLOR *enter during these last speeches.*)

KING: And who is this wretch of whom you good ladies are speaking?

PRINCESS: They are speaking of the writer of these papers, Sire.

KING: Papers? What papers? Who has been meddling in my papers?

BLUE PENCIL BRIGADE (*In horror*): *Your* papers, Sire? Impossible!

PRINCESS: King Syntax, your little game is over. You can no longer play at being King of Grammaria. You have fooled the people long enough.

CHANCELLOR: Be careful, Your Highness! Think of your brother.

PRINCESS: I *am* thinking of my brother. (*Throws back draw curtain revealing* PETRIFIED PRINCE *standing stiffly at attention*) There he is, the right and true King of Grammaria. Take your choice, Uncle. Restore him to life and to his throne or stand trial before the people. Your state papers are a disgrace to Grammaria.

KING: But my grammar is perfect.

PRINCESS: And your writing is atrocious. Written English is just as important as spoken English.

KING: But I was in a hurry. . . . Perhaps I was a bit careless . . . but . . . well, you can understand what I wrote. The thought is there.

CARTER: Boy, oh, boy! That excuse doesn't go over with *our* teacher. She says you must be doubly careful when you put your thoughts in writing.

CHANCELLOR: King Syntax, this is a serious offense. What have you to say?

KING: What do you want me to say?

PRINCESS: Say the magic words that will bring my brother back to life. Say that you will abdicate and let him be King.

KING: But you know he can't speak a decent, English sentence.

PRINCESS: And you can't write one.

CHANCELLOR: Perhaps we could make what the Americans call "a deal." Our poor Petrified Prince could help King Syntax with his writing, and the Ex-King could coach the Prince on his speaking.

KING: An excellent arrangement.

PRINCESS: It will all depend on my brother. Release him at once.

KING: Very well, Your Highness. (*Goes to curtain and swishes it back and forth violently as he intones*)

> Nouns and pronouns, gerunds too,
> All my wicked work undo.
> Parts of speech with me connive,
> Make the Prince to come alive!

(*As he gives the curtain a final tug, the* PETRIFIED PRINCE *steps out of the cabinet.*)

PRINCE: Hello, everybody. What's going on here? Who are all these people?

PRINCESS: Don't you know me? I am your sister.

PRINCE: Of course I know *you*, Sis. But who are those people? (*Pointing to girl and boy*)

PRINCESS: These are our visitors from America.

PRINCE: Gee! I've always wanted to meet someone from America. Hiya, kids. How's tricks? (*They all shake hands.*)

KING (*Holding his head*): Is that any way for a Prince to talk?

PRINCE: Oh, hello there, Unc! I didn't see you. Just as cranky as ever, ain't you?

CHANCELLOR: Come now, my dear boy. You really must get hold of yourself, if you are to be King?

PRINCE: King? How can I be King when everybody knows I can't make the proper speeches?

KING: We . . . er . . . we all make mistakes, Your Highness . . . er . . . that is . . . Your Majesty. If you will be good enough to let me help you with your speeches, that is your *public* speeches, I think we can get along very well together.

CHANCELLOR: Maybe you would like to try on the crown, Your Highness. (*Removes it from* KING's *head and places it on the* PRINCE.) There! A neat fit, if I do say so.

PRINCE: Thank you, Lord Chancellor. I feel most comfortable. In fact, I feel quite accustomed to it. It seems very natural.

CHANCELLOR: Your Majesty! (*All kneel.*) You are talking better already.

PRINCE: It must be the dignity of the crown. Suddenly I feel quite able to cope with the English language. You can be assured I will endeavor to uphold the honor of the Kingdom of Grammaria.

PRINCESS: Oh brother! That is . . . I mean, thank fortune, Your Majesty. And now, what is to be done with this wicked man who held you prisoner for so many years?

KING: I thought we were going to make a deal. I thought I was to help him with his speeches and he would help me with my writing.

PRINCE: I doubt if I will need help from this day forth, Uncle. I suddenly understand my responsibility and pledge myself to speak with the dignity that becomes the crown. As for you, Sir, I feel no need for vengeance. I merely sentence you to eight hours a day in the custody of the Blue Pencil Brigade. When you can write a hundred-word paragraph with no errors in punctuation or spelling, you may be released. Take him away, ladies. (BLUE PENCIL BRIGADE *exits with* KING.)

PRINCE (*Seating himself on the throne*): And now I wish to speak to my American friends. (*Beckons them to the throne*) If you will seat yourselves by my side, I would like to increase my vocabulary with a few lessons in baseball terms. Tell me, please, what is the meaning of the curious expression . . . "to catch a fly"? (LESLIE *and* CARTER *talk excitedly with the* PRINCE; CHANCELLOR *and* PRINCESS *beam in approval as the curtains close.*)

THE END

A Travel Game

(Transportation)

Characters

CHAIRMAN	BOB
MARY	KITTY
BILL	HELEN
RUTH	PHYLLIS
TOM	DAN
SUE	DICK
PAUL	SALLY
ED	FATHER
FRED	SON
JEAN	DONKEY
MILDRED	FARMER
KEN	WOMEN, *five*
BETSY	MEN, *two*

AT RISE: *Children are seated at a long conference table, on which are displayed a model train, airplane, sailing vessel, or any other model mentioned in the script. The following cardboard letters should also be ready for the speakers to hold up as they talk: R, D, Y, L, A, E, T, N, H, W. The* CHAIRMAN *speaks first.*)

CHAIRMAN: Good afternoon, everybody, and welcome to our (*Name of school*) Travel Game. The rules of the game are very simple, and I am sure you will have no trouble catching on. This is how we play. For several weeks our class has been studying TRANSPORTATION, so we are familiar with many different modes of travel. We will now name the various types of transportation, but here's where the fun begins. Each method of transportation that we name must begin with the *last letter* of the previous word.

MARY: Oh, dear! You're making it sound very hard. Let's give an example to show how the game is played. The earliest form of transportation was on foot. If you were sending a package or a message to someone who lived in the next village, or the next town, you had to give it to a carrier or bearer. Some of these messengers were called RUNNERS.

CHAIRMAN: You have actually named four words: CARRIER, BEARER, MESSENGER and RUNNER, and every word ends with the letter R. (*Holds up letter* R.) This means that our next player must name a form of transportation that begins with R. How about it, Bill? Can you think of a form of transportation beginning with R?

BILL: R . . . R . . . That's a hard one! I can't think of any means of transportation beginning with R, but what about the word ROAD? Transportation has always depended upon a road of some sort, whether it was just a path through the jungle, or a well-paved, modern highway.

CHAIRMAN: What do the rest of you think? Do you think the word ROAD is satisfactory?

ALL: Yes, ROAD is all right.

CHAIRMAN: Very well. We accept the word ROAD because it is so vital to transportation, and we have seen in our class study how roads have improved with new and better means of transportation. Now we're stuck with the letter D. (*Holds up* D.) What means of transportation starts with D?

RUTH: In desert lands the DROMEDARY is a beast of travel.

MARY: And what about the DONKEY? People in South America, Spain and Mexico couldn't get along without the patient little donkey.

SUE: That's right. Ever since Bible times, the donkey has been a beast of burden, so I think D for DONKEY is a good suggestion.

PAUL: A donkey is such a little animal to carry such heavy burdens. In some of the pictures I have seen, the riders look as if *they* should be carrying the donkey . . . as this little poem suggests:

> A donkey is a friendly beast,
> So patient and so small,
> And yet his riders sometimes are
> Quite heavy and quite tall.
>
> I've seen tall men astride their backs,
> Feet almost to the ground.
> I think the tables should be turned
> The other way around.
>
> I'd like to see the riders walk
> Along the road so wide,
> And give our little donkey friend
> The pleasure of a ride.

CHAIRMAN: That poem reminds me of the famous old story about the Man, the Boy and the Donkey. A man and his son were once going to market with their donkey and this is what happened. (FATHER *and* SON *enter, right stage, leading a third* BOY *costumed as a donkey. A* FARMER *enters from the opposite side of the stage.*)

FARMER: Good day to you, my friends! Where are you going?

SON: To market. But the way is long and the sun is very hot.

FATHER: Aye, 'tis a greater distance than we thought.

FARMER: How foolish can people be? There you have a strong donkey! What is a donkey for but to ride upon? Why not take things easy and be fresh and rested when you get to town?

FATHER: An excellent idea! Quick, my boy. Climb up on the donkey's back and ride into town in state.

FARMER: That's more like it. (*Exits as* WOMAN *enters from other side.*)

WOMAN: Well! Well! Well! There's a sight to wring your heart with pity! That lazy, selfish boy! He rides, while his poor, old father walks. What is this world coming to! (WOMAN *walks off, clicking her tongue in disgust and disapproval.*)

SON: Quick, Father. Let me get down! I did not mean to be so selfish. (BOY *dismounts*) I'll help you up on the donkey's back. There! up you go! (FATHER *gets on donkey as two* WOMEN *enter.*)

1ST WOMAN: Look at that selfish old man, riding while his poor little boy trudges along in the dust and heat!

2ND WOMAN: Some men are like that . . . selfish to the core!

1ST WOMAN (*As they exit*): Poor child! He'll be dead tired when they get to town!

FATHER: Did you hear what those women said, my son? I cannot bear to be a selfish father. Climb up behind me. We'll both ride into town.

SON: There isn't very much room, but I'll hold on to you. (SON *gets on donkey as a* MAN *enters.*)

MAN: For shame, you lazy louts! Aren't you ashamed of yourselves for overloading that poor little donkey! He can hardly stagger along beneath such a heavy weight. Get down from there before I report you to the law! (FATHER *and* SON *dismount as* MAN *pats donkey*) Poor little beastie! They'd do better to carry you! I never can bear to see an animal mistreated. (MAN *exits as* FATHER *and* SON *stare in amazement.*)

SON: Do you really think we should carry the donkey, Father?

FATHER: I would not want anyone to think we were mistreating him! Maybe we can manage, if you take his front feet and I take his hind feet.

SON: We can try (*They manage to drag the donkey offstage. Enter two* WOMEN *and a* MAN, *all laughing.*)

1ST WOMAN: Did you see those crazy people, trying to carry a donkey!

2ND WOMAN: They must have lost their wits!

MAN: How they'll get across the bridge with him, I can't imagine! (*Sound of splash and yells offstage.*)

1ST WOMAN (*Pointing offstage*): Look! Look what's happened!

2ND WOMAN: Those stupid people have dropped that poor donkey in the river!

MAN: Quick! Let's run to the rescue before he is drowned! (*All exit.*)

CHAIRMAN: And that is a very old story that proves a great lesson . . . "Please all, and you will please nobody in the end!"

SUE: And it also goes to show that the DONKEY is a familiar form of transportation in many parts of the world.*

CHAIRMAN: And after all this talk about the donkey, we don't want to forget our next letter. (*Holds up* Y) Since the word DONKEY ends with a Y, we'll need a new transportation word that begins with Y.

ED: Wow! Y is a difficult letter. Maybe we'll get stuck on that one.

FRED: I saw a word in a crossword puzzle last night that begins with Y. I think it was YAK . . . Y-A-K. Isn't a YAK some kind of animal that is used as a beast of burden?

CHAIRMAN: I think you're right, Fred, but Jean and Mildred have something to say.

JEAN: YACHT is a form of transportation that begins with Y.

CHAIRMAN: We usually think of a YACHT as a pleasure boat, but it does carry passengers.

---

* If desired, they may sing "My Donkey Diodoro," SING ALONG, The World of Music Series, Ginn & Co.

MILDRED: My word is YAWL. Y-A-W-L.

ED: That's a real ship all right. A YAWL is a two-masted vessel, and that's good enough for me.

CHAIRMAN: This is a hard one to decide. Y-A-C-H-T and Y-A-W-L, both spell transportation words and both mean ship.

JEAN: This would be a good place to have a song, because in the early days of sailing ships, much of the work was done to the music of old-time sea chanteys. (*They all sing "Blow, Blow, Blow the Man Down," or any other appropriate sailing song.*)

RUTH: What letter do we start with now?

CHAIRMAN: The last word was YAWL. That means we start with L.

PAUL: What about LEGS? Your own two legs are a sure way to get where you're going.

CHAIRMAN: No, LEGS won't do this time, because we have already mentioned transportation by bearer and messenger. That would be the same thing.

KEN: What about LLAMA . . . the kind you spell with two L's?

CHAIRMAN: I'm not sure if the LLAMA is ever used in transportation.

KEN: Sure, it is. In some parts of Peru, the LLAMA is tamed and used in the same way you'd use a camel. In fact a LLAMA even looks a bit like a camel.

MARY: I know a little rhyme about a llama.

> "A one-L Lama, he's a priest.
> A two-L llama, he's a beast.
> And I will bet a silk pajama
> You've never seen a three-L lllama." *

---

* From *The Face Is Familiar* by Ogden Nash; Little, Brown & Co. Copyright, 1931, by Ogden Nash. Reprinted by permission.

CHAIRMAN: I guess we'll have to accept the word LLAMA for our transportation list. Now that brings us to a word starting with A. (*Holds up* A *card.*)

TOM: That's easy . . . AIRPLANE.

CHAIRMAN: Good! And we can count all kinds of AIRPLANES including the model planes that some of our classmates have built in their spare time. (*Several boys display model planes and tell about them. They sing any airplane song suitable for the grade producing the program.*)

RUTH: I think we should use the word AUTOMOBILE for the letter A. Automobiles are even more common and just as important as airplanes.

BETSY: If we name the AUTOMOBILE, we must be sure to mention TRUCKS. Most of our food, furniture and supplies are brought to our homes by truck.

BOB (*Holding up toy truck*):

> Listen to the sound of trucks,
> Roaring down the road,
> The hum of tires, the screech of brakes!
> Bet they've got a load!
>
> See the drivers at the wheel,
> They plow through snow and sleet,
> And bring their trucks to city folk
> With bread and milk and meat!
>
> Trailer trucks and tractors
> Rolling by at night
> So we have our daily food
> By the morning light!

ED: And don't forget the big BUSSES that travel our modern highways. Millions of Americans in both city and country depend on the BUS for transportation.

CHAIRMAN: Now let me see. The words AIRPLANE and AUTO-

MOBILE both end in the letter E. (*Holds up* E) Who is ready with a word that starts with E?

BOB: ELEPHANT.

CHAIRMAN: ELEPHANT? What on earth made you think of ELEPHANT?

BOB: The elephant is an important animal of transportation depending on where you live.

CHAIRMAN: I know that elephants are used for heavy transportation in a circus.

BOB: In Burma, India and Siam trained elephants are used to drag logs for road building. An elephant can pick up a heavy log and put it down exactly where his rider or trainer tells him. I think ELEPHANT is a good word for our transportation game.

KITTY: So do I, and since ELEPHANT ends with T, I'll suggest the word TRAIN.

CHAIRMAN: There's no argument about that. TRAIN really belongs in our transportation game, all trains—freight trains, passenger trains and, of course, the modern streamliner. (*They sing, "Down by the Station," "Chattanooga Choochoo" or any song dealing with trains.*)

PHYLLIS: There we are with that letter N again. (*Holds up letter*) Train was a good word, but I wish it ended with some other letter.

HELEN: What about the word NAVIGATION?

BILL: Not that one! We'll be right back where we started with another N.

DAN: I know, NASH.

CHAIRMAN: That's another automobile but I guess we'll have to let it stand. That brings us up to H. (*Holds up* H.)

BILL: And that suggests the word HORSE . . . the most important transportation animal in all the world. We've all read horse stories and cowboy stories and stories of the Wild West, where the HORSE was the real hero of the day.

RUTH: There are lots of famous fiction horses like "Black Beauty," and "The Black Stallion" and "My Friend Flicka."

MARY: And just plain ordinary horses like the plow horse and the milkman's horse and the old gray mare. (*They sing, "The Old Gray Mare."*)

ED: I like the cowboy horses best. Let's sing the Cowboy's farewell to Old Paint. (*They sing, "Goodbye, Old Paint."*)

CHAIRMAN: Now we have another hard one, the letter E again.

DICK: We were almost stuck with that one before, until Bob thought of elephant.

CHAIRMAN: I hope somebody thinks of a word quickly.

DICK: I have one, but I don't know what you'll think of it.

CHAIRMAN: Let's hear it, Dick.

DICK: I'd say E for ELEVATOR. True it stays in one place, but it does transport people and freight up and down.

ALL: That's a good one.

CHAIRMAN: It's a good one all right, but it ends in R. (*Holds up R*) and R is almost as hard as E. Do we have any suggestions for R?

SALLY: RICKSHAW, the favorite Japanese method of transportation.

MARY: And RICKSHAW ends in W and that means WHEEL to me. After all, the invention of the wheel was the most important contribution to transportation. Without the wheel, we wouldn't have any of these other forms of transportation, not even a two-wheeled cart or a wheelbarrow.

CHAIRMAN: So let's end our game with the song, "*Wagonwheels*," in honor of all the men who have helped to develop the wonderful system of transportation we have today. (*They sing, "Wagonwheels," as the curtain falls.*)

THE END

The Polka Dot Pup

(*Fire Prevention*)

Characters

MISS DOYLE, *teacher*	HENRY
FIRE CHIEF WAGNER	MAC
FIRE DRIVER WILSON	MILDRED
DENNIS	RANDY
LAURA	GORDON
BILLY	DANNY
STELLA	REBA
GRETCHEN	JEFF

SETTING: *A classroom.*

AT RISE: *The children of* MISS DOYLE'S *classroom are arranging an exhibit of Fire Prevention posters and other aids to Fire Safety.*

MISS DOYLE (*To children arranging posters*): They look very nice, boys and girls, and I think the committee made a wise choice. Be sure to leave room for the chart that Dennis made. Dennis, are you sure you can explain your chart clearly when the Fire Chief makes his visit?

DENNIS (*Holding up chart on which he has been working*): I think the chart explains itself, Miss Doyle. It shows the number of fires in our town recorded by months.

MISS DOYLE: Can you point out a reason why we had so many fires in December?

DENNIS: I'm not sure, but December was a very cold month, so perhaps overheated furnaces had something to do with it. People are always using electric heaters and oil stoves around that time of year, too, for extra heat, and you know how careless some folks are.

LAURA: I'm afraid Christmas had something to do with that fire record, Dennis. I remember two bad fires that were caused by candles and Christmas tree lights.

MISS DOYLE: It's terrible to think of the most joyous season of the year being marred by such tragedy.

BILLY: Maybe we should have Fire Prevention Week in December instead of October.

STELLA: I don't think we could change the date, Billy. Mrs. O'Leary's cow settled that when she kicked over that lantern that started the Chicago fire on the ninth of October, 1871.

GRETCHEN: I think October is a good month to observe Fire Prevention Week because campers and hikers need to be reminded about forest fires at that time of year.

HENRY: And that's the time folks start their furnaces for the winter, so they need to be reminded about cleaning their furnaces and chimneys.

REBA: Oh, Miss Doyle, do you think our room will win the ride on the new fire engine?

ALL: Sure, we will.

MISS DOYLE: Now, don't be too sure, boys and girls. I know you've done everything possible to help Room 17 win that ride on the new Eagle fire truck, but the other rooms have worked hard, too. Remember, the ride goes to the room which makes the most outstanding contribution to Fire Safety. I think our contribution is splendid, but you mustn't be too disappointed if the judges don't consider it the most outstanding.

DENNIS: But, gee whiz, Miss Doyle! It's got everything! Just look at all these posters.

REBA: And our Fire Hazard Exhibit. Look—I brought this old electric light cord. See how frayed it is. That might have caused a fire.

DENNIS: And I brought a glass jar.

MAC: A glass jar? How could that be a fire hazard?

DENNIS: I found it in our basement. Someone had put gasoline in it. A glass jar should never be used as a container for gasoline. Gas belongs in an unbreakable, metal container, and it should be kept out-of-doors.

MISS DOYLE: You people on the Fire Hazard Committee have really kept your eyes open. What in the world do you have, Mildred?

MILDRED: I have a paper streamer and a cardboard jack-o'-lantern—Halloween decorations. Cornstalks and party trimmings often start fires.

DANNY: Here is an oily rag I found near a pile of shavings in our cellar.

MISS DOYLE: I see you understand the secret danger of spontaneous combustion.

RANDY: I bet the Fire Chief will wonder why I brought these two articles. (*Displays a candle and a section of window curtain*)

MISS DOYLE: Maybe you'd better explain them to me too, Randy.

RANDY: "A candle by a curtained winder
             Can turn a cozy home to tinder."

MISS DOYLE: That's the rhyme we learned from our safety magazine, and you've demonstrated it very well.

BILLY: I brought a cigarette. That's the worst fire hazard I could think of.

MILDRED: Here is a whole page of newspaper clippings all about fires that were started by cigarettes. See—forest fires, fires on the farm, brush fires, factory fires, rubbish fires—

all because careless smokers threw their burning cigarettes away.

BILLY: And you haven't even mentioned "Smoking in bed's a sure way to drop dead."

LAURA: Let's practice the Cigarette Song, may we, Miss Doyle?

MISS DOYLE: I think you like to sing that best of all.

ALL: We do. (*All singing to the tune of "La Cucaracha"*)
La cigaretta, la cigaretta, burning, glowing in the dark,
La cigaretta, la cigaretta, danger lies in every spark.
La cigaretta, la cigaretta, when you careless smokers tire,
La cigaretta, la cigaretta, quickly you can start a fire.

(*Verse*)
Careless smokers on the highways
Toss their cigarettes on byways,
Much too late their lesson learning
When they see the forests burning.
Careless smoking is a danger,
Feared by every forest ranger,
So, be sure that you remember
Every word that we will sing.

(*Repeat chorus*)

GORDON (*Entering in great excitement*): They're coming, Miss Doyle! They're coming! On my way back from the library I saw the Fire Chief and his driver coming out of Room 16. They'll be here any minute.

MISS DOYLE: There's no need to get so excited, Gordon. Everything is ready. Do you have your word picture of Prometheus?

GORDON: Yes, all the letters are ready in my desk.

MISS DOYLE: Good. Oh dear! Where is Jeff King? He has the story about our trip to the Firehouse.

GORDON: I saw him running out of the building a few minutes ago. He said he forgot something.

GRETCHEN: I saw him coming to school this morning, and he looked as if he had been crying.

MISS DOYLE: Crying!

GRETCHEN: Yes. His eyes were all red and he didn't answer me when I talked to him.

MISS DOYLE: I hope he isn't sick.

DANNY: But we need his story about our trip to the Firehouse, Miss Doyle. Our report won't be complete without that.

MISS DOYLE: What about the rest of the committee? Do you have your papers?

GORDON: We gave all of them to Jeff. He was the Chairman.

MISS DOYLE: Well, it's too late to do anything about it now. We'll just have to skip that part. Randy, be sure to show our visitors the whole exhibit. I believe they're coming now. (*Enter* FIRE CHIEF *and* FIRE DRIVER.)

MISS DOYLE: Good afternoon, gentlemen. We've been expecting you.

FIRE CHIEF: Good afternoon, Miss Doyle, and good afternoon to Room 17. I am Chief Wagner and this is Driver Wilson. I believe you know why we are here.

RANDY: Yes, sir, and I would like to show you our Fire Safety Exhibits, and introduce our speakers who will make their reports.

DRIVER WILSON (*Looking around the room*): I can see your Poster Committee has been hard at work. Look at this, Chief. Here is a chart that shows the number of city fires listed by month.

FIRE CHIEF: You can easily see what a bad month December was for us.

RANDY: On this table we have our display of Fire Hazards.

FIRE CHIEF: Good! Excellent! I see you have included almost everything from gasoline to cigarettes.

FIRE DRIVER: And here's a box of matches with a timely warning. (*He reads verse attached to box of matches.*)
> Danger almost always catches
> Little boys who play with matches.
> So, mothers, tell each little tyke,
> There's no such thing as lucky strike.
> And keep those matches stored away
> From little children at their play.

RANDY: Now, if you gentlemen will be seated, Gordon Blake and ten members of our class will show you the helpful side of fire with the story of Prometheus.

GORDON: Prometheus is a pretty big word for our class to pronounce, but since we learned his story, even his name seems like an old friend. If you were to pass by Rockefeller Plaza in New York City, you would see a beautiful but strange statue. It is the figure of a man who seems to be falling between two worlds. He has a firebrand in his hand. This man is Prometheus who, according to Greek legend, snatched a brand of fire from the gods on Mt. Olympus and gave it to man. Prometheus was cruelly punished for his theft, but mankind has always been grateful to him. I will call on some of my classmates to demonstrate the many blessings of the wonderful gift of fire. (*Ten children come to front of stage, each carrying a letter.*)

1ST CHILD: P is for power that is furnished by fire
For boilers and engines that never can tire.

2ND CHILD: R is for roasting our savory meat
And making it juicy and tender to eat.

3RD CHILD: O is for ovens to bake our day's bread
All over the world where people are fed.

4TH CHILD: M is for melting the mineral ore,
Heating in furnaces for steel-men to pour.

5TH CHILD: E is for energy, power for machines,
To run a steam engine, fire is the means.

6TH CHILD: T is for temperature, always just right,
When fire is on duty, morning and night.

7TH CHILD: H is for heat to drive out the cold
And furnish warm comfort for young and for old.

8TH CHILD: E for experiments, scientists' clue
To many discoveries, vital and new.

9TH CHILD: U is for useful, our most useful tool
When under control and guarded by rule.

10TH CHILD: S is for service that fire gives to man
From cradle to grave, throughout his life span.
(*Children return to their seats.*)

RANDY: And now a report from our Inspection Committee, Danny Mathews, Chairman.

DANNY: It was the job of our committee to inspect the school building for Fire Safety. We are proud to say that our school is right in line with safety regulations. There are fire extinguishers on all floors and our Principal says they are checked regularly. Our classroom doors open easily into broad halls. Our monthly fire drills show that we can empty the entire building in two minutes and forty-five seconds. The building custodian showed us through the furnace room and workrooms in the basement. Everything is in apple-pie order. Trash is disposed of promptly and there are no open paint cans or oily rags in the basement. We looked up a report on the construction of this school and found that it is built of fireproof materials with extra fire walls in the boiler rooms. It is the opinion of this committee that our parents can feel we are reasonably safe from fire when we are in school.

RANDY: That is a very complete report, Danny, and I want to announce that every pupil in the class has made a check of the private home or apartment house in which he lives for possible fire hazards. Some of the findings of this committee are displayed in the Fire Hazard Exhibit.

MISS DOYLE: And that just about completes our Class Report on Fire Safety, gentlemen. We had some interesting material on our visit to the Eagle Firehouse, but unfortunately, the chairman of that committee is absent this afternoon.

FIRE CHIEF: I think your class has covered the subject amazingly well, Miss Doyle, but it is very difficult to decide on the winning room. You see, the teachers and pupils in this building are unusually conscious of their duties and responsibilities in maintaining Fire Safety. Every room in the building has made an outstanding contribution to our Fire Safety Program. It is, therefore, very difficult to come to a final decision. (*Enter* JEFF KING.)

JEFF: Excuse me for being late, Miss Doyle. I do hope I am in time for my report.

MISS DOYLE: We don't like to have anyone late for school, Jeff, especially our committee chairman.

JEFF: I think I can explain, Miss Doyle, if you'll just let me make my report.

MISS DOYLE: If our guests have time to listen, we'll be glad to hear your report on our visit to the Eagle Firehouse.

JEFF: When our class received an invitation to visit the Eagle Firehouse on (*Uses suitable date*), we were all excited because there were so many things we wanted to learn about firemen and how they lived. The trip was a success in every way. We saw all the new equipment. We learned about modern methods in fighting fires. We saw the teamwork and cooperation of the firemen, each with his job to do and his post of duty. And we learned how much every fire costs the taxpayers of this city. Because we enjoyed our visit so much, and because we discovered how much we owe the brave men who are constantly on duty to protect our lives and our property, we decided to do everything we could from then on to help the firemen. The members of this committee will now report our resolutions.

1ST CHILD: We resolved to report any signs of fire promptly by using the fire-alarm box nearest the scene of the trouble.

2ND CHILD: We resolved to join in all clean-up campaigns necessary to prevent fires.

3RD CHILD: We resolved to observe all safety regulations regarding campfires and day-to-day fire hazards.

4TH CHILD: We resolved to help the firemen at the scene of a fire by keeping out of the way and helping to keep crowds at a safe distance.

JEFF: And let's back up those words with some music, boys, to prove we really mean what we say.

COMMITTEE (*Singing to the tune of* "*I've Been Workin' on the Railroad*"):

> We resolve to help the fireman
> Every way we can.
> We resolve to help the fireman,
> He's a brave, brave man.
> When we hear the siren sounding,
> Any day or night,
> We are sure the fireman's ready,
> Ready for the fight.

JEFF: This afternoon on my way to school I got another idea of how we might help the firemen of the Eagle Firehouse. It was too late to ask Miss Doyle or the members of my committee about it, so I had to act on my own. I hope they will approve of what I did.

MISS DOYLE: Does this idea of yours have anything to do with your being late for school, Jeff?

JEFF: It has everything to do with it, Miss Doyle. You see, we've had some pretty bad news at our house this week.

MISS DOYLE: Bad news?

JEFF: Yes. Our house was sold and we have to move to the Delroy Apartments.

MISS DOYLE: Well, that doesn't seem like such bad news, Jeff. The Delroy Apartments are very pleasant.

JEFF: Yes, ma'am. They're all right, but the management doesn't allow dogs. Dad told me last night we would have to get rid of Polka.

CLASS (*Sympathetically*): Oh! Aw! etc., etc.

FIRE CHIEF: Polka? That's an odd name for a dog, sonny.

JEFF: Polka is short for Polka Dot. You see, he is a Dalmatian, and Polka Dot seemed just the right name for his black and white spots.

FIRE CHIEF: I see. It's a terrible thing to have to part with a dog.

JEFF: I knew you'd understand, sir, especially since Polka is a Dalmatian. I was worried sick about what to do with Polka until just this afternoon when I discovered that you, too, had a sad experience with dogs.

FIRE CHIEF: You mean you found out about poor Jackie.

JEFF: Yes, I missed seeing him at the Firehouse for a couple of days, but I had no idea what had happened to him until one of the boys told me just this afternoon that he had been killed.

FIRE CHIEF: It was a blow to all of us down at the Eagle. We had had Jackie ever since he was a puppy. Why, that old dog knew more about fire fighting than the rest of us put together.

FIRE DRIVER: It doesn't seem like the same place without Jackie.

JEFF: I knew how you must feel, so, the minute I heard about it, I ran back to the house to get Polka.

MISS DOYLE: You brought Polka here?

JEFF: Yes, ma'am. He's out in the cloakroom. I thought maybe the Fire Chief would take him right along back to the Firehouse this afternoon so he could get used to his new home.

FIRE DRIVER: You mean you're giving Polka to the Firehouse, Jeff?

JEFF: It seemed like the best thing to do, sir. Your men need a dog, and Polka's going to need a new home. I think he'll love living at the Eagle and riding on that new hook-and-ladder.

FIRE DRIVER: That's a great idea, Jeff. And you can be sure Polka will live like a king.

JEFF: Dad says it's in his blood to follow horses. I know the Eagle doesn't have any more horse-drawn engines, but I think he'll like the truck almost as well.

FIRE CHIEF: You bet he will. I can't remember the time the Eagle firemen didn't have a coach dog as their mascot, and Polka will get a royal welcome. (*Whimpering noises from cloakroom*)

JEFF: I think he's getting tired of being tied out there. May I bring him in, Miss Doyle?

MISS DOYLE: Of course. We all want to see him. (JEFF *goes to cloakroom and returns with* POLKA. *A real Dalmatian may play the part, if available. Otherwise a toy dog, or enclosed box can be used to fake the scene, as children and firemen gather around.*) Now stand back, children. Don't get Polka too excited.

FIRE CHIEF: Hello, there, Polka. Hello! Did you know you're going to be a firehouse dog from now on?

FIRE DRIVER: And ride up front with me when we go to all the fires?

JEFF: Go along now, Polka. There's your new master. But remember, I'll be coming up to the Firehouse every day to see you.

FIRE CHIEF: And you'll be welcome, Jeff. Come as often as you like. That goes for the rest of you boys and girls too. Up to this point, it was pretty difficult to decide which room had made the biggest contribution to Fire Safety.

But with Polka in the balance—well—this statement is not yet official . . . but I think Room 17 can safely count on a ride in that new fire truck before very long.

ALL (*Cheer and then sing to tune of "How Much Is the Doggie in the Window"*):

> Hooray for the doggie at the Firehouse,
> The one with the polka dot ears.
> Hooray for the doggie at the Firehouse,
> Let's give him three rousing big cheers.
> In Maine or the state of California,
> The firemen all cherish a pup,
> A polka dot doggie in a firehouse
> Is boosting their spirits right up.
> Hooray for the doggie at the Firehouse,
> His name may be Jackie or Bob,
> But one thing you sure can depend on
> That doggie is right on the job!

THE END

Girls in Books*

(Book Week)

Characters

STUDENT CHAIRMAN
GUEST PANEL
ANNE OF GREEN GABLES
MARILLA
FRAULEIN
HEIDI
JOSEPHINE MARCH
MRS. JARLEY
LITTLE NELL
AMY LAWRENCE
BECKY THATCHER
SPEAKER
ALICE IN WONDERLAND

SETTING: *A school stage.*
AT RISE: *The* GUEST PANEL *sits in a semicircle on one side of the stage. The* STUDENT CHAIRMAN *comes forward to open the program.*

CHAIRMAN: No doubt everyone here remembers the old nursery rhyme which contains a recipe for making little girls. "Sugar and spice and everything nice" . . . that's what the

* This program may be performed using visiting mothers or female members of the faculty as a guest panel. With slight alterations, a guest panel composed of students may also be used.

recipe calls for and we are sure the ladies who are our guests this afternoon were fashioned with that formula. It is my pleasure to present our guests at this time. (CHAIRMAN *introduces each of the women on the platform*.)

And now, on with our program. Throughout the history of literature, there are many famous heroines. Today our class will present a group of glamorous girls of fiction, and we are going to ask our guests here on the platform to identify them. Our first scene takes place on Prince Edward Island and represents a real tragedy in a young girl's life. I will place this chair center stage where our heroine can find it because when she enters she will be so blinded with tears she can scarcely see a thing. (*Puts chair center stage. Enter girl in old-fashioned gingham dress, her head closely bound in a large towel. She is crying bitterly, and throws herself into the chair, hiding her face in her hands. In a few seconds she is followed by* MARILLA, *an older woman, dressed very plainly to indicate her severe character*.)

MARILLA: Mercy on us! Have you been asleep, child?

GIRL (*Between sobs*): No.

MARILLA: Are you sick, then?

GIRL: No. Please, Marilla, go away and don't look at me. I'm in the depths of despair. My career is ended. Please go away.

MARILLA: Did anyone ever hear the like? Now get up right this minute, and tell me what you've done. Take that towel off your head, this minute, I say. Now what is this all about?

GIRL: I can't let you see. I simply can't. Oh, Marilla, it's my hair!

MARILLA: Your hair! Let me see! (*Pulls at towel until she sees some of the hair but does not remove covering*) Heavens above! What have you done to your hair? Why, it's green!

GIRL (*Sobbing*): Yes, it's green! I thought nothing in the world could be as bad as red hair; but now I know it's ten times worse to have green hair. Oh, Marilla, what can I do?

MARILLA: I don't know how you got into this fix, but you've got to tell me. What did you do to your hair?

GIRL: I dyed it.

MARILLA: Dyed it? Dyed your hair? Didn't you know that was a wicked thing to do?

GIRL: Yes, I knew it was a *little* wicked, but I meant to be extra good in other ways to make up for it.

MARILLA: Well, if I decided it was worth while to dye my hair, I'd have dyed it a decent color at least. I wouldn't have dyed it green!

GIRL: But I didn't mean to dye it green. He said it would turn my hair a beautiful raven black. How could I doubt his word?

MARILLA: Who said? What are you talking about?

GIRL: The peddler that was here this afternoon. I bought the dye from him.

MARILLA: How often have I told you never to let one of those peddlers in the house?

GIRL: I didn't let him in. I remembered what you said, and I went outside and looked at his things on the step. Then I saw the bottle of hair dye. The peddler said it would dye any hair a beautiful raven black that wouldn't wash off. The price was seventy-five cents and I had only fifty cents from my chicken money, but the peddler had such a kind heart he let me have it for fifty cents. I put it on just like the directions said . . . and now . . . oh dear! I can't bear to look at it! Oh Marilla, what shall I do?

MARILLA: Goodness knows what's to be done, but we'll start by giving your head a good washing! . . . Come along! (*They exit.*)

CHAIRMAN: Dear me! What a tragedy! And now while you

ladies are trying to identify the girl with green hair, we'll remove this chair and make way for our next female of fiction. (*Stagehand removes chair*) This scene involves a much younger girl . . . a very unhappy, homesick little girl who is determined to run away. However, she is stopped in her tracks, by a very strict German governess who does not understand what it means to be homesick. (*Enter a small girl wearing a long cloak with a hood. She carries a little basket containing a few rolls. As she tiptoes across the stage,* FRAULEIN *enters and seizes her arm.*)

FRAULEIN: So there you are! What have you dressed yourself like that for? What do you mean by this? Have I not strictly forbidden you to go running about the streets? And here you are ready to start out again, looking no better than a beggar!

CHILD: I was not going to run about. I was going home.

FRAULEIN: What are you talking about? Going home! You want to run away? And what is the matter with *this* house, I should like to know. Have you ever in your life had such a house to live in, such a table or so many people to wait on you?

CHILD: No.

FRAULEIN: You have everything you could possibly want here! You are an ungrateful little thing! It's because you have too much that you have nothing to do but think what naughty things you can do next.

CHILD: Indeed I only want to go home, for if I stay away so long, Snowflake will begin crying again, and Grandmother is waiting for me, and Greenfinch will be beaten because I am not there to give Peter any cheese, and here I can never see how the sun says goodnight to the mountains . . . and . . .

FRAULEIN: Heaven have mercy on us! The child is out of her mind! And what do you have there in your basket?

CHILD: Only a few white rolls for Grandmother . . . please . . .

FRAULEIN: Rolls! So that is why I found a heap of stale rolls in your clothes closet. I demand an explanation (*Seizing basket*) before I throw them out!

CHILD: No, no, please do not throw them out! The rolls are for Grandmother. She has never tasted such fine white bread. Please, please, Fraulein, let me take them to her. (FRAULEIN *exits with basket as the child follows, pleading all the way*.)

CHAIRMAN (*To* GUESTS): Now your problem is to identify this unhappy little girl who is so far away from home. I'm sure you will know her name because she is a great favorite with little girls and big girls all over the world. Our next heroine is a New England lassie of Civil War days. Strangely enough, her problem right now concerns a matter of hair-dressing. Only in this case, the young lady *sold* her hair to help raise money for her father who was in a Civil War hospital. We'll listen to her tell her story to her mother in her own way. (*Enter girl in Civil War costume*)

GIRL: I hadn't the least idea of selling my hair at first, but as I went along, I kept thinking what I could do, and feeling as if I'd like to dive into some of the rich stores and help myself. In a barber's window, I saw tails of hair with the prices marked and one black tail, not nearly as thick as mine, was forty dollars. . . . So I walked right in and asked if they'd buy mine. The barber stared at me at first and said he didn't care much for mine because it wasn't a fashionable color. But I begged him to take it . . . finally, I got so excited I told him the whole story, all about Father being in the hospital and how much we needed the money to buy things for him. His wife heard me talking and she said . . . "Oh, take it, Thomas, and oblige the young lady." It turned out their son was in the army, too. So the barber agreed. I took a last look at my hair while he got his scissors. But I must admit I felt a bit queer when I saw the dear old hair laid out on the table and felt only the short, rough ends on my head. It almost seemed as if I'd lost an arm or leg. The woman saw me and she gave me a lock to keep. Here it is, Marmee, I'll give it to you to remember past glories. (*She exits.*)

CHAIRMAN: And her past glories *are* remembered today by everybody who reads the book in which she is one of four central characters. Now for our next scene, we will need two properties: a chair and a sign. (*Stagehand brings in chair and a sign "Jarley's Waxworks."*) You will have to imagine that this chair is placed just outside of a little house on wheels presided over by a kindly and spirited old lady. (*Enter* Mrs. JARLEY) We'll tell you the name of the old lady, but it's your job to guess the name of the little girl who will enter in just a moment. She is traveling with her grandfather who has sat down to rest for a few minutes just beyond our range of vision. (Mrs. JARLEY *sits on the chair and the little girl enters.*)

Mrs. JARLEY: Come nearer, child. Are you hungry?

CHILD: Not very. But I'm very tired and it's a long way.

Mrs. JARLEY: Well, hungry or not, you'd better have some tea.

CHILD: Thank you, ma'am. Grandfather and I will like that.

Mrs. JARLEY: There, child, can you read that sign?

CHILD: Jarley's Waxworks.

Mrs. JARLEY: That's me. I'm Mrs. Jarley. See, there—(*Pointing offstage*) the only stupendous collection of real waxworks in the world.

CHILD: I never saw a waxworks, ma'am. Is it funnier than Punch and Judy?

Mrs. JARLEY: Funnier! It's not funny at all! It's calm and classical. And the figures are so lifelike, you'd think they'd move and talk. If you're really disposed to employ yourself, child, I could use you to point out the figures to the company. The duty's very light and genteel, and the exhibit takes place in our larger towns.

CHILD: But what about my grandfather? I couldn't leave him.

MRS. JARLEY: There would be plenty for him to do. He could dust the figures, take the checks, and so forth. What do you say, dearie?

CHILD: We are very much obliged to you, ma'am, and gratefully accept your offer.

MRS. JARLEY: Come along, we'll speak to your grandfather right away. (*Exit* MRS. JARLEY *and child. Stagehand removes chair and sign.*)

CHAIRMAN: I think it would be fun to work in a waxwork show, especially with such a nice employer as jolly Mrs. Jarley. For our next scene, we'll need a small bench, just big enough for two girls to sit on. (*Stagehand brings in bench.*) And here they come now, on their way home from school. (*Enter two girls dressed in gingham dresses and bonnets. They carry a few books, lunch pails and slates, and sit on the bench.*)

FIRST GIRL: Do you like rats?

SECOND GIRL: Of course not. I hate 'em. Whatever made you ask such a question?

FIRST GIRL: Oh, I don't know. I was just thinking. Do most boys like rats?

SECOND GIRL: I guess so. But I'm not sure. I've seen some boys who collect dead ones, just to swing them around on a string and chase the girls.

FIRST GIRL: Umm. Boys are funny, aren't they? What else do they like besides dead rats and candy and getting into fights?

SECOND GIRL: Circuses, I guess. Most boys I know like circuses more than anything.

FIRST GIRL: Even more than they like girls?

SECOND GIRL: Oh, sure. They only like to chase girls and hear them scream and make them cry.

FIRST GIRL: I don't believe all boys are like that!

SECOND GIRL: You don't? Do you know any that are any different?

FIRST GIRL (*Hesitatingly*): I—I think so. Say, were you ever engaged?

SECOND GIRL: Oh, yes. A long time ago.

FIRST GIRL: Was it nice? What was it like?

SECOND GIRL: Well, it wasn't like anything. You only tell a boy you won't have anybody but him, ever, and then you kiss, and that's all. Anybody can do it.

FIRST GIRL: Did *you* kiss the boy you were engaged to?

SECOND GIRL: Sure. That's part of it. Then it's all done, and after that you can't love anybody but him. And you can't ever marry anybody but him, ever, ever, ever.

FIRST GIRL: And he never marries anybody but you, ever, ever, ever.

SECOND GIRL: That's right. And when you're coming to school or going home, you walk together. And you choose him and he chooses you at parties, because that's the way you do when you're engaged.

FIRST GIRL: It's so nice. I never heard of it before today.

SECOND GIRL: Oh, it's ever so nice . . . why, me and Tom Sawyer . . .

FIRST GIRL (*In distress*): Tom Sawyer? You mean *you* were engaged to TOM SAWYER? Then I'm not the first girl he's been engaged to! Oh, dear! (*Starts to cry*) I hate him! And I hate you too! Go away, you wicked girl, I'll never speak to you again as long as I live, or to him either! So there! (*Runs off stage followed by* SECOND GIRL)

SECOND GIRL (*Calling*): Please, please . . . wait for me! It was a long time ago. Let me explain! (*Stagehand removes bench.*)

CHAIRMAN: But all we have to explain is the identity of these two little girls, both engaged, at different times, to the same little boy. Their names are famous the world over, wherever books are read and people smile at this childish love story. Now here's another little girl, equally as famous as our two rivals, but her description comes in poetry rather than prose.

SPEAKER (*Entering and coming forward*):

This useful little lady's come to our house to stay,
And wash the cups and saucers up, and brush the crumbs
    away,
And shoo the chickens off the porch, and dust the hearth
    and sweep,
And make the fire, and bake the bread, and earn her board
    and keep.
And all us other children, when the supper things is done,
We sit around the kitchen fire and has the mostest fun,
A-listenin' to the witch tales the stranger tells about,
And the gobble-uns 'll git you
Ef you don't watch out! (*She exits.*)

CHAIRMAN: Now there's a character you should recognize right away. Be sure you're not confused by this next character who seems to be in pretty much of a muddle herself. (*Enter child in Alice-in-Wonderland costume*)

CHILD: Dear! Dear! How queer everything is today. I wonder if I've been changed into something else during the night. I'll see if I know all the things I used to know. Four times five is twelve. And four times six is thirteen! And four times seven is. . . . Oh dear! I'd better try geography. London is the capital of Paris, and Paris is the capital of Rome, and Rome is . . . no! That's all wrong! I'll try reciting "How Doth the Little Busy Bee."

How doth the little crocodile improve his shining tail,
And pour the waters of the Nile on every golden scale.
How cheerfully he seems to grin, how neatly spread his
    claws,

And welcomes little fishes in with gently smiling jaws. (*She exits.*)

CHAIRMAN: It's plain to be seen this little girl is mixed up. She doesn't know her own name, but no doubt our experts can supply it. We'll ask the official spokesman to come out here with me as we call our performers back for proper identification. First, the young lady with the green hair. (*Enter* ANNE OF GREEN GABLES)

SPOKESMAN: *Identifies the girl if possible and* CHAIRMAN *takes her cue accordingly.*

CHAIRMAN: That's right. (*Or*) Perhaps we can help you out. The young lady is Anne of Green Gables in the book of that name by L. M. Montgomery. We'll ask her to explain how she happened to live at Green Gables.

ANNE: I went to Green Gables to live with Marilla and Matthew when I was a little girl. They had expected a boy to help them on the farm, but after they got to know me, they grew to love me, and I loved them too, although they didn't understand my many many problems. (*She exits.*)

CHAIRMAN: And that green hair episode was only one of dozens. I'm sure *Anne of Green Gables* would be popular with girls of every country and every age. Just as popular as this little girl from Switzerland. (*Enter* HEIDI. *To* SPOKESMAN) Can you tell us her name?

SPOKESMAN: *Gives answer.*

CHAIRMAN: Yes, Heidi is a little girl we all know, and love. Tell us, Heidi, who was that cross governess?

HEIDI: Oh that was Fraulein. She took care of me in the city where I went to live with Clara but I was never happy there.

CHAIRMAN: Did you ever get back to your beloved mountains?

HEIDI: Oh yes, indeed, and wonderful things happened there. But you'll have to read the book for yourself. I know how to keep a secret. (*Exit*)

CHAIRMAN: Here comes our next character . . . the girl who

sold her hair. Do you know her name? (*Enter* JOSEPHINE MARCH)

SPOKESMAN: *Gives name.*

CHAIRMAN: All the world loves Josephine March in Louisa Alcott's *Little Women*. Let's ask Jo about her sisters.

JO: If you know me, you also know Meg, Beth, Amy and Marmee. We lived in the Orchard House near Concord, Massachusetts. If you ever go traveling that way . . . be sure to stop and see us. We won't be at home, but there's something about the house that makes everybody feel welcome. (*Exit*)

CHAIRMAN: Now for the little English girl who wandered around the countryside with her aged grandfather. (*Enter* LITTLE NELL)

SPOKESMAN: *Gives name.*

CHAIRMAN: Little Nell of the *Old Curiosity Shop* led a short unhappy life, but she made many lasting friends among the readers of Charles Dickens.

LITTLE NELL: Poor grandfather. He needed me to protect him. If you read about him, you'll love him as much as I did. (*Exit*)

CHAIRMAN: Speaking of love . . . here are the little girls who got engaged when very, very young. (*Enter* BECKY THATCHER *and* AMY LAWRENCE.)

SPOKESMAN: *Gives names.*

CHAIRMAN: Hello, Becky Thatcher and Amy Lawrence. Did you two ever make up?

BECKY: Of course, we did.

AMY: We're really pretty good friends.

CHAIRMAN: And did you ever forgive Tom for his first engagement, Becky?

BECKY: Yes, I did. You could never stay mad at Tom. Read about us and our great adventure when we were lost in the cave. It's really thrilling. (*They exit.*)

CHAIRMAN: And we have Mark Twain to thank for a very entertaining book . . . *The Adventures of Tom Sawyer.* Next, our poetry girl. Can you identify the stranger "who's come to our house to stay"?

SPOKESMAN: *Gives name.*

CHAIRMAN: "Little Orphant Annie" by James Whitcomb Riley holds an honored place in American poetry. And here's another child who holds an honored place in English literature. (*Enter* ALICE.) Do you know this "child of the pure, unclouded brow"?

SPOKESMAN: *Gives name.*

CHAIRMAN: That's right. It's Alice in Wonderland. And we want to say that all of these girls you have met this afternoon are right out of the wonderland of books. Alice, are you still as confused as ever?

ALICE: Not right this minute. But I am going back to my book shelf before I get mixed up again. You can read more about me in your school library. Goodbye. (*Exits*)

CHAIRMAN: Goodbye, Alice, and goodbye to everybody who has helped us enjoy this visit with our book friends.

As for you girls in the audience, you'll have to decide for yourselves what kind of girl each of you will be. That decision will be influenced by the girls you meet, by the women you know and by the books you read. Right now, there are many patterns to choose from . . . but for most of us, no girl could ever take the place of the "Girl Who Married Dear Old Dad." If we make *her* our model, we can't be very far wrong. So let's close our program today by singing . . . "I'll Be a Girl Just Like the Girl That Married Dear Old Dad."

THE END

Boys in Books*

(Book Week)

Characters

STUDENT CHAIRMAN
GUEST PANEL
PIP
THE CONVICT
JIM HAWKINS
BEN GUNN
TOM SAWYER
HUCKLEBERRY FINN
TOM BROWN
VELVETEENS
MR. WILLIAMS
SAM WILLIAMS
OLIVER TWIST
THE ARTFUL DODGER
STUDENT READER

SETTING: *A school stage.*

AT RISE: *The* GUEST PANEL *sits in a semicircle on one side of the stage. The* STUDENT CHAIRMAN *comes forward to open the program.*

* This program may be performed using visiting fathers or male members of the faculty as a guest panel. With slight alterations, a guest panel composed of students may also be used.

CHAIRMAN: Many popular and unpopular authors have set themselves up as authorities on boys, and a few have even dared draw up definitions. Herbert E. Smith defines a boy as "a man minus pride, ambition, pretense, greed, and about one hundred and ten pounds." Another American author, Louis Redmond, says that a boy "is an inexpensive device for pulling legs off chairs, leaving fingerprints in paint, abandoning bicycles in living rooms, falling into ponds, and correcting pomposity in his elders." This same authority specifies that good places to look for boys are "sand lots, marshes, the bottoms of quarries and the rafters of buildings under construction." We wish to point out that boys are also to be found in school buildings during weekdays, Monday through Friday.

Our guests on the platform today have one important factor in common. At one time or another, they were all boys, and that is why they were invited here today. It is my pleasure to present our guests at this time. (CHAIRMAN *introduces each of the men on the platform.*) We hope you gentlemen enjoy the program that has been prepared for you and now let's get down to business. Throughout the history of literature boys have made an important contribution to great books. Many famous authors in Europe and America have used boys as their heroes. Today our class will present a group of famous boys in fiction and we are going to ask our guests here on the platform to identify them. After all, since each of these gentlemen has had the experience of being a boy, he should know what makes a boy tick, whether he's real flesh and blood or a character in a book.

Here comes our first boy involved in a rather desperate situation. We'll give you one very important clue: The scene takes place in an English cemetery. (*Enter a boy and a man. The boy is dressed in knee breeches and blouse. The man wears a convict's suit and drags a heavy ball and chain with him. He shoves the boy on stage ahead of him, then seizes him by the throat.)*

BOY: Oh, don't cut my throat, sir! Please! Please!

MAN: Show me where you live! Point out the place!

BOY: Right down there, sir, in the village.

MAN: You young dog! What fat cheeks you've got! Darned if I couldn't eat 'em! Now lookee here, where's your mother and father?

BOY: There, sir. There among the tombstones.

MAN: Who do ye live with, supposin' I let ye live at all?

BOY: With my sister, sir—Mrs. Joe Gargery, wife of Joe Gargery, the blacksmith, sir.

MAN: Blacksmith, eh? That gives me an idea. You know what a file is, boy?

BOY: Yes, sir.

MAN: And you know what victuals is?

BOY: Yes, sir.

MAN: You get me a file, and you get me victuals. You bring 'em both to me tonight, or I'll have your heart and liver out! You do it and you never say a word or dare to make a sign, and I'll let ye live. You fail me, and your heart and your liver shall be torn out . . . roasted . . . and ate!

BOY: I'll do it, sir, I'll do it! Only let me go! Let me go!

MAN: On your way then, and mind ye! . . . I'll be keepin' my eye on ye! Understand? *(Man shoves boy ahead of him off stage and follows slowly, dragging his heavy chain with him.)*

CHAIRMAN: Now, gentlemen, there's your first famous boy in fiction. Can you identify him? We'll give you a minute to jot down his name on your score card and then on to our next boy hero. *(Pause)* Again we are in the field of English literature, and this time our scene is on an island where our young hero encounters a strange character. *(Boy enters cautiously as if exploring strange territory. He wears a blouse, open at the throat, knee breeches, but no shoes or stockings. As he peers around the stage a man enters in a weird costume of rags and goat skins. Each is startled at the sight of the other.*)

Boy: Who are you?

Ben: I'm poor Ben Gunn, I am, and I haven't spoken with a Christian these three years.

Boy: Three years! Were you shipwrecked?

Ben: Nay, Mate, marooned! Marooned three years ago, and lived on goats since then, and berries and oysters. But, Mate, my heart is sore for Christian diet. You mightn't happen to have a piece of cheese about you now? No? Well, many's the long night I've dreamed of cheese . . . toasted mostly . . . and woke up again, and here I were.

Boy: If ever I can get aboard ship again, you shall have cheese by the stone. I promise.

Ben: If ever you can get aboard again, says you? Who's to hinder you?

Boy: Not you, I know.

Ben: What do you call yourself, Mate?

Chairman: That's far enough, boys. You'll have to cut the scene right there and make your exit. I'm sure you've given our guests enough clues for identification. (*Exit* Ben Gunn *and boy*) Our next characters come from American fiction and we have a pair of boys for you to identify this time. These two were great friends and had many adventures together. As we meet these famous boys of fiction they have just come from a gruesome scene in a cemetery where murder was committed before their very eyes. If they seem a bit out of breath, it's because they've been running all the way. (*Two boys enter. Both wear overalls and torn shirts. They are barefoot. One boy carries a flat piece of board.*)

First: Say, can you keep quiet about this?

Second: We *got* to keep quiet about it. You know that. That

Injun Joe wouldn't think any more of drowning us than drowning a couple of cats if we was to tell and they didn't hang him. Now look here, let's swear to each other—that's what we got to do—swear to keep quiet.

FIRST: It's all right with me. Do we just hold hands and swear?

SECOND: Oh no. That wouldn't do for this. That's good enough for little things, like girls. *They* go back on you anyway, and tell if they get sore. But there ought to be writing about a thing like this . . . and blood!

FIRST: That's a good idea. (*Searches in pocket and pulls out a piece of chalk*) Maybe I can write something on this board. Then we can both sign. How's this? (*Writes on board*) "We hereby solemnly swear we will keep quiet about this and we wish we may drop down dead in our tracks if we ever tell."

SECOND: Good! Now for the blood! (*Taking pin from shirt*) Here! I got a pin.

FIRST: Don't do that. A pin is brass. It might make you die. I got a needle here somewhere. (*Gets needle from pocket*) Now. Hold out your hand. (*Much squeezing of fingers to get blood*) That's enough. Here, I'll help you sign.

SECOND: Now it's your turn. I'll stick your finger. (*Repeat performance*)

FIRST: That's good enough. Does this keep us from ever telling? Always?

SECOND: Of course it does. It doesn't make any difference what happens about this. We would drop down dead. Don't you know that? Now come along, and we'll bury this board so no one will ever find it. (*Exit boys*)

CHAIRMAN: Well, that's one way to keep a secret. And while our guests are figuring out the secret of these two names, we'll set the stage for our next boy hero. This time the story calls for a tree, but we're going to use a ladder instead.

(*Stage hand brings in ladder.*) Just put it there on the stage and give our hero time to scramble into place. (*Boy enters with fishing rod, climbs ladder and sits on top step.*) Our hero is an English schoolboy who has been fishing out of bounds and has made the sad mistake of taking refuge from the gamekeeper in a tree.

KEEPER (*Entering*): Oh, there ye be! Now you come down this minute.

BOY (*In a stage whisper*): Now I'm in for it, unless I starve him out! (*In loud cheerful voice*) Hello, Velveteens. (*Raises fishing rod as the* KEEPER *starts up the ladder*) Mind your fingers if you come any higher. I'll crack your knuckles with my fishing rod.

KEEPER: I tells ye, lad, come down at once. It'll be the best for ye.

BOY: Thank ye, Velveteens. I'm very comfortable.

KEEPER (*Sitting down*): Werry well! Please yourself. I'm in no hurry, so take your time. I'll learn ye to call honest folks names before I'm through with ye.

BOY (*In whisper*): I can't sit here all night. I wonder if he'll rise to silver. (*Clearing his throat*) I say, Keeper, let me go for two bob.

KEEPER: Not for twenty, neither . . . and here I stay till ye come down.

BOY: And then what?

KEEPER: Walk ye up to school and give ye over to the Doctor for breakin' the rules. Ye know the law on the subject of fishing.

BOY: Very well. I give up. But hands off, ye know. No collaring or that sort of thing. I'll go with ye quietly.

KEEPER: Werry well. (*Boy comes down ladder and he and the* KEEPER *walk off together. Stage hand removes ladder.*)

CHAIRMAN: Well, it looks like a victory for Velveteens. How about it, gentlemen? Do you recognize the boy in the story? While you're thinking it over, we will remove our "tree" and introduce an American boy who finds himself in hot water with his father, all on account of a phone call from a distracted mother. From the looks of the father, the boy will have some real explaining to do. (*Enter father and son, both in modern clothes.*)

FATHER: Now come here and tell me what you did to Georgie Basset.

SON: Nothin', nothin' at all.

FATHER: What?

SON: We just "nishiated" him.

FATHER: That's *all* you did?

SON: Yes, sir.

FATHER: Georgie Basset's mother has just called me on the telephone, and she says that you and your friends lured Georgie into the cellar and had him beaten by two thugs.

SON: It's not so. We didn't lower him into the cellar. We never thought of goin' to the cellar. He went down there himself first.

FATHER: I suppose he was trying to escape from you. Is that so?

SON: We weren't even chasin' him.

FATHER: Then why did he go to the cellar?

SON: He . . . he . . . fell in.

FATHER: How did he fall in?

SON: Well, the door was open and he kept walkin' around there, and we hollered at him to keep away, and then I noticed we couldn't see him any more and when we went and looked down the steps, there he was on the bottom step shoutin' . . .

FATHER: Now see here! You tell me the whole story! How did George Basset happen to fall down those steps?

SON: He . . . he was blindfolded!

FATHER: Blindfolded was he? I think you'd better come along

with me. I believe I have a treatment that will get to the root of this story in a much shorter time. (*Boy and father exit.*)

CHAIRMAN: Poor Georgie Basset! The boys never did want him in their club to start with! But maybe we'd better save our pity for our poor hero when his father gets finished with him. If you hear any ear-splitting yells you'll know what's happening behind the scenes. But here comes another juvenile hero who seems a bit down on his luck. Let's listen to his story. (*Boy enters with small bundle of clothing tied on the end of a stick. He shows his weariness in his walk and finally sits down on the stage to rest. Presently a second boy enters. He wears a suit that is much too big for him and a battered silk hat which he keeps trying to balance on his head. He walks around the smaller boy, examines him from all angles and then speaks.*)

BIG BOY: Hello, my covey. What's the row?

SMALL BOY: I'm very hungry and tired. I have been walking these seven days.

BIG BOY: Walkin' these seven days? Oh, I see . . . Beak's orders, eh? I suppose you don't know what a beak is, my flash companion.

SMALL BOY: I always supposed a beak was the mouth of a bird.

BIG BOY (*Laughing*): My eyes! How green! Why, a beak's a magistrate. And when you walk by a beak's order, it's not straight forward, but always a-goin' up and niver a-comin' down again. But come. You want grub and shall have it. I'll fork out. Up with you, on your pins. (*Small boy rises*) There! Now then. Hurry. (*They start to walk offstage together*) Going to London?

SMALL BOY: Yes.

BIG BOY: Got any lodgings?

SMALL BOY: No.

BIG BOY: Money?

SMALL BOY: No. (*Big boy whistles in surprise.*) Do you live in London?

BIG BOY: I do when I'm at home. I suppose you want some place to sleep in tonight, don't you?

SMALL BOY: I do indeed. I have not slept under a roof since I left the country.

BIG BOY: Don't fret your eyelids on that score. I've got to be in London tonight, and I know a 'spectable old gen'lman as lives there, wot'll give you lodgings for nothin' and never ask for the change . . . that is, if any gen'lman he knows interduces you. And don't he know *me?* Oh, no! Not in the least! (*Boys leave stage, the older boy laughing heartily.*)

CHAIRMAN: And so we've come to the end of our boy heroes for today. We will now ask the Spokesman for our guest panel to come to the front of the platform as we call our performers to step forward for identification. (*One of the guests comes forward and takes his place by the* CHAIRMAN.) We first call on our little English hero who was almost frightened to death by an escaped convict. (*First boy enters.*) Now, sir, who is this famous boy of fiction?

SPOKESMAN: *Identifies the boy if possible.*

CHAIRMAN: That's right, sir. (*Or*) Let me help you out, sir. This lad is Pip from *Great Expectations* by Charles Dickens. By the way, Pip, how did you ever get such a strange name?

PIP: My father's family name was *Pirrip* . . . P-I-R-R-I-P and my Christian name was Philip. The combination was more than I could say when I was small so I called myself Pip.

CHAIRMAN: And did you help that convict escape?

PIP: Yes, I did. I brought him some food and the necessary file and that was the beginning of a great adventure for me. To learn the whole story, read *Great Expectations* by Charles Dickens. I think you'll enjoy it. (*Exit*)

CHAIRMAN: We've certainly enjoyed meeting Pip and now for

our next hero . . . the boy who promised to bring some cheese for poor Ben Gunn. (*To* SPOKESMAN) Can you tell us his name?

SPOKESMAN: *Gives name, if possible.*

CHAIRMAN: Yes, Jim Hawkins is a well-known hero of British fiction. Come out here, Jim, and tell us the rest of your story. (*Enter* JIM HAWKINS)

JIM: You'll have to let Robert Louis Stevenson do that. He's one of the best storytellers in all the world. If you want to know how I got back on board my ship and all that happened in between . . . read *Treasure Island*. It's in the school library. (*Exit* JIM)

CHAIRMAN: And here come our two boys who wrote their names in blood. (*Enter* TOM *and* HUCK) What are their names?

SPOKESMAN: *Gives answer.*

CHAIRMAN: Tell me, Tom Sawyer and Huck Finn, did you ever tell what you saw in that cemetery?

HUCK: You don't catch us on a trick like that, boy. Remember, we signed that oath in blood.

TOM: And if you want to know what Injun Joe did and what happened to him and us, let Mark Twain tell you in *The Adventures of Tom Sawyer*. (*Exit*)

CHAIRMAN: And here comes our boy who was caught up a tree. (*Enter* TOM BROWN) Do you know this fellow, sir?

SPOKESMAN: *Gives name, if possible.*

CHAIRMAN: Tom Brown could get into plenty of trouble. Tell me, Tom, how did you make out on that fishing deal?

TOM: I had a painful session with our Principal the next morning, but he did let me keep the fishing rod which he could have turned over to old Velveteens if he had wanted to.

CHAIRMAN: I guess your school days were very different from ours.

TOM: I guess you're right, but still I wouldn't want to change places. If you read *Tom Brown's Schooldays* you'll find I didn't have such a tough life after all. (*Exit*)

CHAIRMAN: And here comes our American boy whose father gave him a bad time over little Georgie Basset. (*Enter* SAM WILLIAMS) Do you know his name?

SPOKESMAN: *Gives name.*

CHAIRMAN: Yes, this is Sam Williams. He and Penrod Schofield were always getting into scrapes like this, weren't you, Sam?

SAM: We sure were, but we had a lot of fun. You'll have a lot of fun yourself if you read *Penrod* and *Penrod and Sam* by Booth Tarkington. (*Exit*)

CHAIRMAN: Now back to Merry England for our next characters, a pair of boys from the pages of Charles Dickens. (*Enter* OLIVER TWIST *and the* ARTFUL DODGER.) Do you know these chaps?

SPOKESMAN: *Supplies the names.*

CHAIRMAN: Oliver Twist and the Artful Dodger! What a pair! Tell me, Oliver, were you boys good friends?

OLIVER: No, indeed. And if I had ever guessed where this fellow was taking me on that first night in London I would never have gone with him. That merry old gentleman he talked about ran a school for pickpockets and before I knew it, I was up to my ears in trouble.

ARTFUL DODGER: He never had no interest in his work, he didn't, and never learned to dodge the traps like I did.

CHAIRMAN: What's your real name?

ARTFUL DODGER: Jack Dawkins, they call me, but the Artful Dodger suits me much better.

CHAIRMAN: And I'm sure *The Adventures of Oliver Twist* by Charles Dickens will suit us all for excitement and mystery.

OLIVER: And there's a murder too! Don't forget that.

CHAIRMAN: Thanks for reminding us, Oliver. (*Exit* OLIVER

and the DODGER) And thanks to these friends of ours who have shared our fun with book friends this afternoon. Before we close our program about BOYS IN BOOKS, here is (*Name of student*) to tell us what that great American, Theodore Roosevelt, had to say on the subject of The American Boy.

STUDENT (*Coming forward*): "The boy can best become a good man by being a good boy; not a goody-goody boy, but just a plain, good boy. I do not mean that he must love only the negative virtues; I mean he must love the positive virtues also. 'Good' in the largest sense should include whatever is fine, straightforward, clean, brave, and manly. In short, in life, as in a football game, the principle to follow is: Hit the line hard; don't foul and don't shirk, but hit the line hard!"

CHAIRMAN: And now, in honor of all boys everywhere, from six to sixty, in fact or in fiction, let us sing together "For He's a Jolly Good Fellow."

THE END

Not for Girls

(*Arithmetic*)

Characters

Mr. Finch
Mrs. Finch
Larry Finch
Dora Finch
Annie
Tina
Barbara
Mr. Wizard
Announcer

Time: *Just after breakfast.*
Setting: *The Finch dining room.*
At Rise: Mrs. Finch *is seeing her son and husband off for the day.* Dora *is sitting at the table, pretending to take no interest in the proceedings. She is looking at the paper.* Mrs. Finch *straightens* Larry's *tie.*

Larry: Ouch! Not so tight, Mom. Do you want to strangle me?

Mrs. Finch: No, indeed. I want you to speak up loud and plain. I want to hear everything you and Daddy say on the television program.

Mr. Finch: Larry will be ten times louder and plainer than his dad on this deal. I'll be scared stiff.

MRS. FINCH: Nonsense! You have no reason to be scared. You and Larry are the best father-and-son team in town. Nobody can beat you when it comes to figures. You're the experts all right.

LARRY: Save that till after we come home. We've got some tough competition this time.

MRS. FINCH: Don't let it get you down, son. And remember, win or lose, Dora and I will be the proudest gals in town. Won't we, Dora?

DORA (*Pretending not to hear*): What did you say?

MRS. FINCH: What did I say? I just said you and I will be the proudest gals in town when we see Dad and Larry on the Father-and-Son Math Competence Program.

DORA: I don't see anything so wonderful about an old math team. Now if it were a swimming team or a bowling team, then we'd have something worth cheering about.

MRS. FINCH: Why, Dora Finch! What a rude thing to say. You apologize this minute.

LARRY: Oh, don't mind her, Mom. She's just mad because they call her the Dumb Dora of the arithmetic class.

DORA: I am not! I am not mad. I don't care a fig for arithmetic. I wouldn't want to be on any old math team!

MRS. FINCH: Dora! Dora! Stop that this instant.

MR. FINCH: Now, now, Mother. We don't have time for apologies. Larry and I have to keep our heads clear for those problems the experts will throw at us. Come on, Larry. We don't want to be late.

LARRY: And simmer down, Sis. Maybe when you're as old as Mom, you can add two and two and get four.

DORA: You get out of here! (*Rushes at him with newspaper*)

MRS. FINCH: Dora! Dora!

LARRY (*Ducking out of* DORA'S *reach*): Come on, Dad. Let's run for it. Things are getting too hot for us around here. (*Exit* LARRY *and* MR. FINCH *laughing.*)

MRS. FINCH (*Calling*): Good luck to both of you. (*Turning from door*) Now, Dora, aren't you ashamed of yourself?

DORA: I guess I should be ashamed, but that Larry makes me so cross. He thinks he's so smart just because he can do all kinds of problems in his head and get the right answers.

MRS. FINCH: Well, don't you think that's quite an accomplishment? Larry is really very clever at figures.

DORA: Sure . . . but he's a boy! Boys are always smart at arithmetic.

MRS. FINCH: Nonsense! I never heard a sillier statement. You could get just as good marks as Larry in arithmetic, if you'd make up your mind to work harder.

DORA: But Mother, what's the use? Girls don't especially need arithmetic, you know.

MRS. FINCH: Now that's an argument I don't intend to pursue. I suggest you go straighten yourself up a bit and come along over to Mrs. Garner's to watch the TV program. It certainly is a nuisance that our set has to be on the blink now of all times.

DORA (*With a sigh*): Please, Mother, do I *have* to watch that television program?

MRS. FINCH: But, Dora, don't you *want* to see Dad and Larry compete with the other teams? It's so exciting.

DORA: I've seen them before; and those problems make my head ache.

MRS. FINCH: You're impossible. But I certainly don't intend to force you to go. You may stay home if you like. Annie is in the kitchen and this is baking day, so try not to be a bother.

DORA: I won't, Mother, and thanks for letting me stay here.

MRS. FINCH: You're a funny child, Dora. I should think you'd want your father and brother to win.

DORA: I do want them to win. And I know they will. They always do.

MRS. FINCH: Well, I certainly hope their luck holds today. Goodbye, dear, and be sure to keep out of Annie's way. If you need me for anything, you know Mrs. Garner's number.

DORA: Sure, I know. Goodbye, Mom. (MRS. FINCH *exits.* DORA *buries her head in her arms and begins to sob. Then she raises her head and yells*) I hate it! I hate it! I hate it! (*She buries her head again and continues crying.* MR. WIZARD *enters. He watches* DORA *for a while, then clears his throat softly.*)

MR. WIZARD: Excuse me, miss.

DORA: Go away! Go away and don't bother me.

MR. WIZARD: Beg pardon, ma'am, but is your name Dora?

DORA: Yes. But go away, please.

MR. WIZARD: Dora Finch?

DORA: Yes, Dora Finch. (*Sitting up*) Who in the world are you and how did you get in here?

MR. WIZARD: I am Mr. Wizard, and I was instructed to pay a call on a . . . a (*Consulting card*) Miss Dora Finch. Are you that young lady?

DORA: Yes, I am, but I can't talk to you now. I can't talk to anyone now.

MR. WIZARD: Why not?

DORA: Well, can't you see I'm busy—I'm busy crying. I—I'm dreadfully upset.

MR. WIZARD: Yes, I know. You're upset about your arithmetic, aren't you?

DORA: Yes, but how did you know?

MR. WIZARD: I told you my name is Mr. Wizard, and we wizards are very well informed. We know a lot of things. For example, I bet I can tell you just *why* you're upset about your arithmetic.

DORA: Don't bother. I know that without being told.

MR. WIZARD: But I'll tell you anyhow. You see, I love to talk
—especially when it's about arithmetic.

DORA: Well I hate arithmetic and everything about it.

MR. WIZARD: That's just your trouble. You're miserable about
your arithmetic because you hate it, and you hate it because
you think you can't do it.

DORA: I *know* I can't do it, and if you don't believe me, just
look at my report card. (*Pulls it out from a book in the
bookshelf behind her.*)

MR. WIZARD: So that's where you've been hiding it.

DORA: Did you know that too?

MR. WIZARD: Of course. Wizards know everything. I'll bet I
can tell you what you're going to say next.

DORA: You can?

MR. WIZARD: I can. You're going to say that you can't be
bothered with arithmetic because it's not for girls. Girls
have no use for it, isn't that right?

DORA: That *is* what I was going to say. And it's true too.
Girls have no earthly use for arithmetic. I don't see why
we have to bother with it. Nobody actually uses it anyway,
except boys and men.

MR. WIZARD: Do you really believe that?

DORA: Certainly, I believe it. If I really thought I'd have any
use for figures, I'd get busy and do some of this hateful old
arithmetic. But as it is, it's just a waste of time.

MR. WIZARD: Suppose I could show you that most girls or
women use their arithmetic about twenty times a day?

DORA (*Laughing*): Twenty times a day!

MR. WIZARD: Well, maybe not exactly twenty, but at least
. . . a dozen.

DORA: Even twelve times a day is too much, unless the girl
works in a store or something.

MR. WIZARD: I'm talking about right here at home.

DORA: You're crazy, Mr. Wizard. My father is always working with figures, but not my mother. She never has to worry about arithmetic.

MR. WIZARD: You've just never noticed. I tell you what, Dora Finch. I'll make a bargain with you.

DORA: A bargain?

MR. WIZARD: Yes. If I can show you that problems dealing with numbers keep popping into your everyday life at the rate of . . . well, say ten or twelve a day, will you promise to get down to business and do some good hard work on that arithmetic?

DORA: I promise, Mr. Wizard. But I'm afraid you'll get the worst end of the bargain.

MR. WIZARD: I'll worry about that. Now here's the plan. First of all, we must keep score. Here is a score card. (*Gives* DORA *a card*) Every time a situation arises in which numbers are involved, where you have to do any sort of figuring, a bell will ring.

DORA: A bell? What bell?

MR. WIZARD: A bell somewhere in the house. That bell will be the signal that I have scored another point and you must stop whatever you are doing and mark the score card. Will you do that?

DORA: This is beginning to sound like fun.

MR. WIZARD: Numbers really *are* fun, if you just learn to appreciate them.

DORA: Now you sound just like my Dad.

MR. WIZARD: Don't change the subject. Is it a bargain?

DORA: It's a bargain, Mr. Wizard. (*They shake hands.*)

MR. WIZARD: And remember to mark your score card every time you hear the bell.

DORA: I promise.

MR. WIZARD: By the way, Dora, are you sure you didn't drop

that report card on the floor? (*As* DORA *stoops over to look for the report card,* MR. WIZARD *makes a quick exit.*)

DORA (*Looking on the floor and under the table*): I don't see it any place, Mr. Wizard. I don't see how it could have slipped under the bookcase. Are you sure I dropped it? I say, are you sure I— (*Noticing that* MR. WIZARD *is gone*) Why, he's gone! Mr. Wizard, where are you? (*Enter* ANNIE *from kitchen. She carries a measuring cup and a recipe book.*)

ANNIE: Land sakes, Dora, I thought I heard you talking to someone. Where's your mother?

DORA: Gone over to Mrs. Garner's to look at television.

ANNIE: Now, if that's not the limit! She forgot to measure out this recipe for me. It calls for four cups of milk, and there's only a pint left in the refrigerator. Now I don't know how to make it come out even.

DORA: That's not too hard, Annie. There are two cups in a pint, so you have just half the amount of milk. If you cut the rest of the recipe in half it ought to come out right.

ANNIE: Well bless my soul, Dora, I never knew you could figure things out like that. I always thought you had trouble with arithmetic.

DORA (*Clapping her hand over her mouth*): Arithmetic! (*Doorbell rings*) Oh my goodness: Where's that score card? (*Grabs score card and writes on it hastily*)

ANNIE: You better answer that door, dearie, 'stead of standing there scribbling. I have to go figure out the rest of that recipe. And say! I wonder if you could help me set the oven for the roast. Your mother wrote down the time she wants it to be done, and I know it's to cook twenty minutes to the pound, but I just can't seem to figure out how I should set the time. (*Doorbell*)

DORA: Oh dear! Another bell! That's two points for Mr. Wizard already.

ANNIE: Quick, Dora, answer that bell before they wear it out. I have to get back to the kitchen.

DORA: O.K., Annie. I'll answer it. (*Exits. Speaking offstage*) Oh, hello, Tina. Come in. I'm still eating breakfast. (*They enter.*)

TINA: Oh, Dora, I'm so excited! Mother says I may have a party for my birthday. It's the day after tomorrow, and I don't see how I'll ever get ready in time. I brought this paper over and thought maybe you'd show me how to make those darling favors you had for *your* party. Do you remember how you made them?

DORA: Oh, they were easy as pie. Here . . . I can show you in a jiffy.

TINA: Here's the paper. I don't know if it will be enough.

DORA: How many are coming?

TINA: I thought I'd have twelve. But I'd like to get the place cards out of that too.

DORA: We can make the place cards first. This paper is just the right size. Now you fold the sheet in half, like this. Then fold it again, and then again. That will give you eight place cards out of that sheet. So we'll just need half a sheet for the other four. That will be your twelve place cards. Now for the favors . . .

TINA (*Admiringly*): Say! Miss Trevor should hear you spout off! She doesn't think you can do fractions worth a cent.

DORA: Fractions? Who said anything about fractions?

TINA: Why, *you* did! You just divided a paper into halves, then into fourths, then into eighths!

DORA: Oh my goodness!

TINA: What's the matter? (*Doorbell rings.*)

DORA: Nothing's the matter. Nothing at all! Excuse me a minute, till I fill out this little card.

TINA: But don't you hear the bell?

DORA: I hear it all right.

TINA: Shall I answer the door?

DORA: Please do. (*Exit* TINA) Oh dear! That's three points for Mr. Wizard, and the day hasn't half started.

TINA (*Reappears*): It was the paper boy. He says you owe him for three weeks, but last time your mother paid him a week in advance, so he thinks it's only two weeks. And he says he's short on change, so he hopes you have the exact amount.

DORA: Mercy! That sounds like a Chinese puzzle. (*Calling*) Annie, did Mother leave the money for the paper boy?

ANNIE (*From kitchen*): Yes, she did, but I'd better talk to him because he missed us two nights last week and one night this week. Tell him to come around to the back door.

DORA: Thank goodness you'll handle that.

TINA (*Running to door*): I'll tell him, Dora. (*Phone rings.*)

DORA: Can you beat it! There goes another bell! That's another score for Mr. Wizard. I had no idea poor Mother had all these problems on her hands. (*Phone rings again.*)

DORA: Bells! Bells! Bells! Just a minute. I'm coming. (*At phone*) Hello. . . . Who? . . . The Custom-Made Drapery Shop? . . . No, no, Mrs. Finch isn't here just now. Is there a message? . . . What? Will you repeat that? . . . You say the material is only forty-five inches wide instead of fifty-four inches? . . . Yes, I'll tell her . . . And you want her to be sure to get the measurements for the valance in the sun room? . . . Yes, Yes . . . I understand. Naturally she'll have to buy more material if there's that much difference in width. The price? . . . You say this is two dollars a yard instead of two-fifty? Very well. . . . Yes, I'll have her call the minute she comes in. Thank you for calling. . . . Goodbye. (*Hangs up*) Poor Mother! How will she ever figure that out? *Figure!* There's that hateful word again, and another score for Mr. Wizard. (*Grabbing score card*) I wonder if I can write down the score before another bell rings. (*Bell rings just as she is writing.*)

TINA (*Re-entering*): Don't mind that bell, Dora. I bumped against it accidentally as I was closing the door. You don't need to pay any attention to it.

DORA: That's what *you* think.

TINA: Now, let's get back to my favors.

DORA: Honestly, Tina, so much is happening around this house this morning, I don't believe I can help you after all. (*At desk*) Here, take this pattern. You can draw around it and cut it out.

TINA: Do you think I'll have enough paper?

DORA: For heaven's sake, don't ask me to measure it. You'll have plenty.

TINA: But what about the ice cream? How much do you think I should order for twelve? Mother always counts three servings to a pint.

DORA: Then two quarts would be plenty. (*Bell rings.*)

TINA: I never heard so many bells around a house in my life.

DORA: Neither did I! Oh dear! Where's that score card? I seem to be running into figures at every turn! (*Enter ANNIE. Her face and hands are streaked with flour.*)

ANNIE: I never saw the like of the interruptions on baking day. That was the back doorbell . . . the grocery boy. Now he tells me he doesn't have change for five dollars. Will you run upstairs and see if your mother left any change on the bureau? I'll need sixty-four cents in change. There's a quarter in the house pocketbook. (*Bell rings.*) Land sakes! What's that? Sounds like your Dad's alarm clock.

DORA: It's an alarm all right, Annie. Just a minute till I write something on this card. (*Writes*) Now I'll go look for your change.

ANNIE: And be sure to turn off that dratted alarm. (*Exit* DORA. *In a few seconds the bell stops ringing.*)

TINA: I guess I'd better run on home, Annie. Dora seems in such a dither today. Will you tell her I've gone, please? And tell her she's to be sure to come to the party.

ANNIE: I'll tell her, Tina. Goodbye.

TINA (*Starts to exit and returns holding a letter*): Mother asked me to mail this letter for her, but she's not sure if it has enough postage. Would you know, Annie?

ANNIE: It looks mighty heavy to me, child, but I wouldn't know for sure.

TINA: Oh, dear, I guess I'll have to go down to the post office.

ANNIE: There's a letter scale around here some place. Mrs. Finch often uses it. I think it's somewhere in that desk. Dora should know where it is. (*Enter* DORA)

DORA: Is something lost, Annie?

ANNIE: No. I was just wondering where that letter scale is. Your mother often uses it to check postage before she mails her letters.

DORA (*At desk*): Oh, here it is. Where's your letter, Annie?

TINA: It's mine . . . or rather, it's Mother's. Does it need another stamp?

DORA (*Weighing letter*): Yes, it's three ounces. That calls for another three-cent stamp. (*Bell*)

ANNIE: There! There goes the timer on the stove; I'll have to fly. (*Exit*)

DORA (*With a laugh*): Actually that timer was for me, Annie, but never mind. (*Picks up score card.*) Here we go again.

TINA: I must say, Dora, you're awfully mysterious about that card. What is it anyway?

DORA: Well, it's sort of a secret, Tina, but I'll tell you about it some day.

TINA: O.K. I'm too excited about my party to be very curious right now. I have a lot of errands to do so I'll see you to-morrow. So long, Dora, and thanks for helping me.

DORA: So long, Tina, and I hope your party is a wonderful success. (*Exit* TINA. DORA *mops her face and sighs with relief.*) What a morning! Now I can certainly sit down and enjoy myself for awhile. At least the radio won't be firing arithmetic problems at me. (*Turns on radio. There is the closing strain of music and then the announcer's voice.*)

ANNOUNCER: Attention ladies! Don't miss the sensational values at Roger's semi-annual clearance now in progress. Twenty percent off every dress, coat, and suit in the store is Roger's gift to you. Think of it, ladies. You can now buy lovely nineteen-ninety-eight dresses for only fifteen-ninety-eight. Fourteen-ninety-eight suits and dresses, now only nine-ninety-eight. Remember, twenty percent, one fifth of the actual selling price, is subtracted from every garment in the store. Be sure to shop at Roger's today. Set your own prices by subtracting twenty percent from every price tag. Think what you'll save on a single shopping trip to Roger's on the Square in . . .

DORA (*Turning off radio*): Can you beat it! More number work, even on the radio! (*Bell rings*) That Mr. Wizard isn't giving me a minute's peace! (*Bell rings louder.* DORA *shouts loudly*) Just a minute! I'm coming. (BARBARA GREER *enters.*)

BARBARA: Yoo-hoo! Anybody home?

DORA: Oh, hello, Bobby. Come right in.

BARBARA: Where were you? I almost pushed the doorbell button through the wall, but nobody came.

DORA: Sorry. I was . . . er . . . busy. What's up?

BARBARA: Oh, I'm so excited about our vacation plans. Daddy thinks we can go to the coast on his vacation.

DORA: That would be wonderful.

BARBARA: Yes, but Mother is worried about the driving. She

doesn't think we can drive three thousand miles and back in three weeks.

DORA: Gee! Six thousand miles. That would be almost three hundred miles a day! Not even counting side trips and sight-seeing. (*Telephone bell rings.*)

DORA: Botheration! There goes another bell! Another score for Mr. Wizard.

BARBARA: What in the world are you talking about?

DORA: Oh nothing. Excuse me, please, till I answer the phone. (*At phone*) Hello . . . Hello . . . Who? . . . No, this isn't the Roosevelt Garage. You must have the wrong number. (*She hangs up.*) Humph! Wrong number!

BARBARA: I wanted to ask you to go downtown with me. I have a lot of errands to do for Mother. Have to stop at the lending library for one thing. She must owe a fortune on this book. . . . "The Riddle of the Red Room." It was two cents a day in the first place, plus an extra fee of two cents a day after the first two weeks, and she's had it over a month. She'll owe enough to buy the book. I can't even count it up. (*Phone rings*)

DORA: Never mind counting it now. There's that phone again. Hello . . . No . . . this is the same number you called before. Sorry. Goodbye. (*Hangs up*)

BARBARA: I read the book too while Mother had it. It's pretty good. All about a murder in a town which was practically on the border between the Eastern Standard Time zone and the Central Time zone. The murderer was tripped up on his alibi because of the difference in time between the two zones.

DORA: Please . . . please, Barbara, don't talk any more about arithmetic and numbers.

BARBARA: But why? I was only telling you about the story. It's very interesting. All those time zones never meant anything to me when we studied about them in arithmetic class.

But, boy, oh boy, in this story it was a matter of life and death. (*All sorts of bells begin to ring at once—doorbell, telephone, timer, alarm clocks, striking clocks*)

BARBARA: For heaven's sake, what is going on?

ANNIE (*Running in from kitchen*): Heaven help us! The house must be on fire. Answer the phone. Answer the doorbell.

DORA: It's really nothing, honest it isn't. Just keep calm and you'll see. There's no one at the door and no one on the phone. It's . . . well . . . it's just one of those things.

BARBARA: One of what things? (*Bells stop ringing*)

DORA: There! I told you things would calm down.

ANNIE: I'm going back to my kitchen and stay there till your mother comes home. When she's around there are no such goings on! (*Exit* ANNIE)

BARBARA: And I'm going downtown and get started on those errands. Are you coming with me, Dora?

DORA: Not this time, Barbara, if you'll excuse me. I . . . I have some figuring to do.

BARBARA: O.K. I'll see you later. But you really better get your mother to call an electrician to fix those bells.

DORA: I'll take care of it. (*Walks toward door*) And thanks for asking me to go along. (DORA *and* BARBARA *exit. Speaking offstage*) So long, Bobby. (MR. WIZARD *enters from opposite side of stage just before* DORA *re-enters.*)

MR. WIZARD: Well, my dear, things got pretty hot for you there for a while. Do you have your score card ready?

DORA: Yes, Mr. Wizard, and you win with a perfect score of twelve. I guess you must have been right all the time.

MR. WIZARD: It's nice of you to admit it.

DORA: Now that you've won, what do you want me to do?

MR. WIZARD: I want you to take another look at that report card you were trying to hide when I came in.

DORA (*Getting it from table*): I didn't want to look at it because I was ashamed of it. Larry always gets wonderful marks in arithmetic.

MR. WIZARD: Never mind Larry. Read what it says on the back of your card.

DORA (*Reading*): "With a little effort and serious application Dora could make real progress in this subject, but she doesn't seem to take any interest in it."

MR. WIZARD: Now that you have seen that arithmetic really is for girls as well as for boys, how about that *effort* and *application*, Dora?

DORA: Mr. Wizard, I'll make another bargain with you. Drop around this time next month and I'll show you a report card that will really dazzle you.

MR. WIZARD: It's a deal. In the meantime, I think your whole family would be pleased if you looked in on the second half of that TV program. You *do* want your Dad and brother to win, don't you?

DORA: Of course, I do! And let me tell you, Mr. Wizard, if they have any contests for mother-and-daughter teams, Mom and I are going to go into training.

MR. WIZARD: Wonderful! And now, if you'll excuse me . . .

DORA: Never mind vanishing, Mr. Wizard. You can go out the front door with me. I have an idea that from now on you and I will be seeing a great deal of each other. (*Exit as curtain falls.*)

THE END

Pilgrim Parting

(Colonial Life)

Characters

MASTER CHILTON, *a Pilgrim father*
MISTRESS CHILTON, *a Pilgrim mother*
MILES CHILTON, *their son*
COMFORT CHILTON, *their daughter*
SAILOR HUMPHREY, *of the* Mayflower *crew*
MASTER JONES, *Captain of the* Mayflower
SQUANTO, *an Indian friend*
JOHN CARVER, *Governor of Plymouth*
WILLIAM BRADFORD, *author of the Mayflower Compact*
ELDER BREWSTER, *a leader of Plymouth*
JOHN ALDEN
PRISCILLA MULLENS
MISTRESS HOPKINS
MISTRESS BRADFORD
CROWD, *Pilgrim men, women, and children*

TIME: *Early, on the morning of April 5, 1621.*
SETTING: *The beach at Plymouth, Massachusetts.*
AT RISE: *The* Mayflower *is about to sail on her return journey to England.* MISTRESS MARY *and* MASTER JOHN CHILTON *enter.* MASTER CHILTON *carries a small sea chest. His wife carries two cloaks over her arm and a covered basket.*

MASTER CHILTON: This chest is not over-heavy. Have you packed all the children's things?

108

MISTRESS CHILTON: Everything but their cloaks; and these they will need with them, for the nights will be chill once they are out at sea.

MASTER CHILTON: How about the provisions?

MISTRESS CHILTON: The basket is filled to the brim. I do hope they don't gobble everything at once and make themselves sick.

MASTER CHILTON: We'll turn the basket over to Master Jones. He'll dole out the food as they need it.

MISTRESS CHILTON (*Pointing offstage*): Just look, John, how lightly the *Mayflower* rides the waves.

MASTER CHILTON: Aye, lass. The London merchants will be sore vexed when they discover she comes home without a cargo. The men have loaded her with stones for ballast, but even so, she sits high in the water.

MISTRESS CHILTON: Oh, John, do you not wish . . .

MASTER CHILTON: Aye, Mary. I sometimes wish we were going back with Miles and Comfort, but we have set our hopes in this new land.

MISTRESS CHILTON: 'Tis hard to part with them, John. They are so young!

MASTER CHILTON: Cousin Allen and his wife will give them a good home and they will be well brought up. Miles will have his schooling and Comfort will be taught all the arts a housewife should know.

MISTRESS CHILTON: And best of all, they will be safe. Safe from savages and the plague.

MASTER CHILTON: We have naught to complain of with the savages here, Mary. They have been kind and helpful.

MISTRESS CHILTON: So far! But we know not when they may change! And the sickness! It has taken a terrible toll this winter. Think of it, John, fifteen of the twenty-one boys in the colony, struck down by death, in a single year.

MASTER CHILTON: It has been a dreadful winter. But all that

is behind us now. We face the springtime and summer.

MISTRESS CHILTON: And after that, another winter. I cannot bear to have Miles and Comfort endure another siege of illness. Better to send them back to England where they will be safe and happy.

MASTER CHILTON: Aye, they will be happy there.

MISTRESS CHILTON: Perhaps not at first. I am afraid they are sorely grieved at leaving. Comfort has been weeping and Miles looks like a thundercloud. They prefer to stay here.

MASTER CHILTON: It is not for them to decide. They will do as their elders bid them. Come, Mary, we had better go back to the house and waken them. There is still much to be done 'twixt now and the hour of sailing.

MISTRESS CHILTON: Will it not seem strange, John, to look out to sea and not sight the familiar outline of the *Mayflower?*

MASTER CHILTON: Aye, there will be a lonesome spot on the horizon. She is our last link with home.

MISTRESS CHILTON: We'd better be going before we are beset with homesickness. Look, here comes Sailor Humphrey. He can take the chest down to the shallop.

MASTER CHILTON: Good day to you, sir. 'Tis a fine day you have for sailing.

SAILOR: Aye, sir. That it is. Be these the parcels for the *Mayflower?*

MISTRESS CHILTON: The basket is filled with provisions, so take care to keep it upright.

SAILOR: I'll keep it on even keel, ma'am. Are the children ready for the voyage?

MISTRESS CHILTON: We're letting them lie abed till the last moment. They're loath to leave this place.

SAILOR: Humph! They do not know how lucky they are to be getting back to civilization. Their elders would do well to climb aboard with them.

MASTER CHILTON: No doubt you're right, sir. But this land

has a strange hold upon you, once you've weathered a winter here.

SAILOR: Too strange for me to understand, sir. I can only understand I'm heading back to England where there be towns and cities and no savages prowlin' in the underbrush!

MISTRESS CHILTON: I trust you'll keep a sharp eye on the children, sir. Our Miles is a venturesome youth.

SAILOR: Aye, ma'am. Master Jones will see that he comes to no harm on the voyage.

MASTER CHILTON: Thank you, sir, and good morning. Come, Mary. (*Exit* MISTRESS CHILTON *with her husband.* SAILOR HUMPHREY *picks up the chest, basket and cloaks.*)

SAILOR: My pockets be bulging already with messages and parcels for folks back in England! And I'm ready to set my feet on a rolling deck again and feel a good stiff wind in my face. (*Sniffing at basket*) Umm! Mistress Chilton must have tucked some extra goodies in this basket. The smell fair makes my mouth water. (MILES *and* COMFORT *enter. They are excited and out of breath.*)

MILES: Wait! Oh, please wait, Sailor Humphrey.

SAILOR: Well, bless my buttons, if it isn't our two little passengers! Good morning to you, my little mates.

COMFORT: Good morning, sir. May we please have our cloaks?

MILES: And the basket?

SAILOR: Nay, nay, children. I'm a husky fellow, as a sailor should be. These parcels weigh like a feather on my shoulders.

MILES: But it isn't that, sir.

COMFORT: It's our cloaks. We . . . we want to wear them.

SAILOR: Surely you'll not be needing your cloaks on a fine spring morning like this.

MILES: And the basket, sir. We . . . we . . . well, you see . . . we haven't had any breakfast.

SAILOR: That I understand, young fellow. But I just heard

your mother say she was on her way home to prepare it.
So ye'd better run back to the house and fill your stomach
with a last home-cooked meal.

MILES: But' . . . we don't want any breakfast. You see, we
just—well, please, Sailor Humphrey, we've just got to have
that basket.

COMFORT: And the cloaks too. It will be cold in the forest
and . . .

SAILOR: Cold in the forest? What kind of talk is that for a
seagoing maid?

MILES: Hold your tongue, Comfort. I told you to let me do
the talking. Now you've given our plan away straight off!

SAILOR: Plan? And what plan are you thinking of, Master
Miles Chilton? Whatever it is, I have a notion your father
and mother know naught of it.

MILES: Oh, please, Sailor Humphrey. Please, help us! All we
ask is that you give us our cloaks and the basket of food.

COMFORT: So we do not die of cold and starvation.

SAILOR (*Putting down chest and sitting on it*): Now what is
all this talk of death of cold and starvation when in less than
an hour you will be safely aboard the *Mayflower* bound for
jolly old England?

MILES: But that's just it. We're not going.

SAILOR: Not going?

MILES: No. We're running away.

COMFORT: And hiding in the woods until the ship is safely out
of sight.

SAILOR (*With a whistle of surprise*): So that's the lay of the
land, is it? And what do you think your father will do
when he finds you, you young rascal?

MILES: I don't want to think about that just now, sir. But
nothing he does will bring back the *Mayflower*. No matter
how we are punished, we'll be able to stay here in Plymouth.

SAILOR: Your head must be sadly addled, my boy, to risk the dangers of the forest and your father's anger to stay in this miserable spot.

COMFORT: It's not a miserable spot, sir, but a fine settlement, and we wish to grow up here as the settlement grows. One of these days you will see a fair town on this very spot with streets and churches and towers and steeples, like those you see in London.

SAILOR: Not me, my lass. Not me! Once I set foot on England's soil again, I make no more voyages to the new world. 'Tis fit only for the redskins and the porcupines.

MILES: Please, sir, we do not have time for much more talk. In a few moments everyone will be coming down to the shore to see the *Mayflower* sail.

SAILOR: And in a few minutes I mean to have you two on board where you belong.

COMFORT: There's no persuading him, Miles. We'll have to go without our cloaks and without the food.

MILES: Surely you can understand, Sailor Humphrey. You told me yourself how you ran away from home and went to sea when you were no older than Comfort. Surely what we are doing is not as bad as that.

COMFORT: We are only running away from the sea to stay at home.

MILES: And we will be with our own parents. No matter how angry Father may be or how severely he may punish us for our disobedience, he will forgive us! He will even be glad we have stayed, after his anger cools down a bit.

COMFORT: And even Mother will be glad. She was crying last night at the thought of our leaving.

SAILOR: You are a fine pair with words, I must admit. True, I did run away to sea when I was less than your age. But . . . nevertheless—

COMFORT: Please, Sailor Humphrey, please help us.

SAILOR (*Rising and handing them the cloaks and basket*): Very well! I'll help ye! But don't holler for me when your father takes the birch to ye both! (*Picking up chest*) This chest I'll put in the shallop according to orders. Now make yourselves scarce before you get *me* into trouble along with yourselves.

CHILDREN: Oh, thank you! Thank you!

MILES: We'll have to run for it, Comfort. Any moment now, and they'll discover we've gone.

SAILOR: If the redskins have your scalps before sunset, it's no fault of mine.

COMFORT: They won't harm us, sir. Remember, they have signed a pledge. Massasoit will not let his people hurt our people and we will not let our people hurt his people.

SAILOR: Fine words on paper! Fine words indeed!

COMFORT: But they mean them. Truly they do.

MILES: Hurry, Comfort. There's no time for chatter. Come. (*Exit children.*)

SAILOR: No doubt I am doing wrong, but I cannot resist the look in their eyes! They're just like all the rest who insist on staying in this barren land. Dolts and simpletons I call them, every one! (*Starts to exit as* CAPTAIN JONES *enters followed by* GOVERNOR CARVER, ELDER BREWSTER, WILLIAM BRADFORD, JOHN ALDEN, MISTRESS BRADFORD, PRISCILLA MULLENS, MISTRESS HOPKINS *and a large group of men, women and children*)

MASTER JONES: What's that about *dolts* and *simpletons*, my lad?

SAILOR: 'Tis my opinion, sire, of those who refuse your kind invitation to sail back to England on the *Mayflower*.

MASTER JONES: An opinion which I share, in part, Master Humphrey, but something tells me these dolts and simpletons are men of great courage and strong faith. Better get that gear on board the shallop. We'll be taking off for the *Mayflower* in a few minutes.

MISTRESS HOPKINS (*Pressing forward with a parcel and a letter*): Oh Master Jones, pray deliver this letter and parcel for me, when you reach London.

WILLIAM BRADFORD: Fie, Mistress Hopkins, the man is sorely overladen now with our messages and bundles.

MASTER JONES: Always room for one more, Mistress Hopkins. You may rest assured they will be delivered, have I the good fortune to return in safety. But what about yourselves? Can I not deliver a passenger or two as well? My offer is still open. I will take anyone who wants to go.

PRISCILLA (*Stepping forward*): Anyone at all, Master Jones?

JOHN ALDEN: Surely not you, Priscilla. You would not go back to England, would you?

PRISCILLA: I was only thinking of England in the spring, John. How beautiful it is. The blossoms, and the sweet air of summer! It fair made me homesick—just for a minute.

GOVERNOR CARVER: And I have no doubt the thought of home and springtime has made others homesick too, Mistress Mullens. As Governor of the Colony, I wish to say there is no hold that binds any of you to spend another winter here. Anyone who wants to is free to go. There would be no disgrace in returning home.

MASTER JONES: In my opinion, it is pure folly for some of you to face another winter here, when you are worn from sickness and lack of proper food.

ELDER BREWSTER: 'Tis a sign from Above that we have endured those hardships, Master Jones, and though we thank you for the offer, we would stay where the hand of the Lord has directed us.

MASTER JONES: But the children. Think of the children. Will you have them grow up among the savages.

WILLIAM BRADFORD: The Chiltons are sending their children back with you, and other parents know they have the same opportunity. (*Enter* MISTRESS *and* MASTER CHILTON.)

MASTER CHILTON: How long till sailing time, Master Jones?

MASTER JONES: We'll get under way at full tide, sir, almost as soon as we row out to the *Mayflower*. Where are our little passengers?

MASTER CHILTON: That's just the trouble, sir. Where are they?

MISTRESS CHILTON: Has anyone here seen Miles and Comfort?

MISTRESS BRADFORD: You look frightened, Mistress Chilton. Has anything happened to the children?

MISTRESS CHILTON: Anything might have happened to them in this wilderness. I fear they have wandered off into the forest and are lost.

MASTER CHILTON: Do not fret, Mary. They know every foot of this forest, at least in the immediate neighborhood. And if they have wandered off, they have had a purpose in so doing. If Master Jones grants me the time, I will fetch them back in time to give them a taste of the birch before they go aboard.

MASTER JONES: We must catch the tide at its height, sir. If the children are here in time, they may come aboard, but we cannot delay our sailing.

BOY: Miles said he'd never go back to England, no matter what his father said.

GIRL: Hush, Jonathan! Would you be a tell-tale and get the lad in trouble?

MASTER CHILTON: They'll be in bad trouble when I find them, child. And the lad is no tell-tale to be saying what I already know. They have run away rather than leave Plymouth.

MISTRESS CHILTON: Oh, John, how could they be so disobedient?

SAILOR (*Entering*): The shallop is ready, sir, as soon as you come aboard.

MASTER JONES: I am sorry, friend, but I cannot delay.

MISTRESS CHILTON: The chest! The chest! And the provisions? Where are they?

SAILOR: I will unload the chest at once, ma'am. (*Exit*)

MASTER JONES: It is hard for me to bid farewell to such a courageous and God-fearing people. I have lived among you for seven months. I have seen you face suffering, starvation, and death without complaint. And now I see you ready to face those same dangers again. Truly your faith is great. It is with real sorrow that I bid you farewell. (*Turns to exit*)

GOVERNOR CARVER: Our thanks and our prayers go with you, Master Jones.

ELDER BREWSTER: May you have a safe and blessed journey over the perilous waves. (*Enter* SQUANTO *with* COMFORT *and* MILES.)

SQUANTO: Hold! Squanto bring children back for trip on big water! (COMFORT *runs to her mother.* MILES *and his father face each other.*)

MISTRESS CHILTON: Thank fortune, you have come in time!

MASTER CHILTON (*Shaking* MILES): Shame on you, Miles! 'Tis your good fortune that I have not the time to give you the trouncing you deserve!

MILES: I'm sorry, Father, for running away, and I am glad Squanto made us return.

COMFORT: Squanto says no brave man ever turns his back on trouble.

SQUANTO: White children learn to face danger. Never turn back.

MILES: We thought we were being brave to run away. But now I know we are brave only if we stay and face you and Mother and the rest. Father, we cannot go with Master Jones on the *Mayflower*.

MASTER CHILTON: What talk is this to your father? "Cannot

go" indeed. You *must* go because I, your father, command you.

MILES: Nay, Father. It's not right that you force us to go back to England against our will.

MISTRESS CHILTON: Miles! You must not speak so to your father.

MASTER CHILTON: Who are you to talk of right and wrong, Miles? You are but a child. Your parents know what is best for you.

MILES: But I am speaking of our rights, sir.

MASTER CHILTON (*In anger*): Rights? What rights have you?

MILES: I am speaking of the just and equal laws that Master Bradford wrote about in the Compact you all signed before you left the *Mayflower*.

MASTER CHILTON: Silence! I will hear no more of this talk.

GOVERNOR CARVER: Nay, Master Chilton. Let the lad speak. What is this about the Compact, Miles?

MILES: 'Twas the day we landed at Cape Cod, sir. The men all gathered in the cabin of the *Mayflower* to sign the Compact Master Bradford wrote.

GOVERNOR CARVER: Aye, that we did, lad.

MILES: After the gentlemen left, sir, some of us boys went in, and Master Bradford explained the words to us. It said you all agreed to form just and equal laws for the general good of the colony. We asked Master Bradford if those just and equal laws were for everyone, young and old, rich and poor, and he said they were.

MASTER BRADFORD: That is right, Miles. And so they are. The Compact reads that we agree to "enact, constitute and frame such just and equal laws, ordinances, acts, constitutions, and offices, from time to time, as shall be thought most meet and convenient for the general good of the colony."

MILES: And Comfort and I are part of the colony, sir. We have faced the same dangers, we have done our share of the work, and we feel the same strong love in our hearts for this place. Unless it be for "the general good of the colony" to send us away, we claim it is our right to stay here with the rest.

MASTER CHILTON: You have forgotten, my son, the Scriptures say: "Children, obey your parents in all things, for this is well pleasing to the Lord."

ELDER BREWSTER: But remember also, Master Chilton, the next verse of the same Scripture reminds us: "Fathers, provoke not your children to wrath, lest they be discouraged." Perhaps we would do well to hear the lad and take council.

MASTER BRADFORD: Why do you feel so strongly, Miles, about leaving Plymouth?

MILES: Comfort and I are not too young to remember the talk before we left England. We have not forgotten how our elders spoke of worshiping God without fear in our own way, and told us we would build a strong new colony here in America, where men could work and worship as they pleased. Now we are part of this place. We want to build and work with the rest.

COMFORT: We do not want to go back to the old ways.

MISTRESS CHILTON: But think of your future . . . your schooling.

MASTER BRADFORD: There are scholarly men here, Mistress Chilton. Our children will not grow up in ignorance.

MISTRESS CHILTON: But the dangers . . . the cold, the sickness, the threat of starvation.

SQUANTO: Squanto's friends not starve. Squanto teach white men to plant corn, Indian way. Good harvest. Plenty for all.

ELDER BREWSTER: As for sickness and danger, we can only look for protection to the One who has guided us safely thus far in our destiny.

GOVERNOR CARVER: What say you, Master Chilton? Is it for

the general good of the colony that your lad and lass sail this day on the *Mayflower*?

MASTER BRADFORD: Our colony will need strong young muscles, and clear young minds for the work that lies ahead.

MASTER CHILTON (*Looking at wife*): Is it for the general good of the colony, Mary, or for the peace of our own minds and hearts?

MISTRESS CHILTON: Perhaps we have been selfish, John. I will abide by the decision of wiser heads than mine.

MASTER CHILTON: Well, Miles, it looks as if you have won the fight for yourself and for Comfort. The *Mayflower* sails without you.

MILES *and* COMFORT: Oh, thank you, thank you, Father.

GOVERNOR CARVER: A wise decision, Master Chilton, and one you will never regret. As for you, Miles and Comfort, remember you promise all due submission and obedience to these same just and equal laws we may henceforth make for the general good of the colony. Do you understand?

MILES: We understand, sir, and we are ready to follow your orders.

MASTER JONES: Well spoken, lad. I am sorry I will not have you and your sister aboard. But good fortune to you both.

MILES *and* COMFORT: Thank you, sir, and Godspeed! (*Enter* SAILOR HUMPHREY *with chest.*)

SAILOR: So they caught up with you, did they, just as I said they would. Now I'll have to carry this chest down to the boat again.

MASTER JONES: Nay, leave it here, lad. Our passengers are not sailing with us after all. (*To* GOVERNOR CARVER) Goodbye, sir, and God bless this colony. (*To* SAILOR HUMPHREY) Come, lad, we sail at once. (SAILOR HUMPHREY *and* MASTER JONES *exit as people wave and call goodbyes.*)

PRISCILLA: Oh, John, they're going home, back home to England.

JOHN ALDEN: This is your home now, Priscilla. Our home, for
always. Come, let us all go up to Fort Hill and watch the
Mayflower sail out of the harbor. Captain Standish has
promised a proper salute from our guns.

ELDER BREWSTER: Not without a psalm, my son, and a prayer
for those who go and for those who stay. Let us bow our
heads. (*All bow heads and sing to the tune of "Old Hundred."*)

> "All people that on earth do dwell
>   Sing to the Lord with cheerful voice,
> Him serve with fear, his praise forth tell,
>   Come ye before him and rejoice."

THE END

The Bread and Butter Shop

(Bread)

Characters

GRANNY GRAYSON, *proprietor of the Bread and Butter Shop*

TILLIE
REBECCA
HILDA
CHLOE } *her Saturday helpers*
STELLA
SONIA

SELMA, *a newcomer*

OFFICER DURGIN, *a customer*

TOUGHY
SQUAREHEAD } *his pals*
KNUCKLES

LING FOO
MRS. CADBURY } *customers*

MRS. AVERY, *a Den Mother*

JERRY
PHIL
PETER
RALPH } *the Cub Scouts*
TED
DANNY
BILLY

SETTING: GRANNY GRAYSON'S *shop.*

AT RISE: GRANNY *is kneading bread at her worktable surrounded by six children of different national types who sing as they work.*

CHILDREN (*Singing and going through motions to the tune of "The Mulberry Bush"*):

This is the way we knead our dough, knead our dough, knead our dough,
This is the way we knead our dough, so early on baking morning.

This is the way we pat our dough, pat our dough, pat our dough,
This is the way we pat our dough, so early on baking morning.

This is the way we grease our pans, grease our pans, grease our pans,
This is the way we grease our pans, so early on baking morning.

This is the way we shape our loaves, shape our loaves, shape our loaves,
This is the way we shape our loaves, so early on baking morning.
(*They march around table to stove.*)

This is the way we bake our bread, bake our bread, bake our bread,
This is the way we bake our bread, so early on baking morning.

GRANNY (*Puts loaves in oven. If it is impossible to have stove on stage, she merely passes bread pans off stage*): Now we'll just pop 'em into the oven and wait till they're done.

TILLIE: But look, Granny, you have some dough left over.

GRANNY: Never you mind about that dough, Tillie. I'm going to make a batch of rolls with that. (*Gets muffin pans*)

CHILDREN: Cinnamon rolls, Granny?

GRANNY: I might put a mite of cinnamon and sugar on them just to please you young'uns.

REBECCA: How did you ever learn to bake such delicious bread and rolls, Granny?

GRANNY: Land sakes, it just comes natural. Besides, didn't I ever tell you children who my father was?

ALL: No! Who was he?

GRANNY: Why bless my soul, he was the Muffin Man.

ALL: The Muffin Man?

GRANNY: The very same . . . the Muffin Man who lived in Drury Lane. (*Singing*) Oh, do you know the muffin man, the muffin man, the muffin man?

Oh, do you know the muffin man that lives in Drury Lane?

CHILDREN (*Singing*): Oh yes, we know the muffin man, the muffin man, the muffin man,

Oh yes, we know the muffin man who lives in Drury Lane.

GRANNY: Well, our whole family set a powerful store by baking. 'Twouldn't seem like home if I couldn't smell a batch of bread baking in the oven.

STELLA: But just think, Granny, most of the children in this town had never smelled bread baking in the oven before you opened your Bread and Butter Shop.

SONIA: No. We always got our bread at the bakery.

GRANNY: Well, bakeries smell mighty good, too; and they bake it the same way except that machines do most of the work.

HILDA: But it's more exciting to watch you mix the flour with the yeast, milk, salt, sugar and lard and set it away to rise.

SONIA: That dough you mixed yesterday had puffed up almost twice its size by this morning.

GRANNY: That's what makes it light and fluffy when we take it out of the oven.

HILDA: I feel sorry for people who have to eat dry, hard bread.

GRANNY: Well, you don't need to feel sorry for 'em, child. Plenty of people in the world like their bread hard and dry. They make it that way a-purpose. By the way, where is Selma? She's not with you today.

CHILDREN (*Look at each other in embarrassment*): We . . . we don't exactly know.

HILDA: She hasn't played with us this week in school.

TILLIE: She doesn't laugh and joke with us any more.

GRANNY: Is she angry about something? Did you quarrel over some silly thing?

SONIA: No, we didn't quarrel . . . only . . . well, to tell the truth, I think it's the lunches.

GRANNY: What is the trouble with the lunches?

REBECCA: Since Selma has started carrying her lunch to school, she does not join us at noontime.

TILLIE: No, she eats all by herself.

GRANNY: Do you have any idea why?

STELLA: I think maybe it is her bread.

GRANNY: Her bread?

STELLA: Yes, she carries some funny looking, funny smelling bread in her lunch box. I . . . I think she is ashamed of it.

GRANNY: Ashamed of her bread? No one should be ashamed of the bread he eats.

STELLA: I don't know why she is ashamed of it, Granny, but it *is* different.

TILLIE: And it doesn't look very good.

SONIA: I offered to give her one of my sandwiches but she wouldn't take any.

GRANNY (*Shaking her head*): No, of course not. Poor child!

TILLIE: But what can we do, Granny? We want to be friends with Selma.

GRANNY: If it is her bread that is troubling her, offering her some of yours is not the cure.

TILLIE: But what *is* the cure?

GRANNY: I can't be sure, but if I were you, I'd try asking her for some of hers.

SONIA: But it looks dark and it smells so funny.

GRANNY: But maybe it has a delicious taste. You must learn to be adventurous in your eating. Who do you suppose was ever brave enough to taste the first oyster or eat the first sweet potato?

REBECCA: I think you've given us something to think about, Granny.

GRANNY: And now I must give you something to do. (*Pulling slip from apron pocket*) My grocery list this week is so long, I can easily use six little shoppers to go to the store. Tillie, here's my pocketbook. You girls run down to Mr. Timkin's and bring me my order. First thing you know I'll be plumb out of flour and sugar and yeast and shortening, and milk, and butter and eggs . . . and then I'd be in a pretty kettle of fish.

TILLIE: We're at your service, Granny. C'mon, girls.

HILDA: We'll be back before you can say "Jack Sprat." (*Girls exit.*)

GRANNY: Land sakes! What would I ever do without my Saturday helpers? They keep this place humming busier than a beehive. (*Shop bell rings. Enter* SELMA) Why bless my soul if it isn't my little neighbor Selma. Good morning, dear. What can I do for you?

SELMA: I . . . I want to buy a loaf of bread.

GRANNY: A loaf of bread? And just what kind would you like?

SELMA: I don't exactly know. Just so it's the very whitest bread in your shop and cut in the thinnest slices.

GRANNY: Ummmm. White bread, you say? Are you sure you wouldn't want a nice fresh loaf of brown bread?

SELMA: No! No! It must be white! I hate brown bread!

GRANNY: Why, what a curious thing to say, my dear. Some of the best bread in the world is made from dark flour. That's one good thing about bread, Selma. There's a kind to suit every taste and every climate. *We* use wheat flour in our part of the world, but other countries use rice, oats, rye and even beans for flour.

SELMA: They do? Even rich people?

GRANNY: Rich or poor has nothing to do with it. In some countries people bake their bread in large sheets and store it in the attic until they are ready to eat it, maybe months later.

SELMA: They do? How does it taste?

GRANNY: I don't rightly know, child. But I know it tastes good to the people who make it that way. There's nothing tastes any better than the bread our mothers bake for us.

SELMA: Oh, Granny, you must be a mind reader. My mother bakes dark bread with seeds and spices. We love it at our house, but when I take it to school, all the other children stare. Last week one of the girls offered me one of her sandwiches because she felt sorry for me.

GRANNY: Nonsense, Selma. She offered you the sandwich just to be friendly. Aren't you being just a bit silly to be ashamed of the bread you eat?

SELMA: Well . . . maybe I am . . . but all the other girls. . . .

GRANNY: Now, don't you worry about all the other girls. If you stay in my shop a while, you'll meet all sorts of folks coming in here for all sorts of strange bread and cakes. Would you like to stay and watch?

SELMA: I'd love to, Granny, if I won't be in the way.

GRANNY: There's room for all my friends, Selma, and some of yours will be popping in here in just a few minutes. My regular Saturday helpers went to the store for me . . . and here they are . . . back before I've turned around. (*The six shoppers enter laden with packages.*)

HILDA: We got everything on the list, Granny. (*They see* SELMA.)

TILLIE: Hello, Selma. Where did you come from?

REBECCA: We're so glad to see you. Isn't it fun to be here in Granny's shop?

SELMA: Granny said I may stay and watch the customers.

SONIA: That's fine. You'll love it. We always have such a good time.

GRANNY: Just take the groceries in the back room, girls. (*Girls exit and return quickly*) Selma and I have just been talking about all the strange breads people eat in different corners of the globe.

CHLOE: I guess it's like the old rhyme about pease porridge:

> Some like it hot, some like it cold,
> Some like it in the pot, nine days old.

SELMA: I guess maybe there's nothing strange after all about eating hard, dry bread.

REBECCA: Of course not. I'll bring you a taste of the matzoh we eat at the Passover. It's hard and brittle, but it's very good.

TILLIE: Speaking of hard bread, what could be harder than toast? We dry out fresh bread to make it hard and dry because we like it that way.

HILDA: I love toast. In fact, we know a little poem about it.

> Toast! toast!
> Crisp, crunchy toast,
> All golden with butter
> Is what I like most.

SONIA: Toast! toast!
             Smothered in jam,
             Or holding an egg
             With a wee bit of ham.

TILLIE: Toast! toast!
             And a cup of hot tea
             Will make me feel better
             When sick as can be.

STELLA: Toast! toast!
             Oh, the heavenly smell
             Brings me running to breakfast
             Ahead of the bell!

SELMA: I never realized toast was just hard, dry bread. I thought you girls liked nothing but soft white bread.

CHLOE: That would leave out my good yellow corn bread. We love corn bread and spoon bread at our house.

HILDA: Spoon bread? What's that?

CHLOE: Spoon bread is made with corn meal but it's more like a pudding that you eat with a fork and spread with butter. It's delicious.

TILLIE: And what about shortnin' bread. That always makes me hungry just to sing about it. (*They sing "Shortnin' Bread.*")

SONIA: How about it, Granny? Will you make us some shortnin' bread?

ALL: Please, Granny. (*Sing*) Granny's li'l helpers love shortnin' bread!

GRANNY: Now, go along with you. How do you expect me to get my rolls in the oven with you pestering me all the time? (*Brandishes spoon at them*) Clear out of my way now. These rolls are ready for the oven. (*Puts rolls in oven*) Now, let's clear this mess away.

REBECCA: Don't tell me you've finished baking, Granny.

GRANNY: Just about, although I might stir up a batch of oat cakes for Mrs. McClosky! Poor lamb! She's that homesick for Scotland, she's plumb sick.

TILLIE: How about Mr. Viener's apple strudel? You promised him for sure.

GRANNY: Land o' Goshen, child, I baked that strudel before the sun was up!

SONIA: And the little cakes with the caraway seeds for Mrs. Svenson? Are they finished?

GRANNY: All ready and in one of those paper bags on the counter.

STELLA: Is it true, Granny, that you know how to make all the breads and cakes in the world?

GRANNY: Now what ever put such a thought into your head, child? Course it's not true. I just collect recipes from my neighbors and make the bread and cakes they loved as children. That's all.

TILLIE: I used to be awfully fond of pancakes when I was a child, Granny. Would you make some for me?

GRANNY (*Laughing and clouting her with a spoon*): Your mamma will make you pancakes any time you get hungry for them, Tillie-Sillie. My special baking is for poor, lost, homesick people who are hungry for the tastes and smells of their homelands.

TILLIE: But I really am hungry for pancakes, Granny. Are pancakes bread?

GRANNY: Sure thing. Lots of people in the world make their bread like pancakes. Some of them spread the pancakes with chopped meat and peppers, roll 'em up and eat 'em the same as we eat sandwiches.

SONIA: The Mexicans call their pancakes *tortillas*.

STELLA: I like to watch the cooks baking pancakes in restaurant windows. It reminds me of the poem we learned in school.

(*She recites the poem by Christina Rossetti.*)

> "Mix a pancake,
> Stir a pancake,
> Pop it in the pan.
> Fry the pancake,
> Toss the pancake,
> Catch it if you can."

GRANNY: That reminds me of the story my mother used to tell about the little pancake who ran away.

ALL: Tell us! Tell us! Please!

GRANNY: Hush your clamoring! I can't be telling stories and playing with you children when my rolls are baking.

CHLOE: But we're not playing, Granny. We're helping.

SELMA: And I am learning ever so many things.

GRANNY: I'm glad of that, child. (*Shop bell rings.*) Quick! There's the shop bell. Somebody's coming.

ALL: A customer! A customer!

CHLOE: Let me wait on him, please, Granny.

ALL: No! No! Let me! (*Enter* POLICEMAN *with three boys.*)

OFFICER DURGIN: Good morning, Granny. Here we are for our doughnuts!

TILLIE: What can I do for you, Officer Durgin?

OFFICER DURGIN: You can bring me my regular order plus six extra for my pals. (TILLIE *gets doughnuts.*)

GRANNY: How is the doughnut treatment working, Officer?

OFFICER DURGIN: Just fine, Granny. Toughy and Squarehead and Knuckles haven't had a single fight since we've been coming here for doughnuts.

GRANNY: Boys can't fight very well with their tummies full of my doughnuts.

OFFICER DURGIN: You've got something there, Granny. If a doughnut a day will keep fights away, I'm all for 'em. How about you, fellows?

TOUGHY: We think they're swell.

SQUAREHEAD: The best I ever ate, ma'am.

KNUCKLES: I'm gonna take one of mine home for my kid brother. Maybe it will help him get in a better humor and stay there.

GRANNY: Bring your little brother around and I'll see what some bread and butter and brown sugar can do for him. That's what I always fed my little boys when they were cross and fidgety.

TILLIE: Here are your doughnuts, sir. Hope you enjoy them.

OFFICER DURGIN: You can be sure of that, sister. This whole neighborhood seems to be a different place since Granny opened her Bread and Butter Shop. Got anything new I ought to try today, Granny?

GRANNY: Well, let me see. Have you had any more trouble with those two fellows from Denmark?

OFFICER DURGIN: No trouble exactly, Granny. But they're still pretty standoffish and unfriendly. I don't think they trust me.

GRANNY (*Fixing a paper bag*): Then here. I have the very thing. Some good fresh "Weinerbrod" or Danish pastry. Give them these the next time you see them, and I'll bet they'll be your friends for life.

OFFICER DURGIN (*Peering into bag*): Ummm! They look good. I'll have to sample them myself. What are those little specks on top?

GRANNY: Those are cardamom seeds—taste spicy like ginger. You'll like 'em.

OFFICER DURGIN: Well, thanks a lot, Granny. Now come on, boys, before we let our eyes get bigger than our stomachs. (*Exit* OFFICER *and boys*)

TILLIE: My goodness, Granny, we could study geography right here in your shop.

GRANNY: Best way in the world to learn about people is to

study the bread they eat. (*Shop bell rings.* LING FOO *enters.*)

LING FOO: Hello, Granny.

GRANNY: Good morning, Ling. What can I do for you?

LING FOO: Nothing today, Granny. Today *our* house sends *your* house a present. (*Extends plate covered with napkin*)

GRANNY: Ummm! These look delicious, Ling. What are they?

LING FOO: Chinese almond cakes. You'll find the recipe in this envelope. My honorable mother wishes you to have it in exchange for your secrets on American baking powder biscuits.

GRANNY: Thank you, Ling. I'll try some of these tomorrow. And tell your mother to visit me any time. We can exchange lots of baking secrets.

LING FOO (*Bowing*): I will tell her, Granny, and thank you many times. Now our poor house enjoys many good things you teach my mother to make . . . things our honorable ancestors never heard of.

GRANNY: And I have eaten some things my honorable ancestors never heard of either since I've known the Foo Family. (*Exit* LING FOO)

SELMA: Granny, you know the most interesting people.

GRANNY: People are just as interesting as the foods they eat, Selma, and here in my shop I get to know people who eat many different and exciting kinds of bread. (*Shop bell rings. Enter* MRS. CADBURY.) Oh, good morning, Mrs. Cadbury. Tell me, how were the crumpets last week?

MRS. CADBURY: Perfection, Mrs. Grayson. Absolute perfection. The best I've tasted since I left London. Albert agreed with me too, and Albert is a man who really knows his crumpets.

GRANNY: What can I do for you today, ma'am?

MRS. CADBURY: I've brought you a recipe for scones. Albert

and I are having a few friends to tea next week, and I would like to have some real scones.

GRANNY (*Looking over recipe*): Ummmm! It doesn't look too difficult.

MRS. CADBURY: Of course, you may have some trouble with the measurements. You see, all our British recipes are in pounds and ounces instead of cups.

GRANNY: So I see. Four ounces of flour, one ounce of butter.

MRS. CADBURY: That would be a cup of flour and a tablespoon of butter.

GRANNY: I'll try some tomorrow, just to get my hand in.

MRS. CADBURY: And be sure to let me know the next time you bake Indian pudding, Mrs. Grayson. Albert and I are just dying to try it.

GRANNY: I'll be sure to let you know, Mrs. Cadbury. (*Exit* MRS. CADBURY)

HILDA: Dear me! She's very friendly, isn't she? My mom always said she was "stuck-up."

GRANNY: It's hard to be "stuck-up" when you're talking about bread, Hilda. Mrs. Cadbury shares her recipes with me and I share mine with her. Now we're really getting to know each other.

SELMA (*To girls*): I guess it wasn't very friendly of me to refuse the sandwich you girls offered me. I should have offered you some of my black bread in return. Then you could have tasted mine and I could have tasted yours.

STELLA: Be sure to bring an extra slice or two on Monday, Selma, and we can sample each other's bread. (*Shop bell rings and seven Cub Scouts enter with their Den Mother.*)

GRANNY: Gracious sakes alive! What's all this?

MRS. AVERY (*Den Mother*): Good morning, Granny. I hope you don't mind the invasion, but the boys insisted I bring them over here to find out how to make flapjacks. We're going on a camping trip.

GRANNY: Well, now, I haven't baked any flapjacks for a long

time, but I think I have the recipe here somewhere. Hilda, (*Handing her a recipe book*) look through this scrapbook and see if you can find my recipe for flapjacks.

DANNY: My mom says you know how to make everything.

MRS. AVERY: Now, while you're here, boys, you better take a good look around. Our troop has taken up "bread" as our project, Granny, and we've just come from visiting the Merryvale Bakery.

BILLY: But it didn't smell as good as your shop, Granny.

JERRY: You ought to see all those machines, Granny. One big machine mixes all the dough, and another machine cuts it into pieces that are just the right weight for a loaf of bread.

PHIL: Then it is dropped into pans and stays there till it's nice and light.

PETER: Boy, oh boy! You ought to see those ovens, Granny. The men put the loaves of dough in at one end, and by the time they come out the other end, they're all baked as brown as can be.

RALPH: After the bread is cooled, the loaves are sliced by a slicing machine and wrapped in waxed paper.

DANNY: We saw them baking pies and cakes too, Granny. All the work was done by machinery.

PETER: They've even got a pretzel machine. Boy, you ought to see how that thing twists the dough into pretzels.

GRANNY: I can see you had a wonderful time at the bakery.

TED: I liked the farm visit best, though, Granny. Last week Mrs. Avery took us to a farm where we saw the wheat and talked to the farmer.

GRANNY: Now you know the whole story of bread from the wheatfield to the grocery counter.

JERRY: Not quite, Granny. We haven't been to a mill yet. I want to see how the grain is made into flour.

MRS. AVERY: We've made arrangements to visit a grist mill next week.

GRANNY: When I was a little girl we used to play a game

called "The Jolly Miller." Would you like to learn how to play it?

ALL: Yes, yes.

GRANNY: Have you found the recipe for flapjacks, Hilda?

HILDA: Yes, here it is. (*Gives it to* MRS. AVERY)

GRANNY: Thank you. Now, all of you girls and boys take partners and form a circle. Boys on the outside. I'll stand in the center and be the Miller. Now, this is how it goes. (*She sings "Jolly is the Miller" from* GAMES AND DANCES *by William A. Stecher.*) When you sing "The right steps forward and the left steps back" . . . you follow those directions and the miller scrambles to get a partner. Whoever is left out takes his turn as the new miller. Now, let's try it. (*Children sing and play game.*)

MRS. AVERY: That was a lot of fun. We'll have to play that again, boys. Now come along, we'll have to be on our way. It's almost noon.

GRANNY: And that's almost closing time for me.

GIRLS: And lunch time for us.

GRANNY: But wait a minute, girls and boys. There's one more thing I'd like to teach you before you leave . . . something I want you to remember every day when you eat your bread and butter.

CHLOE: What is it, Granny?

GRANNY: It's a very old verse that children have learned in every country about the bread they eat.

> "Back of the loaf is the snowy flour,
> And back of the flour the mill;
> And back of the mill, the wheat and the shower,
> And the sun and the Father's will."

(*Children repeat verse as curtains close.*)

THE END

Paul Revere Rides Again

(Communications)

Characters

TEACHER	COPY BOY
PAUL	NEWSPAPER EDITOR
HIS FRIEND	REPORTER
MARY	NEWSBOY
GARY	ALEXANDER GRAHAM, *radio*
AL	*announcer*
VIC	MR. CABOT
HAZEL	BOY
ROY	TV ANNOUNCER
GOLDIE	FARMER PYNCHEON
MARCIA	TV CAMERAMEN, *two*
SHIRLEY	MIKE OPERATOR
STANLEY	ATTENDANT
PHYLLIS	MAIL CARRIER
SALLY	TELEPHONE OPERATOR
	TELEGRAPH BOY

BEFORE RISE: *A group of children is seated on the apron of the stage listening to the* TEACHER *reading from Longfellow's poem, "Paul Revere's Ride."*

TEACHER:

Listen, my children, and you shall hear
Of the midnight ride of Paul Revere,
On the eighteenth of April, in Seventy-five:

137

Hardly a man is now alive
Who remembers that famous day and year.
He said to his friend:

PAUL (*Springing to his feet and clapping a three-cornered hat on his head, addresses a boy who pantomimes the part of his friend*):

'If the British march
By land or sea from the town tonight,
Hang a lantern aloft in the belfry arch
Of the North Church tower as a signal light,—
One, if by land, and two, if by sea:
And I on the opposite shore will be,
Ready to ride and spread the alarm
Through every Middlesex village and farm,
For the country folk to be up and to arm.'

TEACHER (*As boys pantomime farewell and exit*):
Then he said 'Good night!' and with muffled oar
Silently rowed to the Charlestown shore,
Just as the moon rose over the bay,
Where swinging wide at her moorings lay
The Somerset, British man-of-war.

Meanwhile his friend, through alley and street,
Wanders and watches with eager ears,
Till in the silence around him he hears
The muster of men at the barrack door,
The sound of arms and the tramp of feet,
And the measured tread of the Grenadiers,
Marching down to their boats on the shore.

Then he climbed the tower of the old North Church,
By the wooden stairs with stealthy tread,
To the belfry chamber overhead,
By the trembling ladder, steep and tall,
To the highest window in the wall,

Where he paused to listen and look down
A moment on the roofs of the town,
And the moonlight flowing over all.

GIRLS (*In unison, as* PAUL *re-enters and pantomimes action*):
Meanwhile, impatient to mount and ride,
Booted and spurred, with a heavy stride
On the opposite shore walked Paul Revere.

BOYS (*In unison*):
Now he patted his horse's side,
Now gazed at the landscape far and near,
Then, impetuous, stamped the earth,
And turned and tightened his saddle girth:

GIRLS:
But mostly he watched with eager search
The Belfry Tower of the old North Church,
As it rose above the graves on the hill,
Lonely and spectral and sombre and still.

BOYS:
And lo! as he looks on the belfry's height
A glimmer and then a gleam of light!

GIRLS:
He springs to the saddle, the bridle he turns,
But lingers, and gazes, till full on his sight,
A second lamp in the belfry burns!

SOLO GIRL: A hurry of hoofs in the village street!

SOLO BOY: A shape in the moonlight, a bulk in the dark,

SOLO GIRL: And beneath, from the pebbles in passing, a spark
Struck out by a steed flying fearless and fleet!

ALL: That was all! And yet, through the gleam and the light,
The fate of a nation was riding that night!

TEACHER: Can't you just feel the excitement and tension of
the poem, boys and girls, when we read it together?

MARY: I like that last line, Miss Eaton—"The fate of a nation
was riding that night!"

GARY: But gee willikers, Miss Eaton! The fate of the whole nation depended on those two old lanterns in the church tower. Suppose one of them had conked out at the last minute!

AL: Yeah! That would have messed up the whole thing. Paul Revere would have thought the British were coming by land instead of by sea. He would have given the wrong message.

VIC: We might have lost the whole war before it even started!

HAZEL: Wasn't it pretty risky, Miss Eaton, to depend so much on a lantern? The boys are right. Suppose one of them, or even both of them had failed to work at the last minute?

TEACHER: That was the risk they had to take, Hazel. After all, can you think of any better way they might have sent the message?

ROY: They could have used signal flags.

GARY: It was at night, stupid!

ROY: Oh, yeah. I forgot that.

GOLDIE: And you forget that most of our methods of communication hadn't been invented yet.

AL: I guess the lantern wasn't such a bad bet after all.

VIC: At least it worked all right.

MARCIA: But think how much easier the whole thing would have been if they had our sure-fire inventions.

TEACHER: Maybe you have touched on something important, Marcia. Suppose we all think about it and figure out how we'd handle things if Paul Revere should ride again.

SHIRLEY: What do you mean, Miss Eaton?

TEACHER: I mean we change the date from the 18th of April, 1775, to the eighteenth of April in the present year. General Gage has sent a body of British troops to arrest Hancock and Adams at Lexington and seize some military stores at Concord, eighteen miles northwest of Boston. It is our job to take the place of Paul Revere.

STANLEY: You mean it's up to us to warn Hancock and Adams and let the Minutemen know that the enemy is coming?

PHYLLIS: And we can use any method of communication that exists today?

TEACHER: Any, and all, methods are at your service.

VIC: Say, fellows, this is keen. I'd use radio.

SALLY: We could easily phone from Boston to Lexington.

GARY: What about the walky-talky?

TEACHER: Not so fast! Not so fast! I suggest you plan your campaign carefully and give your reports next week. Would you like to appoint some committee chairmen?

ALL: Yes! Yes! (*Much waving of hands, everyone clamoring to be chairman of something.*)

TEACHER: Very well. We'll need a general chairman. Then we should have committees for newspapers, radio, television, mail service, telephones and telegraph.

GARY: Let's get organized right away.

TEACHER: Before we take any further action, I think we should adjourn to the library where we can find some of the information we'll need. We'll also want to make arrangements to visit the newspaper office, the radio station, and the television studio. But our first stop is going to be our own school library. Come along. (TEACHER *exits with class.*)

MARY (*Entering from opposite side of the stage after a brief pause or musical interlude*): A week has passed, and our class is now ready to present a modern version of Paul Revere's warning . . . so . . .

Listen, good people, and you shall hear
Of the present-day ride of Paul Revere.
The British are coming! There's no time to lose,
But modern invention is spreading the news
To all who are waiting in doubt and in fear.
Observers are posted. If the British dare

To march away from the town tonight
The news will be covered by press and by air—
No need to depend on a lantern light.
If they're coming by land, if they're coming by sea
By phone and by radio, wire and TV,
Reporters are ready to flash the alarm
To every Middlesex village and farm
For the country folk to be up and to arm!
(*She exits as curtains open.*)

SCENE 1

SETTING: *City Room of the Boston* Star. *A desk marked* NEWS EDITOR *is at left, and there is a telephone booth at right.*

AT RISE: EDITOR *is talking to* COPY BOY.

COPY BOY: Any news, Boss?

EDITOR: Nothing, Joe. But I'm expecting a call from Ed any minute.

COPY BOY: It better come soon, Boss. The presses are ready to roll.

EDITOR: We're bound to hear soon, son. Ed always gets his story.

COPY BOY: Maybe he ran into a British Patrol or something.

EDITOR: Not Ed. He's too slippery for them. (*Light goes on in phone booth. Phone rings on* EDITOR's *desk. He grabs the phone and the audience hears the two-way conversation between him and* ED.)

EDITOR: City Desk, Boston *Star*. Bill Higgins speaking.

ED: This is Ed Morley. I've got your story. Are you ready?

EDITOR: Shoot. (*Grabbing pencil and pad*)

ED: It's a sure thing that the British are planning to move tonight. I have a hot tip from one of our men who hangs around the barracks. They've issued arms and the men have been mustered out.

EDITOR: Any news of Hancock and Adams?

ED: They're safe enough for the moment. But they want every able-bodied man in the Concord and Lexington area to be on the alert and ready for action at a minute's notice.

EDITOR: Any idea how many British troops are being called out?

ED: About eight hundred. Not too strong a force for our farmers to handle, if they get the jump on them.

EDITOR: How about the route? Are they coming by land or water?

ED: I wasn't able to find out. It's all very hush-hush, you know. I'll call you back in an hour.

EDITOR: That will be too late. We're holding the presses for this story now.

ED: Sorry. That was all my man was able to get, but he'll report the minute he gets the rest of the dope.

EDITOR: O.K. We'll urge people to use their radios and TV sets for last-minute flashes.

ED: That's all you can do. Be sure to keep a wire open for me at all times. I'll phone in every hour.

EDITOR: Right. So long, Ed, and good luck. (*Light in booth goes out.*)

EDITOR (*Tearing off sheet of notes and sticking paper into typewriter*): Stand by to rush this to the press room, Joe. This edition must hit the streets on time. (*Curtain closes as* EDITOR *types frantically.*)

NEWSBOY (*Crossing stage from left, crying his papers as he goes*): Extra! Extra! Read all about it! British expected to move on Concord tonight. Hancock and Adams reported safe! Farmers in Concord and Lexington area urged to arm and prepare for action. Extra! Extra! British prepare to attack Concord! 800 British Regulars on the march! Extra! Extra!

MARY (*Entering left as* NEWSBOY *exits right*): And so by telephone and the magic of the printed page, the citizens of Boston are informed of the movements of the British troops. The farmers, however, and citizens of the outlying districts depend largely on their radios for up-to-the-minute news coverage. We take you now to Radio Station WBTZ. (*She exits as curtains open.*)

SCENE 2

SETTING: *Studio at Radio Station WBTZ.*

AT RISE: JOHN CABOT *and* ALEXANDER GRAHAM *are seated at a table on which there is a microphone.* GRAHAM *is reporting.*

MR. GRAHAM: This is your XYZ Commentator Alexander Graham reporting to you, the people, from the studios of Station WBTZ. The big news at the moment is the movement of the British troops from the City of Boston. For weeks there has been speculation as to the proposed move of the British against John Hancock and Samuel Adams. To-day it is a known fact that the British forces plan to seize patriot stores at Concord. Observers have reported British troops being mustered out of their barracks and armed for the attack which may come at any moment. We repeat . . . which may come at any moment. Highways between the city and outlying districts are closed to all commercial traffic until further notice. Citizens of the Lexington-Concord area are warned to stay indoors. Keep tuned to your radios for further announcements. Remember, this may mean war. Members of the Provincial Militia are ordered to inspect their arms and stand ready for action. This station will give the alarm the instant the British move out of Boston. And now, here is John Cabot, a member of the Committee of Safety, with a few words of advice in this moment of peril and crisis. Mr. Cabot.

MR. CABOT: The Committee of Safety urges every American

to stand his ground and do his duty in this time of emergency. Women and children are asked to stay indoors. Keep tuned to your radio and TV sets for up-to-the-minute news and official reports. Danger is threatening us all, but there is no cause for panic. Above all, keep calm and follow instructions. See that every weapon of defense is ready and available for instant use. Women and children can be useful in melting lead for ammunition and preparing bandages. See that all medical supplies are in order. Have plenty of food and water on hand. Make sure that your cattle and horses are under shelter. Do not use your telephones except in emergency. Remember your Provincial Congress and Committee of Safety are taking all necessary precautions, but if this be war, let it begin here and now.

MR. GRAHAM: Thank you, Mr. Cabot. We hope that every one of our listeners will carry out your instructions to the letter. (BOY *enters and hands* GRAHAM *a bulletin*.) News has just been received from New York and Philadelphia that the people are ready to follow any example the Colony of Massachusetts may set. Charleston, South Carolina, reports their Provincial Congress ready to "sacrifice their lives and fortunes." All this is the greatest encouragement. Our Colony does not stand alone. (BOY *enters with second bulletin*) Just a moment, ladies and gentlemen . . . This may be the news we have been waiting for. (*Consults slip*) And it is. . . . We have just received an official bulletin that the British are leaving Boston by sea. We repeat . . . the British are leaving Boston by sea! Stay tuned to this station for further official reports and news bulletins. Attention, all militiamen in the Concord-Lexington area! The British are leaving Boston by sea. (*Curtains close as* GRAHAM *repeats message*.)

MARY (*Entering from left*): And so the farmers and their families were alerted to the movements of the British troops.

The Minutemen rush for their rifles and race out of doors to mass at the little bridge in Concord. A few farmers gather to halt the British column at Lexington. In the meantime, the news flashes continue to come from radio and television stations in an effort to keep the people informed. We take you now to a television studio in the heart of Boston.

Scene 3

Setting: *A Boston TV studio. Two cardboard cameras and a boom microphone made from a tin can suspended on a pole represent the equipment.*

At Rise: *Two* Cameramen *and a* Mike Operator, *all wearing earphones, handle the equipment. The* Announcer *and his guest, the* Farmer, *are seated at a desk at left. At right there is a flip board on which posters are turned according to the script. Camera 1 is on the* Announcer.

Announcer: The Colony of Massachusetts faces a grave situation as the British troops march against our military stores at Concord. We place our defense, however, in the hands of brave and trusted men . . . the farmers and citizens of the Middlesex area, who even now are standing by to answer the call to arms. We have in our studio at the moment one of these staunch-hearted gentlemen who is on his way home from a brief visit in Pennsylvania. We know that Farmer Caleb Pyncheon is eager to reach his own homestead and join the ranks of the militiamen, but we feel that he has a message for all of us. Farmer Pyncheon, what do you think of our chances against the British? (*Camera 2 moves in on* Farmer Pyncheon *and boom mike is moved directly over his head.*)

Farmer: The best in the world, sir. The enemy won't stand a chance when they face the muskets of our militia.

Announcer: You seem pretty sure of that, sir.

Farmer: Dad rat it! Of course, I'm sure. Those men are

neighbors of mine. They're dead shots when it comes to killing squirrels and rabbits and foxes and the other varmints that plague their fields; so it won't be any trick at all to shoot down those red-coated critters.

ANNOUNCER: I'm sure you're right, Farmer Pyncheon. This country was born with a rifle in its hand, and I think the British realize to some extent what they're up against. One of our English visitors who returned to his own shores just last winter wrote, "There is not a man born in America that does not understand the use of firearms. It is almost the first thing they purchase and take to all the new settlements and in the cities, you can scarcely find a lad of twelve who does not go gunning."

FARMER: That's right, sir. My boys, David and Ezra, can hold their own with the best of them.

ANNOUNCER: Well, now, Farmer Pyncheon, I know you're anxious to get home and we don't want to keep you a minute longer than necessary, but we feel you have something important to tell us about your trip to Pennsylvania and what you found there.

FARMER: Yes, siree. (*Holds up wooden rifle in front of camera*) I got myself one of these here new-fangled Kentucky rifles down Lancaster way and I'm mighty anxious to show folks up here how they work.

ANNOUNCER (*Examining rifle*): You say this is a *Kentucky* rifle, but it is made in Pennsylvania?

FARMER: Yep. They been making them down near Lancaster since long about 1725, but folks up here haven't had much truck with them. Folks in Kentucky, though, think right smart of them, and I figured they'd come in mighty handy up here.

ANNOUNCER: It surely has a long barrel.

FARMER: About thirty-six or thirty-eight inches; and that gives you the extra handling weight you need for better shooting.

ANNOUNCER: How do you load this contraption?

FARMER (*Pantomimes as he talks*): It's a mighty fast-loading weapon, mister. First you measure out a charge of powder into the barrel. (*Pretends to pour powder into his hand and put it in gun.*) Then you wrap your lead in a bit of cloth or buckskin and ram it down the barrel with this ramrod. (*Pantomimes action*)

ANNOUNCER: That's a new idea . . . that patch of cloth.

FARMER: And a mighty good idea. It gives you straighter shooting, faster loading, and it cleans the barrel of any powder left over from the last shot.

ANNOUNCER: You say it's a faster loading gun than our smoothbore rifle?

FARMER: A good rifleman can load his weapon and be ready to go in thirty seconds.

ANNOUNCER (*Whistles in surprise*): What about the range?

FARMER: Well now, folks argue about that. Some say 150 yards, others say more or less. Some declare they've hit a target at 200 yards.

ANNOUNCER: Well, that's some rifle, Farmer Pyncheon, and I hope you get back to Concord in time to use it.

FARMER: That's what I aim to do. And I figure when men up here see the Kentucky rifle in action, they'll be using it right and left.

ANNOUNCER: Thank you, Farmer Caleb Pyncheon, for giving us this timely information on the Kentucky rifle. And now, a closing reminder from your Committee of Safety. (ATTENDANT *removes cards from flip board as the* ANNOUNCER *reads his concluding speech.* CAMERAMAN *focuses on cards which are arranged in the following order*:

1. HOLD FAST WITH HANCOCK!
2. STAND BY SAM ADAMS!
3. TAXATION WITHOUT REPRESENTATION
4. "GIVE ME LIBERTY OR GIVE ME DEATH!"

5. Don't tread on me! (*Slogan printed below picture of coiled snake.*)

ANNOUNCER: People of Massachusetts, the hour of crisis is at hand! Keep calm! Obey your leaders. HOLD FAST WITH HANCOCK! STAND BY SAM ADAMS! If you *must* fight, remember you are fighting against TAXATION WITHOUT REPRESENTATION. Men, prepare to defend your homes. Women, make ready to stand shoulder to shoulder with your husbands, fathers, and brothers. Remember the words of Virginia's Patrick Henry— "GIVE ME LIBERTY OR GIVE ME DEATH!" The shots fired at Concord will be heard around the world, a warning to our enemies everywhere—DON'T TREAD ON ME! (*Curtains close*)

MARY (*Entering from left*): And so, ladies and gentlemen, if Paul Revere were to ride again to join Hancock and Adams, he would not ride alone. These people would be with him: (*Enter MAIL CARRIER with bag of mail.*)

MAIL CARRIER: The United States mails would carry letters and messages to the most remote farmhouse regardless of weather conditions. Every letter carrier knows the motto of the United States Post Office: "Neither rain nor snow, nor heat, nor gloom of night can stay these couriers from the swift completion of their appointed rounds." (*Enter TELEPHONE OPERATOR with earphones and mouthpiece.*)

TELEPHONE OPERATOR: In small villages and big cities telephone operators stick to their posts in time of emergency. In the cities and open country our telephone linemen are at work around the clock and the calendar to keep telephone service in operation. (TELEGRAPH MESSENGER BOY *enters.*)

TELEGRAPH BOY: The dots and dashes of the telegraph carry messages to army personnel and to civilians. News reports are sent by telegraph to newspapers and radios in all our big cities. Wherever news is being made a telegraph operator is at his post. (*Enter NEWSBOY.*)

NEWSBOY: From editor to newsboy from pencil to press, the American newspaper service is on the job in every national emergency, giving the people the facts and the instructions they need to carry on. (*Enter* RADIO ANNOUNCER *with hand microphone.*)

RADIO ANNOUNCER: America's free radio stations report the news as it happens and cooperate with military authorities and officers of Civilian Defense. (*Enter* TV CAMERAMAN *with cardboard camera.*)

TV CAMERAMAN: Through television Americans *see* as well as *hear* the news of the day. Announcers, writers, cameramen, engineers, and actors help keep America informed of events and inventions in the world around them. (*Enter* PAUL REVERE *wearing his three-cornered hat.*)

PAUL: And so, if I were to ride again to every Middlesex village and farm, I would find an informed and alert people, ready for action. The Minutemen would be at their posts before I arrived; houses would be stocked with provisions— the men, women, and children prepared for any emergency, thanks to our modern methods of communication. But speaking as Paul Revere of 1775, long before men ever heard of these modern miracles, I say many thanks to the man who hung those trustworthy lanterns in the Old North Church.

MARY: And many thanks to Mr. Longfellow whose famous poem always reminds us of the great debt we owe to a silversmith from Boston, Massachusetts:

"For borne on the nightwind of the past,
Through all our history to the last,
In the hour of darkness and peril and need,
The people will waken and listen to hear
The hurrying hoof-beats of that steed,
And the midnight message of Paul Revere."

THE END

Star Cadets

(*Astronomy*)

Characters

BARRY ⎫
RICKY ⎬ *three overnight campers*
MAC ⎭

BARRY ⎫
RICKY ⎬ *campers in dream sequence*
MAC ⎭

CHIEF DEEGA-MORIS, *an inhabitant of Venus*
DOC BAILEY, *adviser to the Stargazers*

KITTY ⎫
STEVE ⎪
JEN ⎪
ERIC ⎬ *Stargazers*
PAM ⎪
WEB ⎭

SETTING: *An open field not far from the Ramsay farmhouse.*
AT RISE: BARRY, RICKY *and* MAC *are lying in sleeping bags extreme right stage.* MAC *is sound asleep, snoring lightly from time to time.* RICKY *and* BARRY *are awake.* BARRY'S *bag is littered with comic books and some are on the ground beside him.*

BARRY (*In a stage whisper to* RICKY *who is next to him*):
Psst! Hey, Ricky, are you asleep?

RICKY: How could I be asleep with this buzz-saw next to me?

BARRY: I'm not asleep either. Isn't it quiet out here?

RICKY: What do you mean "quiet"? This guy Mac is making as much noise as a truck.

BARRY: Yeah, but it's quiet in a different way. And jiminy crickets! Just look at the stars!

RICKY: *You* look at 'em! (*Turning over and covering up*) I'm going to sleep.

BARRY: Well, don't go to sleep first. I don't want to be lying here awake, all by myself.

RICKY (*Half sitting up*): What's the matter? Are you scared?

BARRY: Of course not. I've slept outdoors before. And anyhow, we're only about two miles from Mac's uncle's farmhouse.

RICKY: You sound scared to me, kid.

BARRY: Well, I'm not! (*Pause*) Gee willikers! Look at that big star right over our heads, Ricky. It seems to be looking right down on us. What do you suppose it is?

RICKY: How would I know? And what difference does it make? Now shut up and let me get some sleep.

BARRY: I wonder if it could be a planet. Say, Rick, maybe it's Venus, the planet Venus.

RICKY: So what?

BARRY: Well, gee whiz! You know all about the planet Venus. That's where the space ships go. All sorts of queer creatures live there, and do they ever make it tough for the earth men!

RICKY: What earth men?

BARRY: The earth men who visit Venus in their space ships and go exploring. (*Reaching for comic book and getting flashlight from under pillow.*) Look! See . . . here's a picture of the *Polaris* landing on Venus. Look!

RICKY (*Pulling sleeping bag over his head*): I don't want to look. You read too many comic books in the daytime, without trying to read them at night. Now shut up and let me sleep.

BARRY (*Tossing comic book aside and settling down*): O.K.! O.K.! Just the same I wonder if that *could* be Venus! (*Voice gets fainter and sleepier*) Golly, when I shut my eyes the earth seems to be spinning round and round and yet I can still see the stars. Round and round and round she goes . . . and where she'll stop nobody knows! Maybe we won't stop at all! Golly, I feel dizzier and dizzier! And dizzier and dizzier! (*As his voice fades out, he falls asleep. A spotlight lights up the main portion of the stage as three boys enter, in space costumes. The boys address each other as* BARRY, RICKY *and* MAC.)

BARRY: Hey, fellows, I'm getting so dizzy I can hardly walk. I don't know what's the matter with me.

MAC: Maybe it's that thing on your head. You look as if you're wired for sound.

RICKY: Well how do you think *you* look in that flying saucer hat you're wearing, Mac?

BARRY (*Feeling his head*): Say, what are these things anyhow? Some kind of aerials?

MAC (*Twisting his own wires*): Maybe we could tune in on something and find out where we are.

RICKY: I think I know where we are.

MAC *and* BARRY: Where?

RICKY: I think we're on another planet. Venus maybe.

MAC: What makes you think so, Ricky?

RICKY: Well, look at the sky.

BARRY: Golly, the sun has grown smaller and smaller, and I see two moons in the sky. Say, let's get out of here.

MAC: Maybe we've turned into Space Cadets.

BARRY: If only we could talk to somebody. Let's try our aerials again. (*All twist their aerials and suddenly hear a tapping sound.*)

RICKY: Hear that! Maybe it's some sort of code.

MAC: Maybe we can contact the FBI.

BARRY: The tapping sounds louder when we move in this direction. (*Points left*) Let's follow the sound.

RICKY: I wish we had a Geiger counter or something.

MAC: Maybe it's a trap.

BARRY: Yeah, but then again, maybe it isn't. We got to take a chance. Come on. (*The boys creep left. Suddenly* CHIEF DEEGA-MORIS *appears behind them. He should be as horrible and fantastic as possible. He carries a long silver spear which he brandishes at the terrified boys as he speaks.*)

CHIEF DEEGA-MORIS: Stop! Stop, you earth men and prepare for death! (*Boys whirl around in surprise and fright.*) Your hour has come, you vile invaders. Prepare to die.

MAC: Listen, mister, you . . . you've got us all wrong. We aren't invaders.

BARRY: We're just campers from down in Ramsay's meadow.

MAC: Mr. Fred Ramsay is my uncle. He . . . he can vouch for us.

CHIEF DEEGA-MORIS: Silence! It makes no difference who you are. You are the first earthlings to pierce our cloud screen and spy on us, so you must die.

RICKY: But, golly, mister, we aren't spying.

CHIEF DEEGA-MORIS: Quiet! Or I will shrivel you into dust with my atomic spear!

RICKY: Now I ask you, sir, is that any way to treat visitors? We don't mean any harm.

CHIEF DEEGA-MORIS: By the rings of Saturn, you are speaking lies! You have come to rob us of our treasure.

BARRY: Look, look, mister. We don't want any treasure, honest we don't. We just want to get out of here, and fast!

MAC: If you let us go, we won't touch a thing. Honest we won't.

CHIEF DEEGA-MORIS: Promises won't save you. The penalty

for trespassing on the planet Venus is *death!* (*Blows traffic whistle and shouts*) Guards, do your duty! (*The spotlight goes out and there is the sound of chasing and screaming in the darkness.* BARRY, *in his sleeping bag, is thrashing about yelling for help.* MAC *and* RICKY *wake up.* RICKY *shakes* BARRY *to get him awake.*)

BARRY: Help! Help! Let us go! Let us go! Help! Help! Look out, Mac, there he comes. He's going to get you. Help! Help!

RICKY: Wake up, Barry. Wake up. Barry! Barry! What's the matter?

MAC: What's going on? What's happened?

RICKY: It's Barry. He's having some kind of nightmare.

BARRY: Look out, Ricky, he's aiming that spear straight at you. Duck! (*Dives into sleeping bag*)

RICKY: Come on, Barry. Get awake. You're having a bad dream.

BARRY: Gee whiz! Where am I? Oh, it's you, Ricky. Say, we got to get out of here and fast.

MAC (*Coming over to* BARRY's *sleeping bag*): What's the matter, pal?

BARRY: Gee, I don't know if I'm awake or asleep.

RICKY: You're awake now, old fellow. But you sure were having a terrible dream. What was it all about?

BARRY: I thought we were on another planet. It was that star up there. (*Pointing overhead*) I'm getting out of here.

MAC: Don't be silly, Barry. It was only a dream.

BARRY: I don't care. I'm not staying out here with that planet, Venus, right over my head.

MAC: How do you know it's Venus?

BARRY: It's Venus all right. I can tell. I'm going home.

RICKY: Oh for Pete's sake! Going home just because you're scared of a comic-book dream.

MAC: I always said you were space happy. All you do is read

these things till you're all hopped up over inter-planetary rays and solar cruises and zodiac traps and all kinds of silly talk like that.

BARRY: I don't care what you say. I'm going home.

MAC: But it's five miles back to town.

BARRY: Then I'll go to your uncle's place.

MAC: And have everybody kidding the life out of us because we're afraid to sleep outdoors all night.

RICKY: Sh! Quiet! I hear somebody coming.

MAC: Don't tell me you're getting scared too.

RICKY: Who said anything about being scared? I just said I hear somebody coming. Listen. Can't you hear voices? And look . . . I can see a light . . . out there beyond those trees.

MAC: You're right. It *is* a light.

BARRY: I'm leaving right now.

MAC (*Grabbing him*): Don't be a goon, Barry. Let's wait and see who it is.

RICKY: Let's give them a shout or they'll be more scared than we are. (*Shouting*) Hey! Hey! Who goes there!

STARGAZERS (*Give answering shout from offstage*): It's the Stargazers. Who are you? (STARGAZERS *and* DOC BAILEY *come into view. They carry star maps, field glasses, flashlights, and a camera.*)

DOC BAILEY: Hello, fellows. I hope we haven't spoiled your beauty sleep.

RICKY: No, we weren't sleeping at the moment.

MAC: We're just camping out for the fun of it.

BARRY: Only it hasn't been much fun up till now. We can't sleep. (*The boys get up.*)

DOC BAILEY: It takes a little time to get used to sleeping out-of-doors.

KITTY: It was the funniest thing, the first time I tried to

sleep outdoors, the stars kept me awake. Maybe you think that's hard to believe but . . .

BARRY: No, I believe it all right. The stars kept me awake too.

MAC: Did you say you were stargazers?

DOC BAILEY: Yes, that's what we call ourselves.

PAM: It's really our Astronomy Club and Doc Bailey is our adviser. There's nothing he doesn't know about the stars.

BARRY: Is that right?

DOC BAILEY: I wouldn't say that exactly. But I've spent a good many years studying the stars.

BARRY: Then maybe you can answer a question for me. Is that great big star up there Venus?

PAM: Dear me! You'd better join our club. The first thing Doc taught us was that a star is not a planet and a planet is not a star.

MAC: You mean there's a difference?

STEVE: I'll say there's a difference. Stars are like trees in a forest. They extend in every direction to enormous distances. But there are only nine planets.

STARGAZERS (In concert): Mercury, Venus, Earth, Mars, Jupiter, Saturn, Uranus, Neptune and Pluto.

JEN: And each planet revolves around the sun.

BARRY: But you still haven't told me if that one right up there that keeps twinkling down at me is the planet, Venus?

JEN: If it twinkles it isn't a planet, it's a star.

ERIC: Planets appear to shine very steadily but stars look as if they're actually winking at you.

MAC: Hear that? Then you weren't looking at Venus after all.

DOC BAILEY: You wouldn't be likely to see Venus at this time of night. You'd have to look for Venus in the western sky within three hours after sunset or in the eastern sky about three hours before sunrise.

WEB: That's why Venus is known as the Evening Star and the Morning Star.

DOC BAILEY: But why all this curiosity about Venus?

BARRY: I . . . I . . . was just interested, that's all.

MAC: Fact is he was having a bad dream about Venus just before you folks arrived.

ERIC: A bad dream about Venus? Why, Venus is one of the most beautiful sights in the sky. Certainly nothing to be scared of.

WEB (*Picking up comic book*): Maybe this is the explanation. I bet you've been reading about rockets and space ships going to Venus and getting mixed up with all sorts of imaginary creatures.

BARRY: How do you know they're imaginary.

PAM: Well, in the first place, nobody is absolutely sure that there's any life on Venus at all. Remember, Venus is much closer to the sun than we are, so it receives twice as much heat and light as the earth. Maybe the climate isn't suitable for any living creatures to exist.

BARRY: Someday the rocket men will go there and find out.

STARGAZERS (*Laughing*): Rocket men!

WEB: Don't let anybody kid you, chum. Mars, the closest planet, is twenty-eight million miles from the earth. That would be quite a trip even for a rocket.

BARRY: You just don't understand rockets and space ships.

WEB: And I suppose you *do* understand them. Well let me tell you something, brother, after you've had four or five years of chemistry and advanced mathematics, you come around and we'll talk about rockets and space ships. In the meantime, how about learning a little astronomy from Doc and the rest of the gang?

JEN: Actually the stories of the stars are more thrilling and exciting than the wildest space tales you could ever make up.

RICKY: The only stars I know are in the Big Dipper.

DOC BAILEY: Then you have a wonderful start on your first astronomy lesson because the Dipper is the key constellation.

MAC: I guess I'm dumb but I don't even know what a constellation is.

KITTY: Neither did I when I first joined the Stargazers. But it's not hard. A constellation is a group of stars. When you look at the Big Dipper you are really looking at a group of seven stars, four for the bowl, and three for the handle. Steve, pass out the star maps so our new friends can find their way around the sky. (STEVE *passes out maps.* WEB *and* STEVE *then hold up a large star map between them, which* DOC BAILEY *uses.*)

STEVE: Since we're facing the northern horizon, hold the map so the northern horizon is at the bottom. (*Boys adjust their maps*)

MAC: Now I can see the Dipper very plainly.

RICKY *and* BARRY: So can I.

DOC: If you follow the curve of the Dipper on down for about thirty degrees from the last star in the handle, you'll see a big orange-colored star.

MAC: Is that the North Star?

DOC: No, that's Arcturus. Now look up at the sky and find it. (*All look up*)

ALL: I see it! I see it!

BARRY: Golly, that's the star I thought was Venus.

DOC: Venus has a very white, clear light. But Arcturus is red gold.

RICKY: Is it the brightest star in the sky?

WEB: No. Sirius is the brightest star. Arcturus is the fourth brightest that can be seen in this country.

MAC: It really is bright.

DOC: It's hard to realize when you look at the star that the light you see actually left that star about forty years ago.

MAC: Forty years ago! And you mean we're just seeing it this minute!

DOC: Astronomers measure star distances in light years rather than miles. A light year is the distance that light, moving at the rate of 186,000 miles per second, travels in a year.

BARRY: I don't think I understand that.

PAM: Don't bother. Just go star hunting and let the light years take care of themselves. Do you know how to find *Polaris?*

BARRY: Polaris? That's the name of a space ship.

WEB: Pam is just showing off her astronomical knowledge. *Polaris* means the Pole Star or the North Star.

KITTY: Just use the two stars in the bowl of the Big Dipper opposite the handle as the pointers and they'll point directly to the North Star.

MAC: I see it on the map.

RICKY: I *think* I see it in the sky but it isn't nearly so bright as I expected it to be.

DOC: Most people expect the North Star to be much brighter and bigger than it actually is, because they've heard and read so much about it.

STAN: It's the only star in the sky that doesn't seem to move.

WEB: That is why navigators were able to steer their course by the North Star.

JEN: If we were lost in the woods, do you think we could find our way home by the Pole Star?

DOC: You should be able to find true north by drawing an imaginary curve from the zenith, that's right overhead, straight through Polaris and down to the horizon. When you've established north you could certainly find the other points of the compass.

KITTY: Sure, your back would be toward the south, your left hand toward the west and your right hand toward the east. Just the same, I wouldn't like to travel very far on those directions.

Doc: You'd probably do very well. But we'd better move along if we're going to take any pictures of star trails tonight. (STEVE *and* WEB *fold up large star map.*)

MAC: What are star trails?

ERIC: They're really fascinating. You open the shutter of a camera as wide as possible, point it toward a given star, and leave it that way for about half an hour. The developed negative will show the trail of the star as it moves through the sky. We were going up to High Rock to take our star trail picture for tonight.

RICKY: We don't want to hold you up, but what about those star stories you were talking about?

KITTY: The constellations and many of the single stars have interesting myths and legends which are told about them. The Greeks and Romans, the Norsemen, and even the American Indians knew beautiful stories about the stars in the heavens.

PAM: The people of long ago believed that many of the stars and constellations were placed in the sky as memorials to great heroes or to gods and goddesses.

JEN: Take for example, Queen Cassiopeia. Her whole family is up there in the sky. Some astronomers call them the Royal Family.

WEB: Here we go again. These girls like the stories better than the stars themselves.

KITTY: But they're so romantic.

BARRY: What about this Cassi . . . Cassi-what's-her-name?

KITTY: Cassiopeia. Look up on the opposite side of Polaris from the Big Dipper. See all those stars that look like a big W or M.

BARRY: I *think* I see them.

MAC: Here's the constellation on the star map.

KITTY: Well, that's Cassiopeia, the Queen of Ethiopia, sitting on her great throne chair.

MAC: How did she get up there?

KITTY: That's quite a story. Cassiopeia was a very conceited woman who bragged of her beauty and angered the nymphs of the sea so that they appealed to King Neptune for revenge.

RICKY: And did he turn her into a constellation?

JEN: It wasn't that simple. In fact, she's up there to remind us of her story. Because of her bragging, Neptune sent a dreadful monster to ravage the coast of the whole country. Cepheus, the king and Cassiopeia's husband, appealed to Jupiter, who told him that the only way he could satisfy the monster and save his people would be to sacrifice his daughter.

BARRY: Say, I read this story somewhere. Was the daughter's name Andromeda?

JEN: That's right. The King ordered Andromeda chained to a rock overlooking the sea as a sacrifice to the sea monster.

MAC: But I bet the hero got there just in time.

PAM: The hero's name was Perseus. He had just slain another terrible monster named Medusa. In fact he still had Medusa's head in a bag when he rescued Andromeda.

JEN: It's a good thing he had the head or he never would have saved Andromeda from the monster.

RICKY: How did he kill the monster?

KITTY: As he swooped through the air on his winged sandals, he pulled out the gorgon's head and showed it to the monster. As soon as the terrible creature saw the gorgon's head, it was turned to stone . . . and the beautiful Andromeda was saved.

RICKY: That beats any of the space cadet stories I ever read.

DOC: And there are plenty of other stories like that you can read in the sky if you know where to look.

ERIC: Cassiopeia, Cepheus, Andromeda, and Perseus are all

constellations. If you study your star maps and use the Big Dipper as a guide you can find them.

STEVE: The best part about the Royal Family is that they're in the sky at every season of the year.

Doc: Well, come along, boys and girls. We can't tell the whole story of the heavens at one time. Besides, it's getting late.

RICKY: Thanks for talking to us. We've enjoyed it ever so much.

MAC: We certainly have. Camping out is much more fun when you know something about the stars.

Doc: If you're really interested you might organize a stargazing group of your own, for junior members.

RICKY: Say, that's a good idea. But where would we get an adviser?

Doc: I don't think you'd have any trouble persuading a member of this group to act as a guide. We stargazers always like to get new recruits. Think it over, and let us know if you want to organize a group. Here's a card. Just call this number if you want to do some serious stargazing. Now come on, gang. We must get moving. (STARGAZERS *exit with shouts of "goodbye," etc.*)

MAC: Well, Barry, what have you decided to do?

BARRY (*Sitting on sleeping bag studying star map*): Do about what?

MAC: About going home?

RICKY: Are you still scared to stay out here alone under the stars?

BARRY (*Stretching out on sleeping bag, arms underneath his head*): Gosh, no. The stars seem much more friendly, now that I know some of their names. (MAC *and* RICKY *stretch out too.*)

RICKY (*Pointing*): Look, up there I think I can see Andromeda and Perseus.

MAC: And over there's that other fellow . . . the king . . . what was his name? Cepheus, wasn't it?

BARRY: You know, fellows, I guess there's a lot of nonsense written about these solar cruisers and space cadets.

MAC: I guess you're right. The real thing is more interesting than the make-believe.

RICKY: What do you guys say we really do organize a star-gazing club?

MAC: I'm all for it. How about you, Barry?

BARRY: Me? I'm all for it too, a hundred percent. And do you know what? I've even got a name for us.

MAC *and* RICKY: A name? What is it?

BARRY: We'll call ourselves the Cadets. How do you like that, fellows, The Star Cadets.

THE END

The Case of the Balky Bike

(Bicycle Safety)

Characters

REPORTER COLLINS	LES	
PHOTOGRAPHER	DAVE	
OFFICER CLARK	CAPTAIN DANNY	
MRS. GRAHAM	LUCY	The Bicycle-
OSWALD GRAHAM	MARY	Safety
CARLA	TED	Squad
SANDY	BOB	
BUD		

SETTING: *Room in local police station. The Balky Bike occupies a position center stage. It is mounted on a slightly raised platform enclosed by a decorated rope railing. Above it there is a sign:* IF YOU CAN RIDE IT, YOU MAY HAVE IT!

AT RISE: POLICE OFFICER *is seated at a plain table on which is a large book which he is using as a register. A news* PHOTOGRAPHER *is taking pictures from every possible angle while a* REPORTER, *wearing a press sign in his hat, is asking questions of the* POLICE OFFICER.

REPORTER: This is a story to end all stories, Officer, if I have my facts straight.

OFFICER: That's about all I can tell you. The bike's been here about three weeks now. No one has claimed it and no one has been able to ride it.

REPORTER: But how did it get here? Didn't someone bring it in?

OFFICER (*Shaking head*): No. Not as far as we know. It just appeared one morning among the unclaimed vehicles. It looked just like any other bicycle at first and nobody paid much attention to it until we discovered that no one could ride it.

REPORTER: Why not? What does it do?

OFFICER: It doesn't do anything. That's the point. You can't get it to budge an inch.

REPORTER (*Walking over to bicycle and spinning a wheel*): The wheels have plenty of motion all right.

OFFICER: Yes, but wait till you try to ride it. All the boys on the force have tried and it just won't go. In fact Sergeant Moon tried to force it, and the next thing he knew he was in the middle of the floor.

REPORTER (*Laughing*): A regular bucking broncho, eh?

OFFICER: Yep! It's given the Department lots of publicity all right. Kids from all over town keep coming in to try their luck since the Chief has offered to give it away.

REPORTER: Well, I think I have enough information for a story, Officer. How about you, Ed? Do you think you have enough pictures?

PHOTOGRAPHER: I'd like to get a shot of you or the Officer trying to ride it, Joe.

REPORTER: How about it, sir?

OFFICER: No thanks, not me! I don't want to make a joke of myself like Sergeant Moon. In my opinion that thing would throw you as quick as scat!

REPORTER (*Inspecting bike*): It looks in first-rate condition— a bicycle any boy would be happy to own.

PHOTOGRAPHER: Sure. But what good is a bike that won't run?

REPORTER: I just can't believe it won't go when the wheels spin around like that. (*Spinning wheels*)

PHOTOGRAPHER: Why don't you give it a try, Joe? (*Focuses camera*) I'll get ready to snap you at the take-off.

REPORTER (*Mounting bicycle*): I never did have much luck with bicycles, Ed. I was always having spills when I was a kid. (*Pretending to bear down on pedals*) Umph! Umph! Nope! I can't budge it! (*Getting off*) If that's not the strangest thing! (*To* OFFICER) Have you had a good mechanic look this thing over?

OFFICER: Yes, we have. Nobody can find anything mechanically wrong with that bike. It's just plain balky!

REPORTER: Thanks for the headline, Officer. That's the way I'll write the story for my paper. THE CASE OF THE BALKY BIKE.

OFFICER: Well, I hope you solve the mystery, boys. It's too much for us.

REPORTER: I'm afraid it will be too much for us too. How about you, Ed? Got any theories?

PHOTOGRAPHER (*Scratching his head*): It's not my job to get theories, Joe—just pictures, and I have plenty of those.

REPORTER: O.K. Then we'll be moving along. Thanks for the story, Officer.

OFFICER: You're welcome. (*As* MRS. GRAHAM *and* OSWALD *enter*) Psst! If you've got time on your hands, why don't you stick around? Some of the characters who come in here to try to ride Old Balky are stories in themselves. Here comes Mrs. Graham. She brings her kid in here every day. They want Balky for their collection.

REPORTER: Sounds good. I'll wait. You go back to the office, Ed. I'll call you if anything hot happens here.

PHOTOGRAPHER: O.K. So long. (*Exit* PHOTOGRAPHER *as* MRS. GRAHAM *and* OSWALD *approach table.*)

MRS. GRAHAM: Oh, good morning, Officer. Oswald and I just couldn't wait to come over this morning. We were so afraid someone might have managed to ride Balky before we arrived. But I see it's still here.

OFFICER: Yes, ma'am.

MRS. GRAHAM: Oswald has a new theory he'd like to try, if it's all right with you.

OFFICER: It's O.K. by me, ma'am. Just so he doesn't hurt the bike or himself.

MRS. GRAHAM: Oh, he'll be careful. Oswald dear, explain your theory to Officer Clark.

OSWALD: Well, I've been thinking about it, Officer, and I've decided that maybe this bike is balky because it doesn't have any modern accessories.

OFFICER: Accessories?

OSWALD: Yeah. You know . . . all the latest gadgets that help to give a bike real class. I brought some along with me just on a chance. (*Opens small paper bag and brings out a pair of coon tails such as boys hang on bicycles*) I thought these might dress up the handle bars. (*Ties a coon tail on each handle bar*) And one of these fake TV aerials should make it look sharp. (*Takes it out of bag and puts it on bike*) There! Now I'll give it a try and see if my luck is changed. (*Tries to ride bike but in vain*)

MRS. GRAHAM: Oh dear! It doesn't work. Never mind, Oswald. We'll see the Chief and try to buy the bicycle if you really want it.

OFFICER: The bicycle is not for sale, Mrs. Graham.

MRS. GRAHAM: But it's so unusual, Officer, and Oswald really should have it for his collection. Tell the Officer about your collection, Oswald. Oswald is really quite an authority on bicycles, aren't you, dear?

OSWALD: Oh, I'm not exactly an authority, Mom, but bikes are my hobby. Actually the first bicycle was invented about 1790 and perfected about 1810. I have one of the very first models in my collection. It's called a Walk-Along because it's sort of a two-wheeled kiddy-car that you propel with your feet.

REPORTER: That sounds very interesting, young man. You say you have one of these Walk-Alongs in your collection?

OSWALD: Yes, I have. Would you like to see it?

OFFICER: This is Reporter Collins from the *Eagle*. He came over to do a story on our Balky Bike. Maybe Mrs. Graham and Oswald can give you some background.

MRS. GRAHAM: We'll be glad to help you, Mr. Collins, and I know Oswald will enjoy showing you the collection. We have it stored in our garage.

REPORTER: Do you have any of those old-time high-wheelers, son?

OSWALD: Oh, yes. I have several of those. I have one which was made about 1840 called the *Wooden Horse*. Then I have another model from about 1870 that's called the *Bone Shaker*.

REPORTER: I'm talking about the bicycle with the high front wheel and the tiny rear wheel.

OSWALD: Yes, I know what you mean. Those high-wheelers were pretty dangerous because the rider had a long way to fall in a tumble. The big front wheel furnished all the movement; the little rear wheel was used only for steering.

REPORTER: I'm sure glad the bicycle finally decided to come down to earth.

OSWALD: So are all the rest of the bicycle riders in the world. About 1880 the sprocket and chain device was invented to drive the rear wheel, and after that bikes took on a more modern look.

OFFICER: I guess the pneumatic tire, ball bearings and spring saddle had something to do with bicycle improvement too.

OSWALD: I'll say they did.

REPORTER: I can see I'll have to make an appointment to look at your bicycle collection, Oswald.

OSWALD: Drop in any time. But I hope to add this Balky Bike

to the exhibit, if it's at all possible. How about it, Officer?

OFFICER: I'd like to see you have it, son, but I'm afraid you don't have a chance unless you can figure out some way to ride it.

MRS. GRAHAM: Oh dear! That's so disappointing.

OSWALD: Don't sound so gloomy, Mom. I'll go home and read some of my books on the history of the bicycle. Maybe I can find some new information that will help solve the mystery of the Balky Bike.

OFFICER: And while you're at it, try to find something that will solve the mystery of why we have so many bike accidents in this town. There's a lot of pleasure to be had from riding a bike, but only if the riding is *safe riding*. See what your books have to say on that topic, sonny.

OSWALD: I'll do that, Officer. Come on, Mom. Let's go.

MRS. GRAHAM: And remember, Mr. Collins, you may stop any time to see Oswald's collection of antique bicycles.

REPORTER: Thank you. I'll arrange to bring our staff photographer along and we'll take some pictures.

MRS. GRAHAM: Thank you. Good day, Officer Clark. Come along, Oswald. (*Exit* MRS. GRAHAM *and* OSWALD)

REPORTER: Maybe I can do a whole series of articles on bicycles if I stick around here long enough.

OFFICER: Well, be sure to play up the safety angle as much as possible, Joe. "The careful bicycle rider of today is the thinking motorist of tomorrow." That's the biggest safety slogan of all. (*Enter* SANDY *and* CARLA)

SANDY: Good morning, Officer. May we take a look at the Balky Bike?

OFFICER: There she is! You may look to your heart's content. But give me your names first. We are keeping a list of everybody who tries to ride our mystery bike.

SANDY: My name is Sandra Laine and this is Carla Brown. We think maybe the Balky Bike actually belongs to Carla.

OFFICER: Indeed? What makes you think so? After all, it's a boy's bike.

CARLA: Yes, I know. But I had a boy's bike. Actually it belonged to Tom, my older brother. But he let me ride it.

OFFICER: Did you lose the bicycle?

CARLA: Well . . . not exactly. You see I had an accident with it and my parents wouldn't let me ride it any more.

OFFICER: An accident?

CARLA: Yes. It really wasn't much of an accident, but it scared my mother, and Dad said I couldn't ride any more if it made her nervous.

OFFICER: Any accident is pretty much of an accident, young lady. What happened that frightened your mother so badly?

CARLA: Well, I was riding along behind a big truck, and I got closer and closer. . . . I guess maybe a little bit too close, because when the lights changed and the truck stopped suddenly, I flew up against one of the truck wheels and fell off.

OFFICER: And you call that not much of an accident! You're just lucky to be alive. And I don't blame your parents for not letting you ride.

SANDY: But I see lots of boys and girls coasting along with one hand on the back of a truck.

OFFICER: And I've seen lots of boys and girls badly injured from that very trick. This type of accident you describe is second in the causes of all bicycle accidents.

SANDY: Golly, Officer! I didn't know that!

OFFICER: Well now you know it. So beware of bicycle-hitch-hiking.

SANDY: You say that's the second cause of bicycle accidents, Officer? What is the number one cause?

OFFICER: The number one cause is riding two or more on a bicycle. When you carry a passenger on the handle bars, you endanger two lives . . . your own and that of your rider.

CARLA: Oh, I'd never do that, Officer. My brother warned me against that when he gave me the bike.

OFFICER: And you think this bicycle might be yours?

CARLA: Well, I'm not sure. It's the same model and the same color. But, of course, mine was pretty well scratched from the accident. Daddy made me put it away in the garage and it finally disappeared. I thought maybe somebody stole it.

OFFICER: Well, you may look at Old Balky, but I doubt if you'll find any scratches. (*Girls look at bicycle.*)

CARLA: No . . . not a scratch. And the saddle seat isn't the same. This isn't mine.

SANDY: May we try to ride it, Officer?

OFFICER: Certainly, but I doubt if you'll have much luck. (*Girls try bicycle with no results.*)

REPORTER: You policemen really know the inside facts on bicycle accidents, don't you?

OFFICER: Let's say we know the inside facts on bicycle safety. You know we policemen aren't joy-killers. We're not trying to take the fun out of life; we're just trying to take some of the danger out of life. Well, girls, how did Old Balky treat you?

SANDY: Just like all the others, I guess. It wouldn't budge.

CARLA: And I'm convinced it's not mine. Thanks, Officer.

OFFICER: You're welcome, young lady. And if and when your parents let you ride again, just remember to obey the safety rules, will you?

CARLA: I promise, Officer. And I really mean it. Goodbye. (*Exit girls.*)

REPORTER: Never a dull minute in this place, is there?

OFFICER: As long as there are boys and bicycles, I guess we'll always have plenty of excitement. It looks as if we're getting a few more riding recruits. Hello, boys. (*Enter* Bud, Les, *and* Dave.)

Boys: Hiya, Officer.

Officer: Come to try your luck on Old Balky?

Bud: Yes, sir. We figured this would be a good way for one of us to get a new bike.

Officer: All three of your bikes were pretty badly smashed, weren't they?

Les: Yes, sir, but it really wasn't our fault. We weren't riding the bikes at the time of the accidents.

Officer: And lucky for you, you weren't. Let's see now, weren't you the boy who parked your bike in the Safety Zone?

Les: Sure. But I just left it there a minute. How did I know that bus would run over it? The driver should have kept his eyes open.

Officer: You can't depend on the other fellow to protect your property. You should have kept your own eyes open when you parked.

Dave: Yeah, that's what Dad said when I told him I had parked my bike in a store driveway. He said it was my own fault that the delivery truck ran over it.

Bud: I still can't see that it was my fault when that jerk opened his left-hand car door and knocked me out into the middle of the road. Fortunately just my bike was hit by the next car. I jumped to one side.

Officer: Yes, Bud. You have a pretty good case. No autoist has the right to get out on the road side of his car, but every bicycle rider has to keep his eyes peeled when he's passing a parked car, just in case. It's too bad you boys had those smash-ups, but I'm glad none of you were hurt. You're certainly welcome to try your luck with Old Balky. (*Boys take turns trying.*)

REPORTER: Parking can be almost as dangerous as riding from the bicyclist's point of view.

OFFICER: You bet. Every youngster must use good judgment when it comes to parking. So many expensive bikes are smashed to bits because of bad parking manners.

LES (*Having tried and failed to ride the bike*): Well, sir, shall I write my name in your register?

OFFICER (*Offering him book and pencil*): Sign here, my boy.

LES (*Reading as he writes*): Lester Q. Burton. And thanks for letting me try.

OFFICER: You're welcome. Sorry you had no luck. Next!

DAVE (*Taking pencil and signing*): David R. Ross. I think there's some catch to this deal, Officer.

OFFICER: I can assure you there's no catch, Dave. It's just as much a mystery to us as it is to you.

BUD: Then it's some mystery, if it has the police force stymied. (*Writing*) There! There's my name . . . Bud R. Flanders. I guess I'll have to get my paper route back again, so I can earn money for a new bike.

OFFICER: And be sure you take good care of it when you get it.

BUD: You bet I will. So long, Officer, and thanks.

OFFICER: Nice boys, all three of them, but careless.

REPORTER: Well, I guess I'll be on my way back to the office. I think I've seen about all there is to see around here. I'd better go write my story. (*Enter the Bicycle-Safety Squad,* CAPTAIN DANNY, LUCY, MARY, TED *and* BOB.)

OFFICER: Better wait a few minutes. Looks as if we have a real delegation this time.

CAPTAIN DANNY: Good morning, sir. Are you in charge here?

OFFICER: At your service, young man. What can I do for you?

CAPTAIN DANNY: We're the Bicycle-Safety Squad from (*Names school where play is being given*). We've been making a thorough study of bicycle safety and we have a theory about the Balky Bike.

OFFICER: What sort of theory?

CAPTAIN DANNY: Well, we'd like to tackle the problem by the scientific method.

OFFICER: We've had all sorts of methods, so you're welcome to try out your theory. How do you propose to start?

CAPTAIN DANNY: Our Bicycle-Safety Squad has been taught that safety starts with the proper care of the bicycle. So first of all, we'd like to check the Balky Bike for safety features.

OFFICER: Go right ahead.

REPORTER: This sounds interesting.

CAPTAIN DANNY (*To* LUCY): Get your notebook, Lucy. Ted, are you ready to check?

TED: I'm ready. (LUCY *reads safety items from notebook as* TED *checks.*)

LUCY: How about the frame itself?

TED (*Inspecting*): It's good and solid. No cracks at the joints.

LUCY: Now for the spokes in the wheels.

TED (*Inspecting*): None appears to be loose or broken.

LUCY: Handle grips.

TED: Ah ha! Here we find our first trouble. The handle grips are loose and badly worn.

CAPTAIN DANNY: Then they should be replaced at once. A sudden turn can end up in a spill if the handle grips are loose.

BOB (*Opening tool kit and replacing handle grips*): I'll take care of that right away.

LUCY: Next, the headlight.

TED (*Turning on light*) Hummm! The battery seems weak. I doubt if this light could be seen for a distance of five hundred feet.

BOB: I'll take care of that as soon as I fix these handle bars.

LUCY: Take a look at the pedal treads.

TED: They'll pass inspection. They seem as good as new.

LUCY: Now for the reflector on the rear wheel. Is it cracked?

TED: Nope. A dust cloth would help, but I think it's in good shape otherwise.

MARY: I have some reflecting tape Bob can put on. I got an extra supply when the Service Club taped our bikes at school.

BOB: O.K. That's an added safety device old Mr. Balky should appreciate. (*He puts tape on back fender.*)

TED: Have we finished our check list?

LUCY: Brakes?

TED: I'm sure they're satisfactory. This bicycle is strong on brakes if nothing else.

LUCY: Tire pressure?

TED (*Kicking at tires*): Fine. And the valves seem to be O.K.

LUCY: Have you checked the chain and sprocket?

TED: All in good order.

LUCY: Then we've just about finished . . . all but the horn or bell.

TED (*Working horn*): More trouble. Not a peep out of this horn.

CAPTAIN DANNY: Now isn't that crazy? Here we have a bike all trimmed up with fancy coon tails and a worthless aerial, but no sounding device!

BOB (*Tinkering with horn*): I'll fix that in a jiffy. (*Sounding horn*) How's that?

CAPTAIN DANNY: Swell. Does the bicycle pass inspection, Lucy?

LUCY: I'm not sure about proper lubrication.

OFFICER: I can answer for that all right. The bicycle has been overhauled to check for mechanical defects, and it has had a thorough lubrication.

CAPTAIN DANNY: Then it should be ready to roll. Do you want to try it, Ted?

TED: You're the Captain, Danny. We'll let you try first.

CAPTAIN DANNY: All right, I'll try. (*To* OFFICER) You see, sir, our theory is that the strange behavior of this bicycle might be explained by the fact that up to this time it hasn't been safe for the road.

OFFICER: You mean you actually think the bicycle knew it wasn't safe to be ridden, and therefore refused to move?

CAPTAIN DANNY: It sounds pretty crazy, I admit, but my dad says that bicycles are smarter than the people who try to ride them.

REPORTER: I'm anxious to see how this experiment turns out.

CAPTAIN DANNY (*Mounting bicycle*): It won't be long now. Here we go. (*The bicycle actually moves a few inches*)

ALL: It's moving! It's moving.

REPORTER: By George! Your theory seems to be working. Hold it! I must call Ed to come take some pictures. (*Rushes to phone and pantomimes phone conversation*)

OFFICER: Well, what do you know!

CAPTAIN DANNY (*As bicycle stops*): Hold your horses, everybody! The bike is balking again.

TED: Push harder on the pedals.

BOB: Try standing up on them.

MARY: If Danny can't ride it, nobody can. He used to be a regular stunt rider.

CAPTAIN DANNY (*Dismounting and mopping his face*): Yeah! And I guess that leaves me out, Mary.

MARY: What do you mean, Danny? Why you can even ride a bicycle without using your hands.

CAPTAIN DANNY: Not any more, Mary! But that's probably the reason I am disqualified now.

OFFICER: Disqualified?

CAPTAIN DANNY: Yes, sir. The way I look at it, sir, this bicycle is no ordinary bike and it's not going to let itself be ridden by any dumb cluck who thinks he's a circus rider.

OFFICER: I think I see what you mean.

CAPTAIN DANNY: I used to think I was pretty smart, most of the time, the way I could show off with trick riding. Well, I've seen enough bad accidents to convince me that the smart bicycle rider is the guy that keeps both hands on the handle bars and both eyes wide open.

OFFICER: Good for you, sonny. That's the kind of talk I like to hear.

CAPTAIN DANNY: Yeah, but my tricks have queered my chances with this vehicle. How about you giving it a try, Bob?

BOB: I'll try, but I don't think I'll make the grade. (*Tries but the bicycle moves only a few inches back and forth*) Nope, no luck.

LUCY: That's a shame, Bob, because you haven't had any more accidents since you shot out of that driveway onto the main road last year.

BOB: Yes, but once is enough for this fellow. I just don't measure up to the safety standards. Looks as if it's your turn, Ted.

TED: O.K. Wish me luck. (*Tries to ride but succeeds no better than the others*)

MARY: I can't remember any accident you've ever had, Ted.

TED: Maybe you can't remember. But just last summer I was foolish enough to ride on a pavement and I ran into a woman pushing a baby carriage. Golly, was I scared! I might have injured that baby for life! That cured me.

CAPTAIN DANNY: Do you girls want to try?

MARY: Not me! I'll stick to a bicycle that's designed especially for ladies.

LUCY: I'd never succeed. It was only last week that I was

looking in a dress shop window instead of watching the traffic and I just missed having an accident.

CAPTAIN DANNY: Well, it looks as if our scientific approach didn't work after all.

OFFICER: But I still think you're on the right track. You are the first youngsters to come in here who have realized that a bicycle is a means of transportation instead of a toy.

REPORTER (*Returning from telephone*): Ed will be down here in just a minute. Who's the lucky winner?

OFFICER: Nobody as yet, Mr. Collins. But I think these boys and girls have solved the mystery. I think we have a real safe and sane bicycle here.

CAPTAIN DANNY: One that won't let itself be ridden by anyone except a fully qualified safe rider.

REPORTER: And don't you qualify?

CAPTAIN DANNY: Oh, we know all of the rules . . . all the Do's and all the Don'ts.

ALL (*In concert*): Do not ride two or more on a bicycle.
Do not swerve from side to side.
Do not hitch on vehicles of any kind.
Do not leave curb without looking.
Do not ride on icy pavements or in heavy rain storms.
Do not make turns in the middle of the block.
Do not ride at night without lights.

OFFICER (*Pointing to bicycle*): Look! Look!

ALL: What? Where?

OFFICER (*Rubbing his eyes*): There! Look at the bicycle! I distinctly saw the light blink on and off. Like a signal.

CAPTAIN DANNY: It's not blinking now.

OFFICER: But it was. I'm sure I saw it.

MARY: Maybe it's giving us the high sign . . . a nod of approval.

LUCY: Let's try again. Quick, Danny. Get on. (CAPTAIN DANNY *gets on and rides the bicycle back and forth the length of the platform as the others cheer.* PHOTOGRAPHER *enters.*)

REPORTER: Good! You've arrived just in time to take the picture of the lucky winner . . . the boy who has finally managed to ride Old Balky. What's your name, kid?

CAPTAIN DANNY: Danny Keefer. But I don't want my picture taken as the lucky rider, sir.

REPORTER: For heaven's sake, why not? This is a big story.

CAPTAIN DANNY: Yes, sir, but I think Old Balky let himself be ridden because of those "Don'ts for Safe Bicycling" which we recited. I think he'd let any of us ride him now because he's convinced we take our safe riding pretty seriously. Come on, Bob. Try again. (BOB *succeeds in riding bike*)

BOB: Now it's your turn, Ted. (TED *also rides bike.*)

OFFICER: Now there's a pretty kettle of fish! Three winners. I'll have to call the Chief to decide who gets the bicycle.

CAPTAIN DANNY: Don't bother, Officer. We don't really want the bike. We each have one of our own.

TED: Besides you really need it more than we do.

OFFICER: Who do you mean by *we?*

BOB: You, the Police Department.

OFFICER: And why does the Police Department need a bicycle? . . . We have plenty of cruiser cars.

CAPTAIN DANNY: Yes, sir, but as long as you keep Balky here in this room, you'll have the perfect testing machine for safe bicycle riders.

MARY: If a boy or girl can't ride Old Balky, he shouldn't be allowed to ride any bicycle . . . anywhere . . . ever!

LUCY: Because he hasn't passed his safe riding test.

REPORTER: These kids have a great idea, Officer.

OFFICER: I'll have to talk it over with the Chief, but I'm inclined to agree with you.

REPORTER: Now let's get that picture, quick. Set up your camera, Ed. Now Danny, you take the place of honor at the wheel, and the rest of you Bicycle-Safety Squad members line up beside him. Got it, Ed?

PHOTOGRAPHER (*Snapping picture*): I got it, Joe.

REPORTER: And now, Captain Danny Keefer, do you have a statement for the press?

CAPTAIN DANNY (*Still mounted on bicycle*): Just this statement from the Bicycle Institute of America, sir. "Bicycling is one of the safest sports in the world, if you remember that your bicycle is a vehicle which you can ride almost anywhere, as long as you obey the traffic laws, watch the traffic lights and practice consideration for others."

THE END

Right of Adoption

(Trees and Conservation)

Characters

MR. GUTHRIE, *a wealthy gentleman*
PERRY, *his son*
MRS. HAWKINS, *his housekeeper*
LENA, *the maid*
MISS CONWAY, *a teacher*

GINGER
MARGIE
KATE
GWEN } *the Tree Troopers*
ELEANOR
JOAN
SHIRLEY

TIME: *A Saturday morning.*
SETTING: *The living room of the Guthrie home.*
AT RISE: LENA, *the maid, and* MRS. HAWKINS, *the housekeeper, are doing the morning chores of straightening up and dusting.*

MRS. HAWKINS: I can finish here, Lena. You'd better go tidy things up in the dining room.
LENA: I can't do that right now, Mrs. Hawkins. Young Mr. Perry is still dawdling around with his breakfast.
MRS. HAWKINS (*Sniffing in disapproval*): Humph! If I had my

way that young gentleman would be up and out of here long before this. He's getting to be a lazy-lie-abed. It's a wonder his father puts up with it. Such a hard-working, industrious man, Mr. Guthrie! But that boy of his. (*Shakes her head with more disapproving snorts and sniffs*)

LENA (*Smiling*): He's really a nice boy, Mrs. Hawkins. Just a bit lazy and a trifle wasteful, but ever so kind and full of fun! He always has a joke and a smile.

MRS. HAWKINS: Him and his jokes! I've run out of patience with him. Always thinking up ways for his father to be spending more money. What do you think the latest is?

LENA: I wouldn't know. He has about everything.

MRS. HAWKINS: And now he wants a tennis court back of the garage. Gave his poor father no peace till he consented. Now we'll have all that dirt and mess tracked into the house. (*Enter* PERRY *munching on a piece of toast.*)

PERRY: Good morning, Mrs. Hawkins. Hello, Lena. Did you hear the one about the city fellow who was lost and stopped his car to ask directions from a farmer? He said, "Say, Mister, can you tell me where this road goes?"

LENA: And the farmer said: "I never seen it go nowhere, son. Always stays in the same place."

PERRY: Another score for you, Lena. We must read the same joke books.

MRS. HAWKINS: Now be careful of those crumbs, Mr. Perry. Lena and I have just about finished cleaning up in here.

PERRY (*Swallowing last mouthful*): I'll be careful, Mrs. Hawkins. I just came in to tell you the good news.

MRS. HAWKINS: Has your vacation been cut short this year?

PERRY: Now, Mrs. Hawkins! Don't tell me you're so anxious to get rid of me! No, ma'am. It's good news about the tennis court. Dad told me last night the bulldozer will be here this morning. That's why I'm up bright and early. I want to see the men before they start.

MRS. HAWKINS: Then you better go outside and wait for them.

PERRY: I want to tell them to clear the land on the south lawn instead of back of the garage. It's a much better spot.

LENA: Oh no! Not the south lawn, Mr. Perry.

PERRY: And why not? What's the matter with the south lawn? It's the ideal spot for a tennis court.

LENA: But that's where the prettiest trees are. Surely you wouldn't want to destroy them!

PERRY: Trees? We've got hundreds of trees on this place. Who cares about a few trees more or less? We'd never miss 'em.

MRS. HAWKINS: But your father said the courts were to be back of the garage. He never said a word about the south lawn, Mr. Perry.

PERRY: What difference will it make to Dad? He doesn't know a thing about tennis.

LENA: But he knows plenty about trees, Mr. Perry. You better speak to him before you go giving any orders to those men about tearing up the south lawn.

PERRY: Oh, he won't care, Lena. I know he won't. He told me this whole project would be my responsibility. (*Glancing out window*) Oh, boy! Here they are. I'll go talk to the men right away. (*Exit* PERRY)

LENA: Oh dear, Mrs. Hawkins. What do you think we ought to do?

MRS. HAWKINS: Do? I don't know what you're going to do, Lena Bishop, but I'm going straight to that telephone and call Mr. Guthrie before that young rascal takes it into his head to run that tennis court straight through the front hall.

LENA: Mr. Perry will be furious.

MRS. HAWKINS: Never mind about Mr. Perry. It's the trees I'm thinking about.

LENA: Me too, Mrs. Hawkins. I never cared so much about trees until my little cousin Ginger joined the Tree Troopers. Now I've discovered that trees can be almost as friendly and neighborly as people.

MRS. HAWKINS: Tree Troopers? Are they the little girls who walk over here every Saturday morning to look at the trees?

LENA: Yes. I knew Mr. Guthrie wouldn't mind because they never harm a thing on the grounds. (*Glancing out window*) Oh, please, hurry, Mrs. Hawkins. Try to get Mr. Guthrie before those men start work.

MRS. HAWKINS (*At phone, dials number*): Mr. Guthrie's office, please. Hello, Miss Stanley? This is Mrs. Hawkins. May I please speak to Mr. Guthrie right away? It's very important. . . . What? He's gone out? . . . Oh mercy me! Can you tell me where I can reach him? . . . Not before one o'clock! Oh dear! That will be too late. . . . Well, if he should happen to come in in the meantime, please tell him to call his home. . . . Thank you. Thank you very much. Goodbye.

LENA: Now what are we going to do? That bulldozer will have the south lawn a wreck before we can get hold of Mr. Guthrie.

MRS. HAWKINS: I have a good mind to go out there and give those men a piece of my mind!

LENA: It won't do any good, Mrs. Hawkins. You know how Mr. Perry is when he sets his head on something.

MRS. HAWKINS (*As noise of screaming and shouting is heard off stage*): Heavenly days! What's that? Mr. Perry, are you hurt? (PERRY *enters dragging two little girls*, GINGER *and* MARGIE, *who are armed with notebooks and field glasses. Two others,* KATE *and* GWEN, *are attacking him front and rear. It is all he can do to handle his two captives and fend off the others.*)

GIRLS (*Ad lib*): You let us go! Don't you dare touch those trees! We'll call the police. Help! Ouch! You're hurting my arm. Let me go, etc.

LENA (*Running to one of the girls and peeling her loose from* PERRY): Ginger! Ginger! Stop it! What's happened?

PERRY (*Releasing his prisoners*): So you know one of these little law-breakers . . . these trespassers.

GINGER: I told you that Lena knows us and we're *not* trespassers.

JOAN: We have permission to be here.

PERRY: Lena, I demand to know who this little monster is.

LENA: She's my cousin, Ginger Davis, Mr. Perry. I told her she could bring her little friends here on Saturday mornings to look at the trees if they didn't hurt anything.

PERRY: Hurt anything! Take a good look at my face. Look at those scratches. And I'm black and blue from the knees down! They're a bunch of wild cats, every one of them. They should be locked up.

GINGER (*Throwing her arms around* LENA): Oh, Lena, Lena! He's going to cut down our trees! Our beautiful, beautiful trees. We tried our best to save them, but he and those men are bigger than we are.

PERRY: The little idiots threw themselves right in the path of the bulldozer, and fought like tigers when I tried to drag them out of the way. In fact, three others are sitting out there right now daring the bulldozer crew to come a step farther.

MRS. HAWKINS: And what are the bulldozer men doing all this time?

PERRY: Laughing mostly. They seem to think it's all a big joke! But I'll show them it's not so funny before I've finished with them. You keep these girls here while I go out and drag in the others.

GIRLS (*Rushing to the attack*): No! No! Don't you dare!

Stop him! Stop him! Don't let him go! (MRS. HAWKINS *and* LENA *assist in dragging girls away from* PERRY.)

MRS. HAWKINS (*Sternly*): Now stop this commotion, all of you! I'll have no more fighting and scratching and kicking in this house. Shame on you girls for forgetting your manners! And shame on you, Mr. Perry, for fighting with a pack of little girls half your size! What would your father say?

MR. GUTHRIE (*Entering unexpectedly*): What would his father say about what, Mrs. Hawkins? What's going on here?

MRS. HAWKINS: Oh, Mr. Guthrie! Thank fortune you're home.

MR. GUTHRIE: I thought I'd better drop in for a final word with the bulldozer crew before I went to my board meeting. Now what's the trouble and who are all these children? Friends of yours, Perry?

PERRY: They're no friends of mine, Father. They're trespassers, that's what they are.

GIRLS (*Shouting*): We are *not* trespassers.

PERRY: You can decide that for yourself, sir, when you hear how they've been holding up the bulldozer crew for more than half an hour.

MR. GUTHRIE: Holding up the bulldozer crew for more than half an hour! Why, that *is* serious. I'm paying those men quite a sum of money. I want them to get to work immediately.

GINGER: But, Mr. Guthrie, they're going to destroy all our beautiful trees.

JOAN: My holly tree is right in its path.

MARGIE: And my big White Pine.

KATE: And my lovely, lacy Tamarack.

MR. GUTHRIE: What are you talking about? There are no trees at all back of the garage. I'll listen to your story later. Right now I must get those men on the job.

MRS. HAWKINS: But, Mr. Guthrie, sir, that's just the trouble. The bulldozer crew isn't working back of the garage.

MR. GUTHRIE: Then for goodness' sake, where *is* it working?

LENA: On the south lawn, sir.

MR. GUTHRIE (*With a roar of rage*): On the south lawn! Thunderation! How did those stupid blockheads ever make such an error? I distinctly told them the tennis court was to be back of the garage.

PERRY: But, Dad, the south lawn is a much better spot.

MR. GUTHRIE: Much better spot, my eye! Don't you know the finest trees on the place are on the south lawn? (*Pause*) Wait a minute! Perry Guthrie, did you tell those men to tear up the south lawn?

PERRY: Well, gee whiz, Dad. I didn't think it would make any difference to you. I just thought . . .

MR. GUTHRIE: When it comes to tearing up my property, young man, I'll do the thinking. Lena, Mrs. Hawkins, quick! Tell those men to hold everything till they receive further orders from me. Get them stopped immediately. (*Exit* LENA *and* MRS. HAWKINS)

PERRY: I don't think you'll have to stop them, Dad. They haven't even started. These little demons wouldn't let them. And they have three more of their recruits standing guard out there right this minute.

GINGER: Oh, thank you, thank you, Mr. Guthrie, for saving our trees.

MR. GUTHRIE: You're more than welcome, young lady, but I must say I don't understand this. Just whose trees am I saving?

GIRLS: Ours.

JOAN: Oh dear! I guess you don't understand. We know all the trees on the place belong to you, sir, but . . . well . . . you see . . . they belong to us too.

PERRY: What right do you have to say a thing like that?

MARGIE: The right of adoption. You see, sir, we adopted them.

MR. GUTHRIE *and* PERRY: Adopted them?

MR. GUTHRIE: Who ever heard of adopting a tree? (*Enter* MISS CONWAY *accompanied by* ELEANOR, SHIRLEY *and* GWEN.)

MISS CONWAY: Perhaps I can explain, Mr. Guthrie.

GIRLS (*In surprise*): Miss Conway!

JOAN: How did you get here?

ELEANOR: I ran over to her house and got her to come and talk to the bulldozer boss.

SHIRLEY: We were afraid we couldn't keep them from starting to work.

GWEN: But we knew they'd listen to Miss Conway.

MISS CONWAY: I'm Emily Conway, Mr. Guthrie, and these girls are in my class at school. I took the liberty of asking the bulldozer crew to await further orders from you before they actually started to clear the trees on the south lawn. I felt sure you wouldn't want such valuable property destroyed.

MR. GUTHRIE: And you were entirely right. The whole thing was a mistake . . . a very bad mistake made by my son Perry.

PERRY: Golly, Dad, I'm sorry.

MR. GUTHRIE: We'll take care of that later. But right now I want to know about this business of tree adoption. These children have taken a big interest in protecting my property, and I'm curious to know why.

MISS CONWAY: It's because we've been reading and studying about trees and their value in soil conservation, Mr. Guthrie. Each child in our room adopted a tree for a year, so he could study it and get to know it almost as a personal friend. They've kept records for every one of the seasons. They've studied the leaves, and the buds and the branches. They've made leaf prints and taken measurements, and they've reported every item of interest or change that they have noticed in the growth of the tree.

GINGER: We live in Maytown Heights, Mr. Guthrie. It's a new development, and there aren't any trees at all. So Lena said we could adopt some of your trees if we promised not to hurt anything. I guess she should have asked you, Mr. Guthrie, but she didn't think you'd mind.

MR. GUTHRIE: Mind? Of course, I don't mind. I think it's a splendid idea.

GINGER: I adopted the American Elm near the south gate because I love the graceful shape of the tree and because it has played such an important part in our history. William Penn signed his famous treaty with the Indians under an elm tree, and Washington took command of his troops under an elm tree in Cambridge, Massachusetts, in 1775.

MARGIE: My adopted tree is the big White Pine nearest the house. I chose it because it's so easy to recognize with its long slender needles arranged in groups of five. And anyhow, I think it's the most important forest tree in all of North America. The first American homes and much of the pioneer furniture were made from the wood of the white pine.

JOAN: Nobody would want my adopted tree for the value of its wood, but everybody loves it because of its beauty, especially at Christmas time. I adopted the big American Holly tree in the center of the south lawn and when I saw that bulldozer heading for it, I just felt sick all over. Every year hundreds of holly trees are hurt and injured by thoughtless persons, so that they are dying out. It takes so long for a young tree to grow to any size at all that every one should be protected.

KATE: I adopted my tree because it has so many names. Some people call it the Larch, others call it the Tamarack, and still others call it the Hackmatack. It has needles and cones but it is not an evergreen. It loses its leaves every season and looks as if it is dead in the wintertime. But in spring and summer it is a beautiful, lacy green. I always thought the most deadly enemy of my tree was an insect called the saw-fly, but when I saw that bulldozer this morning, I knew that was a lot more dangerous than any saw-fly.

ELEANOR: I never knew how much I loved my great big handsome Scarlet Oak until I saw it was right in the path of that bulldozer.

SHIRLEY: And that's how I felt about my Copper Beech. It never looked so beautiful before.

GWEN: I guess you won't believe it, but I think my tree understood its own danger. I'm sure the leaves on my Trembling Aspen trembled harder than ever when that bulldozer came in sight.

MR. GUTHRIE: I must say, Miss Conway, I never saw children with such an appreciation and understanding of trees.

MISS CONWAY: We've learned from our study and observation that trees live to give, and whenever we look at a tree we think of the gifts it has for us.

MR. GUTHRIE: I wish my son had that knowledge and understanding, Miss Conway.

PERRY: Gee whiz, Dad, you make me feel like a murderer or something. I know all that stuff about trees . . . how they give us shade and shelter, how they help purify the atmosphere, and supply us with many necessary things of life, but well . . . I just didn't think about all that. I was too keen on getting my tennis court.

MR. GUTHRIE: Well, you can forget about your tennis court now, Perry. Until you have learned a better set of values, you don't deserve a tennis court.

PERRY (*Meekly*): Yes, sir.

Mr. Guthrie: Those trees you would so carelessly destroy have taken years to grow and develop. They could never have been replaced in your lifetime.

Joan: Excuse me, Mr. Guthrie, but we were very much like Perry before we started our conservation study. We knew the facts about trees and their importance to man, but we never actually realized what trees do until we began to go on field trips with Miss Conway.

Margie: We visited with farmers and talked to them about their wood lots. We learned how trees actually fertilize and enrich the soil.

Eleanor: And we visited South Mountain after the forest fire last summer. We saw how tragic a mountain can be when the trees have been destroyed.

Shirley: We investigated the source of our water supply and found out that our good drinking water comes from springs that flow from tree-covered water sheds.

Gwen: Then we went to the Water Company and saw their conservation project; how they've planted thousands of trees at the impounding basin to protect us against a bad water shortage or a severe drought.

Kate: But even then, we didn't really appreciate trees as living things until we each adopted one of our own and watched it grow.

Ginger: My best lesson on trees was moving to Maytown Heights. We have a nice home there but I do wish we had some trees! The people are still having trouble with their landscaping and drainage. The terraces are all sliding downhill, there's no shady place for the little children to play, and the whole place is so barren without trees.

Miss Conway: My father used to say the best way to learn to love trees was to plant them. He used to quote a little verse by Henry van Dyke and I've never forgotten it. "He that planteth a tree is a servant of God. He provideth a kindness for many generations, and faces that he hath not seen shall bless him." Perhaps if Perry had a tree-planting project . . .

PERRY: Say, Dad, that gives me an idea. Why can't I plant some trees? Not on our grounds, but somewhere else, some place where they're really needed, like Maytown Heights, for instance.

GINGER: Oh, Perry! Do you really mean it?

PERRY: Sure, I mean it. Anyone who loves trees as much as you girls should have some of your very own. How about it, Dad? I could buy some trees out of my allowance.

MR. GUTHRIE: And I'm sure you could get the support of the Conservation Society and the Water Company. They are only too anxious to have young people plant seedlings and young trees. Go ahead, son, and see what you can do.

PERRY: When can we start?

MISS CONWAY: I'd suggest we make a tour of the town first, Perry, to see what kind of shade trees or evergreens are best suited to a development like Maytown Heights. My station wagon is outside, and we could all pile in and do a little prospecting before we decide on the kind of trees to plant.

PERRY: How about it, girls? Will I be safe from attack if I join your tree-scouting expedition?

GIRLS (*Laughing*): You're safe as long as our adopted trees are safe.

PERRY: Is it O.K. with you, Dad?

MR. GUTHRIE: It's one hundred percent O.K. with me, Perry. From what I've seen of these young ladies, they'll keep you so busy you won't have time to get into any mischief. (*Girls and* MISS CONWAY *exit with* PERRY *in one direction, as* MRS. HAWKINS *and* LENA *enter from the other.*)

MRS. HAWKINS: That bulldozer outfit is starting to get impatient, Mr. Guthrie.

LENA: They said if you don't want them today, they have another job they can do.

MRS. HAWKINS: Shall we send them away, sir?

MR. GUTHRIE: No, thank you, Mrs. Hawkins. I had just about decided to drop the whole idea of a tennis court for this year, but come to think of it, I might take up tennis myself this summer. Perry and I might put in a row of maples right back of the garage so I'll have a shady spot to rest when I get too tired. I'll go out and have a word with those men myself.

THE END

It's a Problem

(Health)

(Characters)

CHAIRMAN OF THE BOARD OF EXPERTS

MARY
SARAH
RUTH
LOUISE } *Members of the Board of Experts*
SUE
BILLY
FRED
JOHN

PROBLEM PATTY
PROBLEM PAUL
PROBLEM PEGGY
PROBLEM PETE
PROBLEM POLLY
PROBLEM PATRICK

SETTING: *The meeting room of the Board of Experts.*

AT RISE: PROBLEM PATTY *is in the consultant's chair.* BOARD OF EXPERTS *are seated around a table.*

CHAIRMAN: Hello, there, and welcome to our (*Mentions grade*) Grade Problem Period. Today we are about to discuss some important Health Problems. Here is Problem Patty with Question Number One.

PROBLEM PATTY: Thank you, Madam Chairman. I really do

need help. I am called Problem Patty because it is such a problem for my mother to get me off to school on time.

MARY: A great many mothers have that same problem, Patty.

PROBLEM PATTY: Yes, I know. But mine seems to be extra special. You see, in the morning, I am always in a hurry. But Mother insists I take time out for breakfast. My problem is how to stop wasting time on breakfast and get to school before the bell rings.

SARAH: The answer to that one is very simple. You'll just have to get up earlier.

PROBLEM PATTY: But I'm too sleepy! Anyhow, why should I bother with that silly old breakfast!

RUTH: It looks as if we'll have to educate Problem Patty about breakfast. Breakfast isn't a bit silly, you know. In fact, it's terribly important because it gets you off to a good start for the whole day. What do you usually eat for breakfast?

PROBLEM PATTY: Whatever I can grab on the run. (*Experts shake heads in disapproval.*)

CHAIRMAN: That will never do! Let's give her the formula for the right kind of breakfast!

EXPERTS (*Singing to tune of "Shortnin' Bread"*):

Get out the juices, get out the toast,
That's what children love for breakfast most.
Get out the dishes for the oatmeal too,
Good hot cereal's the dish for you!

All us li'l children love breakfast, breakfast, all us li'l children love to sit and eat!

All us li'l children love breakfast, breakfast! All us li'l children love a breakfast treat!

Get out the cocoa, get out the milk,
Breakfast's gonna make your skin like silk.
Get out the bacon and get out the eggs,
Gonna build a pair of sturdy arms and legs!
    (*Repeat chorus*)

CHAIRMAN: Give yourself plenty of time for a good breakfast, Patty, and see if your problem doesn't have a happy ending.

PROBLEM PATTY: Very well, I'll try. But I bet my mother will say . . . I told you so! (*Exit* PATTY *as* PAUL *enters*)

CHAIRMAN: Mothers have a way of being right about a lot of things. But here comes Problem Paul. His face is all screwed up as if he has a very tough problem to solve.

PROBLEM PAUL: My problem is really difficult. In fact, you'll have to be good in arithmetic to answer this one.

BILLY: We'll do our best. But I do hope it doesn't involve fractions.

PROBLEM PAUL: If you have twenty-eight teeth when you're eight years old, how many will you have when you're eighty years old?

BILLY: That answer doesn't depend on arithmetic. That depends on you.

PROBLEM PAUL: What do you mean?

RUTH: Your teeth depend on daily care,
        And proper foods to eat.
        Of too much candy, please beware!
        There's danger in a sweet!
        Your teeth will last a good long while,
        If you take care, you bet!
        At eighty you will have your own,
        Or buy another set!

CHAIRMAN: Here's the formula that should solve your problem, Paul.

EXPERTS (*Singing to the tune of "She'll Be Comin' 'Round the Mountain"*):

You should clean and scrub your grinders after meals, after meals,
You should clean and scrub your grinders after meals, after meals,

If you're heedin' our reminders,
You'll be scrubbin' all your grinders,
And you'll soon begin to know how good it feels!

So be sure to brush your teeth four times a day, times a day,
So be sure to brush your teeth four times a day, times a day,
Every night and every morning,
After meals, and that's a warning—
You will find that brushing teeth prevents decay.

CHAIRMAN: I guess you'll have to solve your own problem by taking care of your own teeth, Paul. No one else can do it for you.

PROBLEM PAUL: All right. I'll try to remember. When I'm eighty years old, I'll write you a letter and let you know how your advice worked out. (*Exit* PAUL *as* PEGGY *enters*)

CHAIRMAN: And now we're ready for our next Problem, and this time, it's Problem Peggy. Make yourself comfortable, Peggy, and tell us your troubles.

PROBLEM PEGGY: My problem is also about teeth, but it's quite different from Paul's. You see, my problem is toothpaste. Each of us uses a different kind at our house, and I'd like to know how to tell which one is best.

LOUISE: The best toothpowder or toothpaste to use on your toothbrush is elbow grease.

PROBLEM PEGGY: Elbow grease! That would taste horrible. I like a toothpaste that tastes good.

LOUISE: Elbow grease doesn't have any taste at all. It just means that you should scrub your teeth good and hard when you brush them. If you try using a teaspoon of salt in a glass of water, you'll be making your own toothpaste.

PROBLEM PEGGY: That sounds like a good idea. Elbow grease and salt water! That's a pretty good formula . . . and not at all expensive.

SARAH: But the main idea is to remember to use it four times a day.

PROBLEM PEGGY: Thank you. I'll be sure to take your advice. (*She exits and* PROBLEM PETE *enters.*)

CHAIRMAN: Dear me! Look at this dirty fellow. It must be Problem Pete.

FRED: Yes, that's Pete all right. You'd hardly believe he's a nice looking fellow when he's cleaned up. His problem must be terrific.

CHAIRMAN: Let him state his case.

PROBLEM PETE: I live near a laundry,
But I'm in a quand'ry!
I guess I'm a guy without hope!
I love to see dirt
On my face and my shirt.
I hate to use water and soap!

The water's so wet!
And the soap that I get,
It always throws suds in my eye!
But my friends are so few
I am hoping that you
Will give me advice I can try.

My mother is worried,
My father is flurried,
That I'm such a terrible "dope"!
I go out to play,
And my friends fade away,
Because I hate water and soap!

CHAIRMAN: Dear me! This *is* a problem!

LOUISE: Maybe he should send himself away to be dry-cleaned!

JOHN: Maybe he should get a girl. My dad says there's nothing like a girl friend to make a fellow spruce up and take pride in his appearance!

MARY: Humph! What girl would want to play with him! Just look at his face and hands!

SUE: And I bet his hair hasn't been combed in a week.

CHAIRMAN: But soap and water are his main problem. How can we solve that?

BILLY: There just isn't any other way to cleanliness.

FRED: Or to health, either. My dad's a doctor, and he says disease germs love dirt. He lent us this microscope so we could really see bacteria at work in a single drop of dirty water. Want to have a look, Pete? (*Motions to microscope on large table*)

PROBLEM PETE: I've seen lots of dirt in my day, Fred.

FRED: But nothing like this, I bet. Take a good look. (PROBLEM PETE *looks in microscope.*)

PROBLEM PETE: What are all those squirmy little things?

FRED: I'd have to be a scientist to name them for you, Pete. But that's the sort of wild life you find in dirt, whether it's in a drop of muddy water or on your face and hands.

PROBLEM PETE: Golly! I'd hate to think those things are crawling over me.

FRED: And every time you put your finger in your mouth or put the end of a dirty pencil in your mouth, you get a dose of those creepy, crawly little bugs.

PROBLEM PETE: Maybe there's a point for soap and water after all.

FRED: It's our best weapon against these little killers, Pete.

PROBLEM PETE: O.K., I surrender! I'm a soap and water boy from now on.

SUE: We've scouring pads for pots and pans,
    And cleansers for the sink,
    And polish for the silverware,
    So bright it makes you blink!
    There's cleaning wax for kitchen floors
    That really is a joy,
    But only soap and water will
    Shine up a dirty boy!

PROBLEM PETE: I guess you've got something there and the next time you see me I'll be all shined up like a new penny from head to foot. (*Exit* PROBLEM PETE)

CHAIRMAN: I think Problem Pete is going to be all right. Now, who is next on our list?

LOUISE: I have the name of Problem Polly as our next consultant and here she is. (PROBLEM POLLY *enters*.)

PROBLEM POLLY: Oh dear! I'm really worried! My problem is candy. I have what is known as a *sweet tooth*. I can't pass by a dish of chocolates or gum drops without taking a handful. What can I do?

SARAH: Plenty of people, old and young, have your problem, Polly. It's all a matter of self-control. Try eating a piece of candy after meals instead of between meals and see how it works.

BILLY: Set up a candy budget for yourself—three small pieces a day, one after each meal—and see if you can stick to it. Put yourself in training the way athletes do.

MARY: If you drink enough milk and eat plenty of fresh fruit and vegetables, maybe you won't be so hungry for candy.

PROBLEM PATTY: Oh dear! There's that word *milk* again. How much are you supposed to drink?

MARY: Three or four glasses a day. You really need a quart a day to keep up good health standards.

PROBLEM POLLY (*With a sigh*): Very well, I suppose I'll have to give it a fair trial. But what about all those fruits and vegetables? Why are they so important?

ALL: Vitamins! Eat vitamin foods! Vitamins taste better in food than in medicine!

PROBLEM POLLY (*Laughing*): I guess you're right about that.

EXPERTS (*Singing to the tune of "Skip to My Lou"*):

Choose all your vitamins, skip to my Lou,
Choose all your vitamins, skip to my Lou,

Choose all your vitamins, skip to my Lou,
Skip to my Lou, my darling!

Without any vitamins, what would I do?
Without any vitamins, what would I do?
Without any vitamins, what would I do?
What would I do, my darling?

You'd be a sick-a-bed, boo, hoo, hoo!
You'd be a sick-a-bed, boo, hoo, hoo!
You'd be a sick-a-bed, boo, hoo, hoo!
Boo-hoo to you, my darling!

Eat 'em in oranges, a grapefruit'll do,
Eat 'em in oranges, a grapefruit'll do,
Eat 'em in oranges, a grapefruit'll do,
Grapefruit'll do, my darling.

Lettuce and lima beans have a lot too,
Lettuce and lima beans have a lot too,
Lettuce and lima beans have a lot too,
They have a lot, my darling.

Eat all the dairy foods, do, do, do!
Eat all the dairy foods, do, do, do!
Eat all the dairy foods, do, do, do!
And drink your milk, my darling!

PROBLEM POLLY: You've put up some very convincing arguments. From now on, I promise to be a real vitamin girl
with plenty of fresh fruits, green vegetables and milk! I'll
put the lid on the candy box and keep it on tight! (*Exit*
PROBLEM POLLY)

CHAIRMAN: We have one more appointment, but he seems to
be late.

SARAH: If it's Problem Patrick, he's always late.

RUTH: He's getting slower and slower.

FRED: No pep at all.

SUE: Look, here he comes . . . dragging along at a snail's pace.

CHAIRMAN: Hurry up, fellow, you're keeping us waiting.

PROBLEM PATRICK (*Entering and yawning*): I'm sorry. I just stayed in bed for a little extra snooze, and I must have slept longer than I planned. (*With another yawn*) Excuse me, please.

CHAIRMAN (*With a yawn*): Please try to stop yawning or you'll have us all doing it.

PROBLEM PATRICK: But that's my problem. I'm yawning all the time. In fact, I'm so sleepy right now I can hardly keep my eyes open.

CHAIRMAN: What time did you go to bed last night?

PROBLEM PATRICK: I don't remember. It must have been after eleven . . . or maybe closer to twelve. (*Experts shake heads in disapproval*)

CHAIRMAN: No wonder you're sleepy.

PROBLEM PATRICK: Oh, that's nothing for me! I'm a regular night owl!

FRED: Do you eat mice?

PROBLEM PATRICK (*Startled*): What did you say?

FRED: I asked you if you ate mice. That's what night owls eat.

PROBLEM PATRICK: Don't be ridiculous.

FRED: I'm not being ridiculous. If you want to be a night owl, you should follow his eating habits as well as his sleeping habits. A diet of mice would be just about as good for you as the owl's sleeping habits.

JOHN: If you want to be an owl, you should grow feathers.

PROBLEM PATRICK: You're making fun of me! I came here to get help with my problem of yawning. It's very embarrassing. I yawn all the time, whether I want to or not. I can't seem to help it.

LOUISE: Ten hours of sleep each night would soon fix that.

PROBLEM PATRICK: Thomas Edison got along on only three or four hours sleep a night.

JOHN: First he's an owl, now he's Thomas Edison!

PROBLEM PATRICK: I'm getting out of here! You're just trying to make a dunce of me!

BILLY: You've already done that yourself, boy, by yawning your way through life.

MARY: You need all the rest you can get to build up your energy.

BILLY: It takes more energy than you have now just to grow!

PROBLEM PATRICK: That's a funny statement.

BILLY: But it's true. When you were six years old, you probably weighed about forty-three pounds, and were about forty-three inches tall. In five years, if you kept up to other boys of your age, you gained thirty pounds and added twelve inches to your height.

FRED: Boy, that's work. From the time you're six till you're fourteen, that's only eight years, you're supposed to gain sixty pounds, and grow about twenty inches! You can't do that by yawning, brother.

PROBLEM PATRICK: Golly! No wonder I feel tired all the time. Mom says I'm growing like a weed.

CHAIRMAN: Why don't you give your body a square deal, Patrick?

PROBLEM PATRICK: I never thought of it that way before. I've always wanted to be big and strong, but, well . . . I thought it was sissy to go to bed early.

JOHN: Then we must have a lot of sissy track stars, and basketball players and big-time athletes.

PROBLEM PATRICK: Maybe you're right.

CHAIRMAN: Of course, we're right. That's why we're experts.

PROBLEM PATRICK: You sure know all the answers.

CHAIRMAN: No, we don't know all the answers, Patrick. Nobody knows all the answers to health problems. But we do know that it always pays to follow the rules . . . and we know our health rules backwards and forwards. Maybe we should give you a copy of the list we compiled in class.

FRED (*Handing* PATRICK *the list*): Try to stop yawning long enough to read these. You'll find they solve most of our daily problems. (PROBLEM PATRICK *reads list of health rules that have been compiled by class.*)

PROBLEM PATRICK: These rules should be easy to follow.

CHAIRMAN: Of course. Most of them are just plain, common sense, and I am sure our Problem Pupils will agree with me. (*Enter* PATTY, PAUL, PEGGY, PETE *and* POLLY.)

PROBLEM PATTY: A hearty breakfast every day
                 Will start me on my healthy way.

PROBLEM PAUL: A toothbrush, though it's not so weighty
                 Will save my teeth till I am eighty.

PROBLEM PEGGY: No toothpaste ever can compare
                 With elbow grease and dental care.

PROBLEM PETE: Soap and water are the foe
                 To fight the germs and lay them low.

PROBLEM POLLY: Vitamins are fine and dandy
                 In place of too much cake and candy.

PROBLEM PATRICK: From now on, I will use my head
                 And get sufficient rest in bed.

ALL (*Singing to the tune of "For He's a Jolly Good Fellow"*):
We'll all be healthy and happy, we'll all be healthy and
     happy,
We'll all be healthy and happy, and you can be just the
     same.
And you can be just the same, and you can be just the same,
If all these rules you will follow, if all these rules you will
     follow,
If all these rules you will follow, then you can be just the
     same!

THE END

A February Failure

(Abraham Lincoln)

Characters

MISS MARTIN, *the teacher*
HARRISON HARDWICK, *a February Failure*
MEMBERS OF THE CLASS

ANNOUNCER: Did you ever live through a day when everything
went dead wrong? Well, that's the sort of day it was for
Harrison Hardwick. To begin with, Harrison overslept.
He slept straight through the alarm, and the next thing he
knew, his mother was shaking him awake and warning him
that he would be late for school. Poor Harrison hurried as
fast as he could, but the bell had rung ten minutes before
he pushed open the door to his classroom. The children
were all studying, but they turned around in their seats
and gave him the "Sleepyhead Treatment," as soon as he
walked in.

SETTING: *A classroom.*

AT RISE: TEACHER *is at her desk.* CHILDREN *turn as* HARRISON
enters. They recite the following in a jeering tone.

ALL: Sleepyhead! Sleepyhead! Couldn't you get out of bed?
SOLO: Can't you tell the night from day?
ALL: Sleepyhead! Sleepyhead! Lazy little Lie-a-Bed!

SOLO: What excuse have you to say?

ALL: Hurry up! Hurry up! Take your seat and hurry up!

SOLO: We have no more time to fool!

ALL: Tardy mark! Tardy mark! Now you'll get a tardy mark!

SOLO: Sleepyhead is late for school!

TEACHER: Dear me, Harrison! Now you've spoiled our perfect attendance record for the week! Did you bring your note?

HARRISON: I hurried so fast I forgot to bring it, Miss Martin. I'll bring it for sure tomorrow. I don't know how it happened, but I overslept!

TEACHER: You must really try to be more punctual. Now take your seat quickly, please, and let me see your Lincoln story.

HARRISON: My Lincoln story?

TEACHER: Now don't tell me you forgot that too? You know this is the day of our Lincoln program, don't you?

HARRISON: Oh, my goodness! I forgot it! It was all finished, but I forgot to bring it!

TEACHER: Then sit right down and get to work on another. We were hoping to be able to use yours in our program, but now you have failed us. Mary, suppose you read your story.

MARY: Abraham Lincoln was born so long ago that all the people who actually knew him are dead. But many folks wrote down the things they remembered about Lincoln and the stories that were told about him. Although we do not know if all of these stories are true, some of them are very amusing. Lincoln was a great one for settling arguments. One time two men were arguing about the proper length of a man's legs. Finally they asked Mr. Lincoln's opinion. He studied the problem and then he said: "Well, boys, it's my opinion that a man's legs should be long enough to reach from his body to the ground."

TEACHER: That's a popular Lincoln story, Mary, and you've

told it very nicely. Now, Harrison, let's see what you can do with a Lincoln arithmetic problem. Can you figure out how old Lincoln would be if he were living today?

HARRISON (*Figuring on piece of paper*): Let's see . . . no, that's not right. (*Erasing*) I'd better start all over again.

TEACHER: You shouldn't have any trouble with that, Harrison. It's just a simple problem in subtraction. Don't you know how to do it?

HARRISON: You subtract the year in which Lincoln was born from 1955.

TEACHER: That's exactly right. Now go ahead.

HARRISON: But that's where I'm stuck. I can't remember the year he was born.

TEACHER: We talked about it only yesterday, Harrison. Tell him the date, class.

ALL: 1809.

TEACHER: Now, go ahead. What's your answer?

HARRISON: Forty-six. (*Children laugh*)

TEACHER: I'm afraid you've made Mr. Lincoln far too young. Better take another look.

HARRISON: Oh, now I see. He'd be a hundred and forty-six years old.

TEACHER: That's more like it. Now write this sentence on your paper: "If Lincoln were alive today, he would be one hundred and forty-six years old." (*As* HARRISON *starts to write*) Wait a minute, Harrison. How do you spell *Lincoln?*

HARRISON: L-i-n-c-o-n.

TEACHER (*As other children wave hands in air*): Does anyone have a correction?

FRED: He forgot the second "l." L-i-n-c-o-l-n.

TEACHER: I'm afraid Harrison is forgetting too many things today. But now it's time to practice our program. Let's try our Lincoln song. (*Class sings any song about Lincoln.*)

TEACHER: What's the matter, Harrison? You aren't singing.

HARRISON: I—I don't feel much like singing, Miss Martin. I—I don't know all of the words.

TEACHER: Then perhaps you'd better study them so you can sing them this afternoon. Now where are the children for the Lincoln Portrait? (*Five children take their places. The center one carries a picture of Lincoln.*)

1ST CHILD: Lincoln was a tall man,
   Lean, and brown, and strong.
   Lincoln always had a joke,
   A laugh to pass along.

2ND CHILD: Lincoln was a kind man,
   Quick to sympathize.
   To see a fellow creature hurt
   Brought tears into his eyes.

3RD CHILD: Lincoln was a plain man,
   Simple in his taste;
   Never was a rich man
   With money he could waste.

4TH CHILD: Lincoln was an honest man,
   Always on the square.
   Lincoln was a just man,
   Believed in playing fair.

5TH CHILD: Lincoln was a strange man,
   People called him odd.
   Lincoln was a good man,
   With faith in men and God.

TEACHER: That's a splendid description of Lincoln, boys and girls, and I hope you will remember it, long after our program is forgotten. Now after you children finish the poem, you all sit down, and Nancy hands the Lincoln picture to Harrison as he steps forward to say his poem. Come along, Harrison. It's your turn. (TEACHER *stands waiting for* HARRISON *and hands him the picture as he comes for-*

ward.) Hold the picture, as if you're actually talking to it, Harrison, when you say your poem.

HARRISON: I—I don't believe I can say my poem, Miss Martin.

TEACHER: Why of course you can say it. You knew it perfectly yesterday.

HARRISON: I still know it . . . but I don't think I can say it.

TEACHER: But why not?

HARRISON: It's the picture. It's just as if Mr. Lincoln is staring straight at me and sees what a failure I am.

TEACHER: Why, Harrison, what do you mean?

HARRISON: I've failed at everything all morning. I spoiled our attendance record. I didn't have my Lincoln story. I couldn't do that arithmetic problem, and I even forgot the words of our song. I never do anything right.

TEACHER: I'll admit this has been a bad day for you, Harrison, but we all have our failures you know . . . even Lincoln.

HARRISON: Not Lincoln, Miss Martin. You can see just by looking at his picture that he was never a failure.

TEACHER: Perhaps this is the time for me to give you our Lincoln surprise, boys and girls. You know, every year on Lincoln's birthday, I like to give the class a little gift in his memory. Last year it was this picture. This year it is something different. Sit down, Harrison, and let me show you. (TEACHER *places picture on her desk and picks up a package*.) We all know that Abraham Lincoln is one of our great American heroes. We all know that he was born in a log cabin in the wilderness, and that he rose to success and fame through hard work and courage. But I wonder if we know about his failures?

CLASS: Failures?

TEACHER: This year I didn't know what to bring you on Lincoln's birthday. I thought of a little statue, another picture, some new books . . . and then I saw this— (*Unwrapping gift*) a framed copy of "Lincoln's Failures." Before we hang it on the wall, I'd like you to gather round me and read it.

1ST CHILD (*Reading*): When Abraham Lincoln was a young man, he ran for the legislature of Illinois and was badly defeated.

2ND CHILD (*Reading*): He next entered business, but he failed, and spent the next seventeen years of his life paying up the debts of his partner.

3RD CHILD (*Reading*): He fell in love with a beautiful young woman, but she died.

4TH CHILD (*Reading*): He entered politics, but was badly defeated.

5TH CHILD (*Reading*): Then he tried to get an appointment to the United States Land Office, but he failed.

6TH CHILD (*Reading*): He became a candidate for the United States Senate and was badly defeated.

7TH CHILD (*Reading*): In 1856 he became a candidate for the vice-presidency of the United States, and was again defeated.

8TH CHILD (*Reading*): In 1858 he was defeated by Stephen Douglas.

ALL (*Reading*): But in the face of this defeat and failure, he finally won the greatest success in life, and undying fame, to the end of time.

TEACHER: And that's our Lincoln gift this year, boys and girls . . . a list of Abraham Lincoln's failures. We'll hang it up front right beside his picture, so that when you meet with failure and discouragement, you can say to yourself: "If *he* could succeed after all those failures and disappointments, so can I."

HARRISON: Gee, thank you, thank you, Miss Martin for the present! And now . . . I'd like to practice my poem for the program.

TEACHER: Splendid, Harrison. Go right ahead.

HARRISON: When Lincoln saw the stars aglow

In his Kentucky sky,
Did he feel timid and alone,
And just as small as I?

And when he heard the night wind
Come howling at the door,
Did he slide down inside his bed
And shiver at its roar?

And when he had to go alone
For water in the night,
Did he walk a little faster?
Did he feel a tiny fright?

And when he had some work to do—
Hard work instead of play,
Did Lincoln ever put it off
Until another day?

I'd give a lot to know these things,
For though I plainly see
I'll never be like Lincoln,
Perhaps *he* was like me!

(*Children applaud*)

TEACHER: That was beautifully done, Harrison, and I know
you'll do just as well this afternoon. I think you've turned
your back on failure for a long time to come. And you
know, boys and girls, I think you'll really find the secret of
Lincoln's triumph over failure in the verse we learned yesterday. Let's say it.

ALL: I will if I can, and I can if I try.
I'll keep right on trying and never say *die!*
And if I meet failure perhaps now and then,
I'll never give up, but start over again!

THE END

A Lincoln Museum

(Abraham Lincoln)

Characters

CURATOR OF THE CLASSROOM MUSEUM
ROSE
FRED
BILL
GRACE
ETHEL
SUE
ELLEN
TED
CARLA
NICK
TEN STUDENT COMMENTATORS

SETTING: *A classroom stage.*

AT RISE: *The* CURATOR *stands behind a flag-draped table, downstage center, which has been prepared to receive the Lincoln exhibits.*

CURATOR: Good afternoon, and welcome to our Lincoln Museum. (*Laughs*) Oh, I know what you're thinking! There's nothing in our museum! Well, you just wait and see. In a few minutes, my classmates will be bringing in their Lincoln treasures and this table will be filled up in no time. In case you're wondering who I am, I'll tell you. I am the Curator.

That means the caretaker or guardian of the museum. It's my responsibility to assemble the exhibits, take care of them and see that they are properly explained. Now we're ready to start and here comes Rose with Exhibit A. Dear me! It looks like something she dug out of the attic.

ROSE (*With old-fashioned silk hat*): I guess you're right, and I must admit Exhibit A looks pretty old and battered, but that's exactly as it should be. If you've studied the life of Lincoln, I'm sure you know why it belongs here.

CURATOR: Thank you, Rose. I'll put the hat where it's sure to be noticed. But what on earth does Fred have?

FRED (*With a piece of wood*): Never mind what it is. Just see that it gets a good place on the display table. It might seem to you to be an ordinary piece of wood, but just wait till you hear the story.

CURATOR: Leave it to you to find something unusual. Hello, Grace. What's your contribution?

GRACE: It's a letter. I'm sure it's important because the date is November 21st, 1864, and the closing reads: "Yours very respectfully and sincerely, A. Lincoln."

CURATOR: Here, I'll prop it up against the silk hat so everyone can see it.

BILL: And be sure you take good care of my exhibit. I made it myself. Maybe the printing isn't so good, but I guess you can read it. (*Holds up banner.*)

FRED: Sure, I can read that without any trouble. It says: LINCOLN AND LIBERTY. I must say I can't remember anything about such a banner. Are you sure you didn't make it up?

BILL: I made the banner but I didn't make up the slogan. That's history.

CURATOR: Let's not get into a discussion now, boys. That will come later. Let's see what Ethel has.

GRACE: It looks like a theatre program.

ETHEL: And that's just what it is. Where do you want me to put it? (*She places it on table.*)

CURATOR: We're getting so many sheets of paper, it's hard to know how to arrange them to the best advantage.

SUE: Well, save room for mine. It's a piece of sheet music and I'll tell you right now, I had a terrible time finding it. The pages are yellow and the ink is faded, but I think we can still make out the words and the melody.

ETHEL: Let me see that. That looks interesting.

CURATOR (*Taking sheet music*): Not now, please! If we stop to look at all these things we'll never get the display in shape.

SUE: Ellen is bringing their family Bible. It's so big she can hardly carry it.

ELLEN (*Entering with Bible*): Oh, dear . . . make a place for this quick, before I drop it.

CURATOR: Put it right here.

ELLEN (*Placing Bible on table*): Mother said we're to be very careful because it's one of our family treasures.

CURATOR: We will. I'll be standing guard right here the whole time.

TED: Hi, everybody. Look what I have for the exhibition. (*Displays placard*) One hundred thousand dollars reward. (*Putting it on table*) There! I hope everybody can read it.

CARLA (*In a hurry*): I hope I'm not too late. Here's my contribution.

TED: What is it? It's so little I can hardly see it.

CARLA: Once upon a time it was a dime, but now it's as flat and thin as a piece of paper. (*Puts coin on table*)

CURATOR: That just about completes our collection. We need just one more display.

NICK: And here it is . . . an empty picture frame. I hope it's all right.

CURATOR: It looks fine to me, Nick, and I'll put it in a good location. (*Puts frame on table*)

NICK: Everything looks great! And if anybody should ask me, I'd say I think this is a swell way to pay our respects to Mr. Lincoln.

CARLA: Just think! Every single object on this table is connected in one way or another with his life.

CURATOR: And that's where our museum really gets interesting. As our audience may have guessed by this time, this museum is not an ordinary museum with proper tags and labels. And our exhibits are not ordinary exhibits. We've collected the articles on display from all sorts of places. We've ransacked our houses from cellar to attic to find these bits of Lincoln lore, and now we're going to call in a board of experts from our history class to identify them for you. We have ten exhibits so we'll call ten students. Their names have already been chosen and here they are. (*Ten boys and girls enter.*) Welcome to our Lincoln Museum, fellow students. The members of the Museum Committee have done their best to line up a display of interesting articles associated with the life of Abraham Lincoln. Now it's your job to identify these articles and explain the connections. The boy or girl who brought the object under discussion will decide the correctness and completeness of your answers. (*Calling first name*), we'll ask you to start with Exhibit A.

ROSE: As you can see Exhibit A is a high silk hat. Can you explain why it belongs in our Lincoln Museum?

1ST STUDENT: Well, Lincoln is often pictured wearing a high top hat. It seems to be as much a part of him as his beard or the mole on his cheek. In some pictures, where he isn't actually wearing a hat, you see it on a table beside him. I guess he always wanted it nearby. It seems to me that somewhere I read how he sometimes carried important papers tucked inside his hatband. I guess it was rather like a brief case.

ROSE: I think that's a very satisfactory answer, (*Name*). But

I'd like to ask one more question. Can you think of anything we read in connection with Lincoln that made me think of bringing this hat for the museum?

1st STUDENT: Oh, I think I know what you mean. You're referring to the poem "Abraham Lincoln Walks at Midnight" by Vachel Lindsay. One of the stanzas mentions the hat:

> "A bronzed lank man! His suit of ancient black,
> A famous high top-hat and plain worn shawl
> Make him the quaint, great figure that men love,
> The prairie-lawyer, master of us all!"

ROSE: Thank you, (*Name*), for such an excellent description of my exhibit.

CURATOR: I'm afraid our next observer might have a more difficult job. (*Name of* 2ND STUDENT), we'll ask you to identify Exhibit B contributed by Fred King.

2ND STUDENT: It looks like a piece of wood. May I pick it up?

FRED: Sure, pick it up and examine it. You can't hurt it.

2ND STUDENT: It looks just like ordinary wood to me.

FRED: That's what it is . . . just ordinary wood. But you're supposed to tell why it might belong in a Lincoln Museum.

2ND STUDENT: Ummmm. Well, it doesn't look old enough to be a piece of wood out of the log cabin in which Lincoln was born, but that's one connection it might have with Lincoln.

FRED: I'd call that a pretty good try. Can you think of anything else?

2ND STUDENT: Since Lincoln was called the "Rail Splitter," maybe it's a piece of one of the rails he split. Or it could be part of his wooden ax handle, or that wooden fire shovel he used to cipher on.

FRED: I'd say you made a good score on that piece of wood, boy. And I bet if we had more time you'd be able to think of more ways in which Lincoln's life was connected with plain ordinary wood. How about that store in Salem? Couldn't this be a piece of the flooring, or maybe a part of the wooden sign that hung in front of his law office in Springfield?

2ND STUDENT: You're giving me more ideas. Maybe this is a piece of wood out of the flatboat on which he sailed down the Mississippi . . . or say . . . it might even be a hunk out of that old slave block he saw in New Orleans—the one that turned him against slavery forever and made him say to himself: "If ever I get a chance to hit that thing, I'll hit it hard!"

FRED: Golly! I never thought of half those things when I decided to bring a piece of wood. I just thought about the log cabin and the crude wooden tools he used and the little store at Salem. Your answers are much better than my original idea.

CURATOR: We'll let Grace present her contribution which is Exhibit C.

GRACE (*Holding up paper*): As you can see, it's a letter.

3RD STUDENT (*Examining letter*): Oh, dear! Lincoln wrote so many letters . . . hundreds and hundreds of letters. Can't you give me a clue?

GRACE: The date, November 21, 1864, should give you a clue.

3RD STUDENT: November 21, 1864. The Civil War was in progress at that time. Was it a military letter?

GRACE: Take a look at the signature.

3RD STUDENT: "Yours very sincerely and respectfully" . . . that doesn't sound very military. If he was the commander-in-chief, I don't think he'd use that word "respectfully." It sounds more as if he were writing to a woman.

GRACE: You're on the right track, and I'll add this much . . . it's a very famous letter.

3RD STUDENT: Oh, now I know. It's the letter he wrote to Mrs. Lydia Bixby, the widow in Boston, whose five sons had been killed in the war. Some people think that the letter is as great a masterpiece as his Gettysburg address.

GRACE: Your answer is right. I copied part of the letter itself because I thought it was worth remembering. (*Reads*) "I pray that our Heavenly Father may assuage the anguish of your bereavement and leave you only the cherished memory of the loved and lost, and the solemn pride that must be yours to have laid so costly a sacrifice upon the altar of freedom."

CURATOR: It's really a beautiful letter, isn't it? And it certainly deserves a place in our collection. Now for Bill's banner, Exhibit D.

4TH STUDENT: "Lincoln and Liberty." That sounds as if it could be a campaign banner.

BILL: So far so good. Any further information?

4TH STUDENT: I'd take a guess that it's a slogan from the campaign of 1860 when Lincoln ran against Douglas and won.

BILL: And that information is correct.

CURATOR: Exhibit E.

ETHEL: Here it is, (*Name of student*). You may look it over. (*She hands program to 5TH STUDENT.*)

5TH STUDENT: This is a program from Ford's Theatre in Washington. The date is April 14, 1865. That was a tragic night for Lincoln and for America, because that was the night the President went to see the play entitled "Our American Cousin," starring the famous actress, Laura Keene. Mr. Lincoln was tired and discouraged that evening and probably would have stayed at home but his wife thought it would do him good to see the play and enjoy a hearty laugh. But there were no laughs for Lincoln that night. He arrived at the theatre about 8:30, after the play had already started. About thirteen minutes after ten, John Wilkes Booth appeared at the door of the President's box, raised his gun and fired. The whole theatre was in confusion. They carried the wounded President across the street to a private home where he died at twenty-two minutes past seven on the morning of April 15, 1865.

CURATOR: I wonder if our next exhibit has any connection with the President's death.

SUE: Not at all. (*Holding up sheet of music*) This sheet music has a different and happier association.

6TH STUDENT: It could be the words and music of the song, "We're Coming, Father Abraham." Thousands of copies were printed during the war.

SUE: Better take a closer look, (*Name*). I think you can make out the title.

6TH STUDENT (*Examining music more closely*): Oh, now I see! The title is "Listen to the Mocking Bird." I believe this was said to be Lincoln's favorite song. He was always delighted to hear it played or sung. Some folks believe the words reminded him of his first sweetheart, Ann Rutledge, who died before she became his wife.

CURATOR: Since this was Lincoln's favorite song, I think we might enjoy hearing it right now. (*"Listen to the Mocking Bird" may be sung by the group or by a soloist.*)

CURATOR: And now for Exhibit G.

ELLEN (*Pointing to table*): There it is . . . a large family Bible.

7TH STUDENT: The Bible was part and parcel of Lincoln's life from the time he was a little boy until the day he died. It was one of the few books he read as a child and he knew many of its verses by heart.

ELLEN: Can you think of any official way in which the Bible was associated with his life?

7TH STUDENT: Official? Well, naturally, he used the Bible when he took the oath of office as President of the United States. That would have been March 4, 1861, and March 4, 1865. At his second inauguration, he made one of the most famous speeches of his life . . . the speech from which these lines are taken:

ALL (*In choral reading style*):

"With malice toward none;
With charity for all;
With firmness in the right, as God gives us to see the right,
Let us strive on to finish the work we are in;
To bind up the nation's wounds;
To care for him who shall have borne the battle,
And for his widow and his orphan;
To do all which may achieve and cherish
A just and lasting peace among ourselves
And with all nations."

CURATOR: Our next exhibit is the poster with the words: "One hundred thousand dollars reward."

8TH STUDENT: I think that poster must have been printed after the death of Lincoln in hopes that it would lead to the capture of Booth and his accomplices.

TED: That's right, (Name). Do you happen to know if the reward was ever claimed?

8TH STUDENT: Yes, it was claimed but not by one individual. It was finally split into thirty-four parts. Colonel Conger got the largest portion, fifteen thousand dollars, and Lafayette Baker, head of the Secret Service, received three thousand dollars. John Wilkes Booth was captured and killed on the 26th of April, 1865, and four of the conspirators were hanged on July 7th of the same year.

TED: I'd call that a very complete report. Congratulations, (Name).

CURATOR: And now for this very thin piece of metal which Carla assures us was once a dime.

CARLA: It really was, and this happens to be a real exhibit. My grandmother gave it to me. It's been in her family for . . . well . . . maybe I'd better not say how long . . . or I'd be giving (Name) too strong a clue.

9TH STUDENT: I think I know what it is, Carla, even without a clue. If that object was once a dime, it must have been smashed flat by a very heavy object. Now I do happen to know that as Lincoln's funeral train passed through the country from Washington to Springfield, Illinois, men and women gathered along the tracks and at every station to pay tribute to their martyred president. Many people wanted souvenirs of the occasion so they placed coins on the track as the train approached and gathered them up afterwards to be kept as prize possessions. I'd take a guess that this coin is one of those Lincoln keepsakes.

CURATOR: I must say our Board of Experts is well-informed on the subject of Abraham Lincoln, sixteenth President of the United States. Nick, do you want to say anything about our last display?

NICK: No comment.

10TH STUDENT (*Examining exhibit*): An empty picture frame! Since it's empty, I suppose we could fill it with any one of several items . . . a copy of the famous Emancipation Proclamation, the Gettysburg Address, or even the Bixby letter that is also one of our Exhibits. But I have an idea that Nick brought the picture frame with a painting or photograph of Lincoln in mind. There was a time when every schoolroom contained a picture of Lincoln, and even now his likeness is familiar to all Americans and to people all over the world. Whole books have been compiled of photographs of Abraham Lincoln. Men have done his likeness in oil, wood, stone and in the stained glass windows of churches. I propose that we reserve this frame for our picture of Lincoln . . . so that here in our classroom we can always see the kindly face of the great American we all love, the man who truly belongs to the ages and whose truth is forever marching on. (*The cast joins in singing "The Battle Hymn of the Republic" as the closing song.*)

THE END

Visitor to Mount Vernon

(George Washington)

Characters

THE PATRIOTIC TEDDY BEAR
THE PAINTER
FREDDY
MISS SHELBY
PHOTOGRAPHER
MAN
CLASSROOM PUPILS

PROLOGUE

BEFORE RISE: *The* PATRIOTIC TEDDY BEAR *steps out from behind the curtains to introduce himself and greet the audience.*

TEDDY BEAR: Hello, everybody! I'm the Patriotic Teddy Bear. You can tell by looking at me that I was manufactured in the United States of America, but I must say my colors are the result of accident rather than design. Actually, these red, white and blue clothes that I wear were given to me by a stupid painter in the toy factory where I was made.

PAINTER (*Entering from opposite side*): Just a minute! Just a minute! I resent that! You have no right to call me stupid.

TEDDY BEAR: Won't you admit that you made a mistake when you were painting me and dipped your brush into the wrong bucket?

PAINTER: Sure, I'll admit it. But everybody makes mistakes!

223

If I had been stupid, when I put that splash of red paint on your stomach, you would have been thrown into the trash pile.

TEDDY BEAR: And you would have lost your job!

PAINTER: Exactly so! But I wasn't stupid. I was clever! I decided to cover up my mistake by giving you a whole red coat, with a little white vest and shirt front just to make you look stylish. Then I got the idea of finishing you up in a smart looking pair of blue pants. So there you were . . . a red, white and blue teddy bear! Something new and different! Now do you still think I'm stupid?

TEDDY BEAR: No, I've changed my mind. I think you are very smart indeed. And I guess I owe you a vote of thanks, because if you hadn't painted me red, white, and blue, Freddy might never have noticed me.

FREDDY (*Entering from other side*): Oh, but I did notice you, the minute I saw you standing in that toy store, and I guess it was love at first sight. From the very second I laid eyes on you, I knew you were a patriotic teddy bear.

PAINTER: Hear that? It was my color scheme that made you famous.

FREDDY: That's right. I noticed him right away, because of the red, white and blue, the colors of our own dear flag. (*The* PAINTER, TEDDY BEAR *and* FREDDY *sing a flag song such as "Flag Song," Book 4,* THE AMERICAN SINGER *published by The American Book Company, or the children may want to choose a song about the flag from their music class or compose their own.*)

FREDDY: The Patriotic Teddy Bear was given to me as a birthday present and we got along just fine; but sometimes poor Teddy had his troubles. I'll never forget the day I took him along to school with me. He caused quite a sensation among the other boys and girls. (*They exit.*)

* * * *

SCENE 1

SETTING: *A schoolroom.*

AT RISE: *The* PATRIOTIC TEDDY BEAR *flops lifeless in a chair as a group of children clusters around him.*

BILLY: What a crazy-looking teddy bear! Why don't you throw him away?

FREDDY: Throw him away! I should say not! That old teddy bear is almost as old as I am. It would be almost like throwing away my brother!

BILLY: But he's such a dumb-looking teddy bear! Red, white and blue! Who ever heard of those colors for a teddy bear!

FREDDY: Well, you've heard of them now! I think red, white and blue are good colors for anything. Besides, what does his color matter?

BEN: But teddy bears should be brown or white, or maybe black! Not red, white and blue! I'd throw him away.

FREDDY: Stop talking about throwing him away. He's mine and I like him the way he is. Besides, he has to wear a red, white and blue suit because he's so patriotic.

BILLY (*As all children laugh*): Ah! What does that silly old teddy bear know about being patriotic? Why, I bet he doesn't even know who George Washington was.

FREDDY: Then he can learn. We can take him along on our trip to Mount Vernon. (*To* MISS SHELBY *who joins group*) Can't we, Miss Shelby?

MISS SHELBY: What's this about our trip to Mount Vernon?

BEN: Freddy wants to take his teddy bear along on our trip, Miss Shelby. Did you ever hear of anything so silly?

MISS SHELBY: Oh, I don't know! Maybe Freddy has a good reason for wanting to take his teddy bear.

FREDDY: It's because he's a patriotic teddy bear, Miss Shelby. See . . . he's red, white and blue, just like our flag.

BILLY: I think it would be sissy to take a teddy bear along on a trip. We're too old to play with teddy bears.

FREDDY: This teddy bear isn't a toy. He could be our mascot.

SUSIE: A mascot! That's a good idea! He could be the mascot for our room, like the Navy Goat or the Army Mule.

FREDDY: Now you're talking, Susie. And everybody's heard about the Detroit Tigers and the Chicago Cubs.

BEN: Maybe it's not such a bad idea at that, Freddy. I kind of like the idea of our room having a mascot.

TONY: And what could be better than a patriotic teddy bear?

FREDDY: Then we could take him along to Mount Vernon, couldn't we, Miss Shelby? He wouldn't take up very much room on the bus.

MISS SHELBY: Let's call for a vote. All in favor of adopting the Patriotic Teddy Bear as our official mascot, say "Aye."

ALL (*Loudly*): Aye!

MISS SHELBY: Opposed—"No?" (*Pause*) The "Ayes" have it and the Patriotic Teddy Bear is our official mascot.

RUTH: Now let's vote on taking him to Mount Vernon.

MISS SHELBY: You know how to make a motion, Ruth.

RUTH: Very well. I move that we take our official mascot, the Patriotic Teddy Bear, on our trip to Mount Vernon.

SUSIE: Madam Chairman, I second the motion.

MISS SHELBY: Are you ready for the question?

ALL: Question.

MISS SHELBY: It has been moved and seconded that we take our official mascot, the Patriotic Teddy Bear, along with us on our trip to Mount Vernon. All those in favor, signify their consent by saying "Aye."

ALL: Aye.

MISS SHELBY: Opposed—"No?" (*Pause*) The motion is carried and the Patriotic Teddy Bear goes with us. Remember,

Freddy, you'll have to be responsible for him and see that he is well taken care of.

FREDDY: I will. I'll see to it that he doesn't give anybody a minute's trouble.

MISS SHELBY: And now that we have that important matter settled, let's review some of the facts we learned about Mount Vernon. Freddy, you'd better make the Patriotic Teddy Bear sit up and pay attention so he will be prepared for his visit. Betty, can you tell us something we've learned about Mount Vernon?

BETTY: We learned that Mount Vernon is located about fifteen miles from Washington, D. C., on the Potomac River. It was Washington's home, and he loved it so much that he never left it except when his duty to his country called him away.

RUTH: We learned that Washington liked being a farmer and plantation owner better than being President of the United States.

MISS SHELBY: Since we've done so much reading and reporting on Mount Vernon, I know each of you has some special item you'll want to see on tomorrow's trip. David, what do you want to see?

DAVID: I want to see the room where George Washington was born.

MISS SHELBY: Then I'm afraid you'll be disappointed. Does anyone know why?

SALLY: Because he wasn't born there at all. George Washington was born at another plantation on the Potomac, but the house burned down, and his father built their new home near Fredericksburg on the Rappahannock River.

MARY: When George Washington was eleven years old, his father died, and he went to live with his brother Augustine who lived near the old homestead at Bridge's Creek, where he was born.

DAVID: Then how did he get to Mount Vernon?

MISS SHELBY: I think Carl has been writing a report on that angle of our story, David.

CARL: Although George Washington went to live for a while with his brother, Augustine, he was really under the care of his older brother, Lawrence. It was Lawrence who built Mount Vernon for his bride, Anne Fairfax. The Fairfax family lived on the next plantation, an estate called Belvoir; and when Washington went to visit Lawrence at Mount Vernon, he met Lord Fairfax who later employed him to survey his lands in the wilderness.

MISS SHELBY: Does anyone know how Mount Vernon got its name?

FRANK: Lawrence Washington named his home Mount Vernon in honor of Admiral Vernon under whom he served with the British forces in Jamaica.

MISS SHELBY: And now let's talk about some of the special sights we want to see.

ANNE: I want to see the big library with Washington's own desk and chair.

TED: I'm going to look for the sword he wore when he was inaugurated as the first President of the United States.

RUTH: I want to see the vegetable gardens and the flower gardens.

BILL: I've always wanted to tell time by a sundial. I'm going to look for Washington's own sundial in the gardens.

MARY: I want to see the old-fashioned kitchens and slave quarters.

SUSIE: I'd like to see the pincushion that is covered with a piece of Martha Washington's wedding dress.

TONY: I want to see the bedroom and the big bed where George Washington died.

BOB: And the tomb where he and Martha are buried.

SALLY: I don't like to think about sad things at Mount Vernon.

I want to remember the happy times George Washington had there with his family and friends; the parties and the picnics and the dances and all the fun they had. I can hardly wait to see the music room with the beautiful harpsichord he gave to his granddaughter, Nellie Custis. Do you think we could hear it play, Miss Shelby?

MISS SHELBY: I'm afraid not, Sally. But we're all familiar with the music of the minuet, so when you look at the harpsichord, just imagine that you hear the music and see the beautiful ladies and handsome gentlemen stepping around in the graceful measures of the dance.

SUSIE: Just the way we do it here in school. Let's practice right now, shall we, Miss Shelby?

MISS SHELBY: Why, of course. Choose your partners, children, while Susie puts on the record. (*Children dance minuet, bowing their way off the stage at conclusion of the dance, leaving the* PATRIOTIC TEDDY BEAR *alone. He rises, stretches, and imitating the minuet, moves center stage, where he strikes a pose, and says:*)

TEDDY BEAR: Nobody asked *me* what *I'd* like to see at Mount Vernon; but let me tell you one thing . . . here's a teddy bear who's going to keep his eyes wide open and not miss a trick!

CURTAIN

*   *   *   *

SCENE 2

SETTING: *A bus stop.*

TIME: *Just after the visit to Mount Vernon.*

AT RISE: *The children enter in a long straggling line, herded into place by* MISS SHELBY. *Some carry post cards, souvenir booklets and pennants. Others carry coats, lunch boxes and cameras. All look tired. A few are limping and one carries his shoes.*

Miss Shelby (*Counting the last few children as they enter*): Thank goodness, you're all here. All present and accounted for. And not too soon either because the bus should arrive any minute.

Susie: I can hardly wait to sit down. My feet hurt.

Ruth: So do mine, but it was worth it.

Billy: I'm not a bit tired. I could go through Mount Vernon all over again! Gee! I wish I could slide down those banisters!

Anne: I don't believe we missed a thing! The west parlor, the library, the family dining room, the great banquet hall, the bedrooms! Oh, it was all so wonderful, and just the way we read about it in school.

Mary: How did they collect all that furniture, Miss Shelby? Did it all belong to Washington?

Miss Shelby: Not all of it, Mary. Many of the furnishings actually belonged to the Washington family, but other pieces have been added to make the rooms look as they did when Washington lived there.

David: Does the Washington family still own Mount Vernon?

Miss Shelby: No. It belongs to the Mount Vernon Ladies' Association of the Union. They bought it from John Augustine Washington, the Second, in 1858 and have taken care of the house and grounds ever since.

Tony: I was disappointed that we couldn't walk right into the rooms and look at things close up.

Freddy: Don't be dumb! The place would be ruined in no time if people could walk on the carpets and touch the furniture. Why, in one year alone, my guide book says, more than a million people came to visit Mount Vernon.

They're always making repairs as it is, to keep the house and grounds in proper shape.

TONY: Yeah, I guess they're right. When will the bus come, Miss Shelby? I'm hungry.

MISS SHELBY: We won't have long to wait, Tony, and we can eat our lunch on the bus. I hope you still have yours.

TONY: You bet. I'd never lose my lunch box.

BEN: And I've still got my camera. Dad said I'd be sure to leave it somewhere.

FREDDY: Oh my goodness! I've lost him! Miss Shelby, wait for me, I'll have to go back!

MISS SHELBY: Freddy, Freddy! Come back here! What's the matter?

FREDDY: It's my teddy bear! I've lost him!

MISS SHELBY: But you can't go back! The bus will be here any minute! Besides, it's closing time.

FREDDY: But Miss Shelby, I just can't leave him. He's our mascot! We can't go without him!

MISS SHELBY: I told you to watch out for him. He was your responsibility.

FREDDY: Bill, you were carrying him for a while. What did you do with him?

BILLY: I gave him back to you, don't you remember? It was just before we went into the library.

FREDDY: Then I'll have to go back. Please, Miss Shelby. I'll run all the way.

MISS SHELBY: It's no use, Freddy. You can't get in and we'll miss the bus.

SUSIE: Oh dear! What will become of our Patriotic Teddy Bear? We'll never see him again.

MISS SHELBY: Hush, Susie. Don't be so tragic about it! We'll write to the Lost and Found Department. Someone will be sure to find him.

RUTH: But we can't go home without our mascot!

MISS SHELBY: Dear me! We never should have brought him in the first place. A sight-seeing trip is no place for teddy bears! (PHOTOGRAPHER *enters.*)

PHOTOGRAPHER: Good afternoon, miss. I'm from the *Sunday News.* May I please take a picture of your group?

MISS SHELBY: Certainly, although I'm afraid you'll find us a bit upset. We have suffered a great loss.

BEN: Yeah, Freddy left our mascot at Mount Vernon.

PHOTOGRAPHER: That's too bad. What was your mascot, an animal of some sort?

FREDDY: No, it was my teddy bear.

SUSIE: The Patriotic Teddy Bear we called him because he was red, white and blue.

PHOTOGRAPHER: Well, cheer up! And let's get a picture of you all bright and smiling. (*Starts posing children*) Where is this group from?

FRANK: We're the (*Names grade, school, town, and state*) and this is our teacher, Miss Shelby.

PHOTOGRAPHER: I'm glad to know you. Did you have a good time at Mount Vernon.

ALL: Wonderful, great, swell, etc.

PHOTOGRAPHER: Now hold it steady, everybody, and smile . . .

SUSIE: Oh dear! I can't smile a bit for thinking of our poor Patriotic Teddy Bear lost in that great big house!

MISS SHELBY: Susie! Please! Don't bring up that subject till we get this picture taken. Now back into position, everyone. (MAN *enters carrying toy teddy bear painted red, white and blue.*)

MAN: Excuse me, ma'am. Does this belong to one of your pupils?

FREDDY (*Breaking from posed group*): Why there he is! There's my Patriotic Teddy Bear!

ALL: There he is! There's our mascot!

MISS SHELBY: Oh, thank you, sir. The children have been so worried about him. Where on earth did you find him?

MAN: He was lying right in the middle of George Washington's bed. How he got there nobody knows, but the guard remembered seeing one of the children carrying a red, white and blue teddy bear.

FREDDY: I must have dropped him as I leaned over the rope to see into the room.

BILLY: But how would he get on the bed if you dropped him on the floor?

FREDDY: I just don't know.

TONY: Now there's a real mystery for you!

PHOTOGRAPHER: And there's a real story for my paper! Here, Freddy, you stand in the front row and hold up that red, white and blue Teddy Bear so everyone will be sure to see him. (*Group poses for picture. As he takes the shot*) Now there's a headline that will surely go down in history: PATRIOTIC TEDDY BEAR SLEEPS IN GEORGE WASHINGTON'S BED!

CURTAIN

*   *   *   *

EPILOGUE

TEDDY BEAR (*Enters from behind curtains, chuckling to himself*): Well, I didn't keep my eyes *wide open* after all! But I did have a wonderful nap on that great big bed. You see, there's really no mystery about it at all. When Freddy let me slip out of his hands on the other side of that rope, I just watched my chance and slid under the dust ruffle of that great four poster. It was cool and dark underneath the bed and I got sleepier and sleepier. But the floor was as hard as . . . well, as hard as a floor can be. So, when the guard wasn't looking, I just took hold of the bed rail, gave myself a quick flip, and there I was right in the middle of the counterpane. Before you could count ten I was sound asleep and when I awoke I found myself the most famous teddy bear in America. Because I'll have you know I'm the only teddy bear in the world who ever took a nap on George Washington's bed! (*Enter* PAINTER *to left of* TEDDY BEAR.)

PAINTER (*In disgust*): Oh, there you go again! Always boasting about being so famous! Always raving about having your picture in the Sunday paper! And to think it was all the result of a double accident! First, I made a mistake with that paint job in the factory . . . and then . . . (*Enter* FREDDY *to right of* TEDDY BEAR.)

FREDDY: And then, I just accidentally dropped you inside that historic bedroom . . .

PAINTER: So you really can't take any of the credit for yourself!

TEDDY BEAR: Just the same, I'll never forget that I am *the* Patriotic Teddy Bear who visited Mount Vernon and slept in George Washington's bed! And wherever I go, I'll be humming a patriotic tune to myself that sounds like this: (TEDDY BEAR *sings "Father of the Land We Love" by George M. Cohan, written to commemorate the 200th Anniversary of the birth of Washington, copyright by Sol Bloom, Washington Building, Washington, D. C.; or any other Washington song from a classroom music book may be used. The* PAINTER *and* FREDDY *join in on the chorus, after which all three make their final bow and exit.*)

THE END

The Patriotic Teddy Bear and the UN

(United Nations)

Characters

FREDDY	POLICEMAN
SALLY	JACK-IN-THE-BOX
RUTH	FRENCH DOLL
JIMMY	TOY SOLDIER
PATRIOTIC TEDDY BEAR	CLOWN

SETTING: *Freddy's playroom.*

AT RISE: FREDDY *is showing the room to a group of his class-mates. The toys are standing about the room in character-istic attitudes:* TOY SOLDIER *stands at attention,* FRENCH DOLL *strikes a pose, the* POLICEMAN *stands guard,* JACK-IN-THE-Box *folds his arms, the* CLOWN *is sprawled on the floor, and the* PATRIOTIC TEDDY BEAR, *in his red, white and blue suit, is seated in a chair.*

FREDDY: Of course, I don't play with these toys very much any more. I'm getting a little old for such things.

JIMMY: I know how it is. I don't play with my old toys very much any more, but it's kind of nice to have them around. This is a dandy playroom.

SALLY: Oh, look at the beautiful French Doll! Isn't she lovely?

FREDDY: She belongs to my sister. Every Christmas we put her under the Christmas tree and the Patriotic Teddy Bear al-ways stands beside her.

235

RUTH: Why do you call him the *Patriotic* Teddy Bear?

JIMMY: Can't you see? It's because of his red, white and blue suit.

SALLY: I never saw a red, white and blue Teddy Bear before.

FREDDY: Neither did I, till I saw this one. I was quite small when I got him. He's a little faded now but we still call him the Patriotic Teddy Bear.

JIMMY: He sure wears the patriotic colors.

FREDDY: But that's not the real reason. We call him the Patriotic Teddy Bear because he once took a nap in George Washington's own bedroom!

GIRLS (*Drawing closer to the* TEDDY BEAR): Did he really?

FREDDY: Yes, he really did. One time our teacher took the class to visit Mt. Vernon and I insisted on taking my Teddy Bear along. I got so tired on the long tour of the house that I dropped poor Teddy inside the guard rail as we were looking at Washington's bedroom, and I never even missed him till we were ready to get on the bus. I was just about to run back for him, when a man brought him to me and said the guard found him right in the *middle* of the bed! Nobody knows how he got there, but I guess he's the only Teddy Bear in the world that slept in George Washington's bed at Mt. Vernon.

SALLY: Isn't he darling? Look at his beautiful red coat!

RUTH: And his dear little blue pants! I think he's cute as can be.

JIMMY: He looks downright proud of himself. I think he realizes he is a teddy bear of some importance.

FREDDY: Maybe he does, but we'd better go. Mother said she'd fix some sandwiches and cocoa for us and I feel pretty empty inside.

JIMMY: Me too! Sandwiches and cocoa sound good to me.

SALLY: I could stay here for hours and play with these toys but I suppose you boys would die of starvation.

RUTH: Goodbye, little Teddy Bear! I'll always remember you. (*The children exit.*)

CLOWN (*Jumping to his feet and making a mocking bow*): "Goodbye, little Teddy Bear! I'll always remember you!"

ALL TOYS (*Coming to life and laughing*): Patriotic Teddy Bear indeed!

TOY SOLDIER: I suppose we should stand and salute every time you go past.

FRENCH DOLL: Or make a curtsey in your direction.

POLICEMAN: Or bow three times when you come our way.

TEDDY BEAR: And what's so funny? You're all jealous! That's what's wrong with you. After all . . . I really am the Patriotic Teddy Bear, you know.

JACK-IN-THE-BOX: I'm not so sure of that! You have no right to call yourself "patriotic" just because you slept in George Washington's bed. That could have happened to any toy!

TEDDY BEAR: No, it couldn't. It was hard work climbing up into that bed! And besides, I am a red, white and blue teddy bear!

POLICEMAN: And that's only because the painter spilled a can of red paint on you in the toy shop! He had to fix up his mistake by giving you the blue pants and white gloves and white face. He made a novelty out of you and saved his job! You forget, I was made in the same factory!

TEDDY BEAR: I don't care what you say! I'm the Patriotic Teddy Bear! So the rest of you better keep quiet!

CLOWN: Look here, Teddy Bear, you're getting pretty conceited! You think you know everything about America just because you slept in George Washington's bed.

TEDDY BEAR: So what? Can any of the rest of you say as much?

CLOWN: If you're going to call yourself "patriotic," you'd better start being a better American.

TEDDY BEAR: You can't tell me anything about being a good American, Jo-Jo Clown! I'm proud to be an American and live in the U.S.A. and if you don't like it, you can just take this. (*Gives the* CLOWN *a push and a poke, and the two are soon in a fight*)

FRENCH DOLL: Stop it! Stop it!

TOYS: Stop! Stop!

FRENCH DOLL: Somebody do something quick! Mr. Policeman, blow your whistle!

POLICEMAN (*Blows whistle*): Stop in the name of the law! (TOY SOLDIER *and* POLICEMAN *separate fighters.*) Calm down, both of you! Fighting is against the law in this playroom.

CLOWN: I was just trying to teach him to be a better American.

POLICEMAN: Then you're going about it in the wrong way. Americans are learning to settle their difficulties without fighting. Remember, America is a member of the United Nations, and every American must learn to live in peace with his neighbors.

CLOWN: Thanks, Officer. That's what I was trying to say but I used the wrong language. I want this fellow to understand that no nation, not even America, can lord it over the rest of the world.

POLICEMAN: Good for you, Jo-Jo! If we all learn that lesson, we'll have peace in the playroom.

TEDDY BEAR: Say! What is this? Isn't America the greatest country in the world?

TOY SOLDIER: Sure it is . . . to us Americans.

FRENCH DOLL: But to us French people, France is the greatest country in the world. That's the trouble with you, Teddy Bear. You think because your colors are red, white and blue, you're the greatest, strongest Teddy Bear in the world.

TEDDY BEAR: And what if I do?

FRENCH DOLL: Don't forget—I come from France, and our colors are also red, white and blue!

CLOWN: In the United Nations more than half of the sixty flags have red, white and blue in their designs, so maybe color isn't so important after all.

TEDDY BEAR: Do sixty nations belong to the UN?

JACK-IN-THE-BOX: That's right . . . sixty nations, all pledged to help each other and maintain peace in the world.

TEDDY BEAR: And since when do you know so much about the United Nations, Mr. Jack-in-the-Box?

JACK-IN-THE-BOX: Well, you see . . . to understand the United Nations, you must understand geography and where the different countries are located. Now it so happens, I am an authority on geography. Listen:

> Geography is quite a thrill,
> I really think it's great,
> And I can name each capital,
> Each city and each state.
>
> Madrid is somewhere south of France,
> Kentucky is in Spain,
> The Rocky Mountains form a ridge
> Across the state of Maine.
>
> The East is East and West is West,
> And North is close to South.
> The Amazon and Danube meet
> At Mississippi's mouth.
>
> Geography! Geography!
> I really dote on you!
> We're glad the earth spins round and round
> And gives us such a view!

SOLDIER: I'm afraid your geography is topsy-turvy, my friend, but you have the right idea. Once upon a time, the different people of the world were separated by geographical barriers . . . rivers, mountains, jungles, and deserts. So each nation had very little to do with any other nation. Now the airplane and radio and television have broken down those barriers. Distances are shortened. The world is smaller. So now we must learn to live in peace, as good neighbors should.

TEDDY BEAR: I guess you think I'm not a very good neighbor.

CLOWN: You could be, if you tried.

FRENCH DOLL: We'd like to be good neighbors and good friends if you'd let us.

TOY SOLDIER: You're really a good fellow, if you'd only forget how important you are and learn to be one of the gang.

JACK-IN-THE-BOX: I'll even help you learn more about geography.

TEDDY BEAR: Gee! I'm beginning to feel a warm little glow in the pit of my stomach!

POLICEMAN: I can tell you what that is. That's the warm glow of friendship.

FRENCH DOLL: It will spread all through you if you let it.

JACK-IN-THE-BOX: You'll feel full of sunshine.

TEDDY BEAR: Thanks, everybody. From now on, I'll try to be a better American and a better neighbor.

SOLDIER: Let's give three cheers for Teddy . . . Hooray! Hooray! Hooray!

POLICEMAN: Quiet! Somebody's coming. (*All toys freeze in place as* FREDDY *enters carrying a book. He stands looking down at the* TEDDY BEAR.)

FREDDY: You're a lucky fellow, Teddy Bear! Nothing to do all day but sit around this playroom while I have to go to school and study! And guess what! I have to learn a poem about the United Nations to say in school tomorrow. Just look how long it is! You have nothing else to do so you can listen while I read it. (*He reads poem.*)

> We must be neighborly, we must be neighborly,
> With lands across the sea.
> Let's all help our neighbors, share in their labors,
> That's the way to be.
> We must be neighborly, we must be neighborly
> To build a friendly world.
> With every nation freedom's station,
> Flags of peace unfurled!
> Let each one aid humanity,
> By stretching forth a helping hand.
> Protect this old world's sanity,
> With more attempts to understand.
> We'll all stand firm as one community,
> Nothing can disturb our unity,
> Always these United Nations
> Stand for lasting peace.

(*He pats* TEDDY BEAR.) Dear me, Teddy! I could swear you were really listening. Here. (*Putting book in* TEDDY'S *hands*) You hold this book while I try to say it. (FREDDY *sits down, repeats first few lines several times and dozes off.*)

TEDDY BEAR: Sh! I believe he's asleep!

FRENCH DOLL: I wish we could help him learn that poem.

JACK-IN-THE-BOX: Maybe if we'd sing the words to him, very softly while he's sleeping, they'd sink into his mind, and he'd know them when he wakes up.

POLICEMAN: It's worth trying. I hope we can all keep the tune. Toy Soldier, you be the leader.

TOY SOLDIER: One, two, three, four—here we go! (*He leads the toys as they sing the poem to the tune of "American Patrol."*)

THE END

Hello, Mr. Groundhog

(Weather)

Characters

EXALTED GRAND HIBERNATOR
GRAND HIBERNATOR
1ST *and* 2ND SLEEPERS
CHIEF EYE-RUBBER
ASSISTANT EYE-RUBBER
FLYING SAUCER OBSERVER
INSPECTOR OF SHADOWS
CHIEF ALARM SOUNDER
ASSISTANT ALARM SOUNDER
HONORABLE CHIEF SCRIBE
1ST *and* 2ND ASSISTANT SCRIBLETS
1ST *and* 2ND WARDENS
1ST *and* 2ND GUARDIANS OF GROUNDHOG HOLE
DIRECTOR OF GROUNDHOG RESEARCH AND ASSISTANT
CHAIRMAN OF HONORARY MEMBERSHIP
SCOUTMASTER
SHERRY
GAIL
MARY
ELEANOR
BESS
GERTRUDE
ELSIE
PHOTOGRAPHERS, *three*

Time: *February second.*

Setting: *The woods, near a groundhog hole.*

At Rise: *The members of the Royal Order of Slumbering Groundhogs are seated in a semicircle with their presiding officer in the center. At one side is a placard bearing the words:* groundhog hole. *Two boys stand guard at the sign. The* Exalted Grand Hibernator *calls the meeting to order.*

Exalted Grand Hibernator: The annual meeting of the Royal Order of Slumbering Groundhogs is now in session. Since this is our first official meeting, we will not be able to have the reading of the minutes, but the Honorable Chief Scribe will read the aims and purposes of our organization.

Honorable Chief Scribe: It is the purpose of the Royal Order of Slumbering Groundhogs of (*insert name of school, town and state*), patterned after the original Order of Slumbering Groundhogs at Quarryville, Pennsylvania, to defend the groundhog, and to guard his slumbers, his haunts and his habitations. Our annual meetings shall be held on the second day of February, at which time the Faithful will gather to await the appearance of our friend, the groundhog, and salute his arrival with all due respect after his long months of hibernation. The First Assistant Scriblet will now read our pledge.

1st Assistant Scriblet (*Reading*):

"Let us sit by the side of the groundhog hole, and wait for the prophet who knows,

Who can tell when the winter is over, and gone with its ice and its snows.

Why should we hark to the siren call of those of a spurious clan?

Let us sit by the side of a groundhog hole, and wait for the prophet who can."

EXALTED GRAND HIBERNATOR: The Second Assistant Scriblet will now call the roll:

2ND ASSISTANT SCRIBLET: Since it is the privilege of every member of the Lodge of Slumbering Groundhogs to adopt a special title, I will now call the roll of distinction: (*Calls roll with suitable pauses for responses*) Exalted Grand Hibernator, Grand Hibernator, First Sleeper, Second Sleeper, Chief Eye-Rubber, Assistant Eye-Rubber, Flying Saucer Observer, Inspector of Shadows, Chief Alarm Sounder, Assistant Alarm Sounder, First Warden, Second Warden, First Guardian of the Groundhog Hole, Second Guardian of the Groundhog Hole, Director of Groundhog Research Division, Assistant Director of Groundhog Research, Chairman of Honorary Memberships, Honorable Chief Scribe, First Assistant Scriblet, Second Assistant Scriblet. (*Closes the roll call by answering "here" to his own name.*)

EXALTED GRAND HIBERNATOR: Since we are all present and accounted for, we will rise and deliver the special tongue-twister of the day.

MEMBERS (*Rising and reciting very rapidly*): How much wood would a woodchuck chuck, if a woodchuck could chuck wood?

EXALTED GRAND HIBERNATOR: Members may be seated. We will now have our reports. First Guardian of the Groundhog Hole, what is your report?

1ST GUARDIAN: Nothing, sir. We have kept good and faithful watch, but there is nothing to report. His lordship, the groundhog, must be sleeping late this year.

EXALTED GRAND HIBERNATOR: Can it be that we have been misinformed and this groundhog hole is a booby trap?

1ST GUARDIAN: Impossible, sir. We have it on the best authority that there is a groundhog on these premises and sooner or later he *must* come out of that hole. Do I have your permission to return to my post?

EXALTED GRAND HIBERNATOR: Permission granted. The Director of the Groundhog Research Division will take the floor. I am sure that he will have some interesting information to report.

DIRECTOR OF RESEARCH: On the contrary, sir, I am afraid my findings are rather discouraging. We all know, of course, that February second, our beloved Groundhog Day, was originally called Candlemas, and here is our superstition expressed in rhyme:

> "If Candlemas day be fair and bright,
> Winter will have another flight.
> But if Candlemas day brings clouds and rain,
> Winter is gone and won't come again."

And so we depend on Mr. Groundhog as our weather prophet. If the day is clear, and Mr. Groundhog sees his shadow, when he emerges from his hole, he is frightened and dashes right in again. If it is cloudy, and no shadow appears, our friend, the groundhog, stays out for good, and spring is on its way. My Assistant Research Director will make his report directly on the groundhog itself.

ASSISTANT DIRECTOR: I can give you only a few basic facts about the groundhog. His other name, woodchuck, which we use in our official tongue-twister, is an adaptation of the Indian name, *We-Jack*, but folks around here usually call him the groundhog. I'm afraid he's not a very useful animal. In fact, the farmers consider him quite a pest, because he tunnels under their fields and also destroys a lot of their crops. I do have one other interesting fact about the groundhog, but I hesitate to repeat it without permission of the Exalted Grand Hibernator.

EXALTED GRAND HIBERNATOR: You may proceed with your report.

ASSISTANT DIRECTOR (*In an apologetic manner*): I regret to say that many young groundhogs are caught and killed for the local markets. They are considered very good eating. Of course, I know very well that none of our members would ever dream of eating one of our little weather prophets, but just in case you should ever need it, I have the recipe. (*With a questioning look at presiding officer*) Shall I continue?

EXALTED GRAND HIBERNATOR: Continue. We must know all the gory details.

ASSISTANT DIRECTOR: First boil the woodchuck in water with a teaspoon of vinegar, some onion and salt. When it is soft, roll in flour and fry in lard or butter.

1ST GUARDIAN: Mr. Hibernator, I protest. If the groundhog hears such talk as this, he'll never come out of his hole. I object to any further reports on the cooking and eating of groundhogs.

EXALTED GRAND HIBERNATOR: Objection sustained. We will have no more recipes from our Research Division. Although, I must admit, this one sounded very tasty. Do we have any further reports from our members on animals that affect the weather? First Sleeper, I see you are opening your eyes. What have you to contribute?

1ST SLEEPER: I have often heard it said that a cold winter is indicated if animals acquire an especially heavy coat of fur in the fall.

EXALTED GRAND HIBERNATOR: Any comments?

2ND SLEEPER: Doesn't sound logical to me, sir. Even if an animal *could* predict the weather, I don't see how he could control the growth of his fur. I think the state of an animal's fur is controlled by his food supply rather than by his weather prophesies.

CHIEF EYE-RUBBER: My grandmother used to say if the squirrels gathered an unusually large supply of nuts in the fall, the winter would be long and cold.

2ND SLEEPER: That's not much better than the superstition about an animal's coat of fur. You might just as well try to judge the weather by the amount of coal or fuel oil your neighbor ordered for the winter.

EXALTED GRAND HIBERNATOR: No arguments, please. We must give all our members a chance to report. Any further weather observations about animals?

INSPECTOR OF SHADOWS: The lamb and the lion are mentioned in the old proverb . . . If March comes in like a lion, it will go out like a lamb, and vice versa.

CHIEF ALARM SOUNDER: I found an old English quotation about a weather-minded pig. It goes like this:

"Old Gruntie smells the weather,
Old Gruntie smells the wind.
He knows when clouds will gather
And summer storms begin."

ASSISTANT ALARM SOUNDER: Geese are known to go south before a cold wave and flies are more troublesome right before a rain.

ASSISTANT EYE-RUBBER: Plants are also considered good weather prophets. I found an old rhyme that says:

"Onion's skin, very thin,
Mild winter's coming in.
Onion's skin thick and tough,
Coming winter cold and rough."

EXALTED GRAND HIBERNATOR: I must remind you that this meeting is limited strictly to animals. We must ask the Honorable Chief Scribe to strike that last entry from the minutes. What do the Official Wardens have to report?

1ST WARDEN: We have been especially vigilant this week, sir, and can report that we took two forged membership cards away from Sherry Marsh and Gail Porter.

2ND WARDEN: They're still threatening to crash one of our meetings or form a rival organization of their own.

EXALTED GRAND HIBERNATOR: Good work, Wardens. We certainly have no room for girls in the Royal Order of Slumbering Groundhogs. But since the subject has come up, we'll hear from our Chairman of Honorary Membership.

CHAIRMAN OF HONORARY MEMBERSHIP: Among the honorary members of the nationally famous Quarryville Lodge of Slumbering Groundhogs are the names of such famous persons as President Eisenhower, Ex-President Truman, General MacArthur, Professor Albert Einstein and Captain Kurt Carlsen, Commander of the ill-fated *Enterprise*. For Honorary Members of our own (*name of town*) Order, I propose the following names. (CHAIRMAN *names the Mayor of the Town, Chief of Police and any other well-known town officials or prominent leaders.*)

EXALTED GRAND HIBERNATOR: The Honorable Chief Scribe will notify these gentlemen of their invitation to membership and we hope they will be able to attend our next annual meeting.

CHAIRMAN OF HONORARY MEMBERSHIP: And one thing more. Although our active membership is limited to students of (*name of school*) and natives of (*name of town*), we have invited Scoutmaster Stanley Devon, of Troop Thirteen, as our special guest for today's meeting and associate member of the club. Here he is, Scoutmaster Devon. (*Applause as* SCOUTMASTER *enters*)

EXALTED GRAND HIBERNATOR: Welcome to the (*school and town*) Lodge of the Slumbering Groundhog, Scoutmaster Devon. I'm sure you can give us a lot of tips on groundhog watching.

SCOUTMASTER: It's a real pleasure for me to join you on this historic occasion, the first meeting of your chapter of Royal Groundhog Watchers. I am afraid I won't be too much help on the groundhog watching, but maybe I can give you some real tips on the weather. You know there are two groups of people who have always known a lot about the weather— sailors and farmers. Shepherds and frontiersmen and experienced campers also keep a sharp eye out for weather signs, and some of the things they have learned have turned out to be very reliable.

EXALTED GRAND HIBERNATOR: Can you tell us which are the most reliable?

SCOUTMASTER: From the camper's point of view, I'd say the clouds are the most reliable weather signposts. When danger is near, they thicken. When it passes, they disappear. The cirrus cloud always appears before a storm. Therefore, here's a proverb that is fairly reliable:

> "Mackerel scales and mares' tails,
> Make lofty ships carry low sails."

Careful watching will sometimes enable you to tell whether the tails of the clouds are increasing or decreasing in size.

CHIEF EYE-RUBBER: That word *cirrus* is familiar. We talked about cirrus clouds in our science unit. Aren't they the high, fleecy clouds, usually made of ice crystals?

SCOUTMASTER: Right you are, son.

CHIEF EYE-RUBBER: But I don't understand that part about mares' tails. What are they?

SCOUTMASTER: They're just a form of cirrus cloud. Some people call them mares' tails, others describe them as colts' tails or cats' tails.

ASSISTANT EYE-RUBBER: I don't know if I'd be able to recognize a *mackerel sky*. It sounds sort of fishy to me.

SCOUTMASTER: That's exactly what it is. A mackerel has greenish, blue stripes on his back, and a mackerel sky is covered with rows of small, fleecy clouds, resembling the streaks on a mackerel's back.

EXALTED GRAND HIBERNATOR: What about the old rhyme?

"Sky red in the morning is the sailor's warning.
Sky red at night is the sailor's delight."

SCOUTMASTER: That's an old, old proverb, originating in the Bible, and it's very reliable because it is based on scientific fact. When the sun sets clear, and the evening sky is red, the atmosphere is relatively dry, and there is dust in the air. Therefore, you can expect clear weather. A red sky at morning is a sign of moisture in the air. Another version of that same proverb goes like this:

"Evening red and morning grey
Speeds the traveler on his way.
Evening grey and morning red
Brings down rain upon his head."

FLYING SAUCER OBSERVER: My mother watches the factory smoke stacks before she hangs out her wash. If the smoke goes straight up, she hangs it out; if it settles right down on the ground, she says it will rain.

SCOUTMASTER: The fall of the smoke indicates the moisture in the atmosphere, so your mother has a pretty good weather sign there. But the clouds are even more reliable. When you hear people say, "The higher the clouds, the finer the weather," they're really voicing a scientific principle, because it's the low nimbus and cumulus clouds that usually bring the rain. When you see large, fluffy cumulus clouds early in the day, you may prepare for thunder storms before night.

"In the morning mountains,
In the evening, fountains."

GRAND HIBERNATOR: That's a good rhyme to remember. The nimbus clouds are the dark, stormy clouds and the cumulus clouds do look like mountains, all piled on top of each other.

1st Sleeper: Remember our teacher said that a cumulus cloud looks like a cream puff with a straight, flat bottom, sort of brownish as if it had baked a little too long in the oven.

2nd Sleeper: If it rains on July 15th, St. Swithin's Day, it will rain for the next forty days.

Scoutmaster: Don't be too sure about that. A check was made at the New York City Weather Bureau on the rainfall in 16 cities on St. Swithin's Day and for each day following for the required forty days. Eight cities which had rain on July 15th and eight cities that had no rain on that day were chosen for study. The record showed not one single case where rain on St. Swithin's Day produced rain for forty more days. So I guess we'll have to toss the St. Swithin's Day prophecy out the window.

2nd Sleeper: What about the moon? Can't you tell about the weather by watching the moon?

Scoutmaster: No relation exists between the moon and the weather except in the influence of the tides and the way they affect atmospheric pressure. No, I'm afraid the moon isn't too accurate a weather sign.

Exalted Grand Hibernator: Well, then, Mr. Scoutmaster, you still haven't answered our question. Which are the *best* and most reliable weather signs?

Scoutmaster (*Producing a set of weather flags*): These. These are the official flags of the Weather Bureau established in 1870. The main office of the United States Weather Bureau is in Washington, D. C., but about 300 branch stations are maintained in various parts of the country. These stations make daily reports to the main station and to each other. Daily reports are also received from about one hundred Canadian stations, from Alaska, the West Indies and ships at sea. These reports are based on scientific observations and actual measurements of air pressure, temperature and wind velocity. The Weather Bureau also uses

Sounding Balloons to determine conditions in the upper air, which are as important as conditions near the ground. The information from sounding balloons and from the many weather stations on the ground is sent out by teletype to the main weather stations located in the larger cities. The observers follow the movement of the winds and rain masses from place to place, and this is the information that is used for predicting tomorrow's weather. And here you see the official flags that are the Weather Bureau's signals: (*Displays white flag*) This plain white flag means fair weather. (*Black triangle*) The black triangle stands for temperature. When it is displayed *above* the white flag, it means fair and warmer. When it is displayed *below* the white flag, it means fair and colder. (*White flag with black square in center*) This is the signal for a cold wave. (*Blue flag*) Blue flag means either rain or snow. By combining it with the black flag, you get rain and colder or rain and warmer. (*Demonstrates, then holds up red triangle*) The red triangle means a dangerous local storm. (*Red square with black center*) This is the signal for severe winds.

EXALTED GRAND HIBERNATOR: I think it would be a good idea to have a practice drill on those flags, Mr. Scoutmaster.

SCOUTMASTER: O.K. (*Holds up white flag*)

ALL: Fair.

SCOUTMASTER (*Displaying white with black above*): How about this one?

ALL: Fair and warmer.

SCOUTMASTER (*Displaying red triangle*): And this?

ALL: Storm warning. (WARDENS *at edge of group suddenly catch hold of two girls, one of whom is carrying a large covered box. There is a scuffle with shouts and shrieks.*)

GIRLS: You let us go. Let go of me. Ouch! Help! You'll be sorry.

WARDENS: What do you think you're trying to do? You have no business here.

EXALTED GRAND HIBERNATOR: What's the matter? What's going on back there?

1ST WARDEN: Here are our two gate crashers, your Honor.

2ND WARDEN (*As they drag girls forward*): You should be ashamed of yourselves.

SCOUTMASTER: Looks as if you've caught a pair of stowaways.

EXALTED GRAND HIBERNATOR: What are your names?

GAIL: You know our names as well as you know your own, Mr. Exalted Grand Hibernator.

1ST WARDEN: You and Sherry thought you were pretty smart, making out those false membership cards, didn't you?

2ND WARDEN: Only we were a whole lot smarter and caught you in the act. And now we've caught you the second time.

SHERRY: And speaking of getting caught, my fine friends, what are you going to do or say when you are caught trespassing on private property?

EXALTED GRAND HIBERNATOR: What are you talking about?

SHERRY: Only this. (*Goes to sign marked* GROUNDHOG HOLE *and turns it around, showing sign reading* NO TRESPASSING.) This just happens to be my uncle's farm and he's very strict about his no trespassing signs.

EXALTED GRAND HIBERNATOR: But there must be some mistake.

GAIL: There is. And you've made it. And you're going to pay for it, unless we can come to terms.

EXALTED GRAND HIBERNATOR: But our Guardians of the Groundhog Hole investigated thoroughly and they were assured that there is a groundhog on this property.

SHERRY: There is. Only it isn't there! (*Pointing to hole*) That's the hole my uncle's little terrier dug to bury a bone. Your faithful guardians were led astray by my cousin who was paid fifty cents by Gail and me to give out the groundhog information. My uncle is due home in about ten minutes and he's going to be plenty sore when he finds all you trespassers, isn't he, Gail?

GAIL: You bet. The last ones he caught paid ten dollars apiece, didn't they?

SHERRY: And what's more, you're going to look pretty silly when the photographers come.

EXALTED GRAND HIBERNATOR: What photographers?

SHERRY: The photographers from the High School *Beacon* and the daily press. Gail and I tipped them off and they want to get pictures of the groundhog watchers in action.

EXALTED GRAND HIBERNATOR: Well, as a matter of fact, it *would* be nice to have our pictures in the paper. Too bad we didn't think of it ourselves.

GAIL: Yes, isn't it? And isn't it too bad you didn't think of getting a groundhog?

EXALTED GRAND HIBERNATOR: A groundhog?

SHERRY: You don't want your pictures taken keeping watch at an empty hole, do you?

1ST EYE-RUBBER: But groundhogs are pretty scarce in this region.

GAIL: Not too scarce . . . if you know the right people.

SHERRY: My cousin is quite a hunter and trapper.

GAIL: Maybe we could get together on a really good business deal.

EXALTED GRAND HIBERNATOR: Are you trying to tell us you can get us a groundhog?

GAIL: We already have him, right here in this box.

ALL: A real groundhog?

SHERRY: A real, live, honest-to-goodness groundhog, guaranteed to be in first-class condition.

GAIL: And he's yours, on one condition.

EXALTED GRAND HIBERNATOR: Make it as painless as possible.

SHERRY: That you revise your constitution and admit girl

members to the Royal Order of Slumbering Groundhogs.

SCOUTMASTER: I'm afraid they've got you, boys. (*Sound of automobile horn*)

GAIL: That's either the photographers or Sherry's uncle.

SHERRY: Better decide quick, fellows.

EXALTED GRAND HIBERNATOR: O.K. I'll put it to a vote. Do you want the groundhog under the conditions just laid down? All in favor, say "Aye."

ALL: Aye.

EXALTED GRAND HIBERNATOR: The Ayes have it. Now can we have the groundhog?

GIRLS: He's all yours. (*They hand over the box. Boys open it and crowd around admiring the groundhog.*)

EXALTED GRAND HIBERNATOR: He's really a dandy, but I'm afraid we've paid a terrible price.

SCOUTMASTER: Nonsense. A fine specimen like this would be cheap at any price.

GAIL: If we're really members of the Royal Order, we should have our membership cards.

HONORABLE CHIEF SCRIBE: Here they are, all in proper order. (*Presents each girl with a card*)

SHERRY (*Reading*): This card attests membership in the Royal Order of Slumbering Groundhogs, (*School, town, state*).

GAIL: And it's duly signed by the Exalted Grand Hibernator and the Honorable Chief Scribe. I guess that makes us legal.

SHERRY (*Turning around, speaking to concealed observers*) It's O.K., girls, you may come out now. (*Several girls enter*)

MARY: It's about time. I'm crippled for life from crouching under that bush.

ELEANOR: I think a stone has gone clear through my right knee.

BESS: Do you have membership cards for us too?

EXALTED GRAND HIBERNATOR: A fine pair of Wardens we have

in this lodge! The woods must be full of these spying females.

GERTRUDE: Not too full. We all had plenty of room.

ELSIE: The only trouble was we couldn't quite hear everything that went on. The girls right here at the meeting were the lucky ones.

EXALTED GRAND HIBERNATOR: Girls right here at our meeting? What are you talking about?

GRAND HIBERNATOR: This is impossible. I demand an investigation.

GAIL: It's time to unmask, girls. I think we can guarantee you safe conduct. (*Six members of the group take off their long white robes and remove their hats, revealing themselves as girls*)

GRAND HIBERNATOR: This is outrageous.

SCOUTMASTER: But what can you do about it?

SHERRY: Just issue more membership cards. After all, a bargain is a bargain.

GAIL: And remember, Sherry and I are the Joint-Custodians of the official groundhog.

SHERRY: Wherever he goes, we go, so we're sure to be in on all the fun. The rest already have their titles. (*Enter three* PHOTOGRAPHERS, *each wearing a press card in his hat. They are in a great hurry.*)

1ST PHOTOGRAPHER: Has he come out of his hole yet?

2ND PHOTOGRAPHER: Are we in time?

3RD PHOTOGRAPHER: Has he seen his shadow?

EXALTED GRAND HIBERNATOR: Plenty of time, boys. Don't scare him to death. Easy! Easy! Take it easy! (*Boys get in position to take picture and others crowd around.* SCOUTMASTER *stands to one side*)

GAIL (*To* SCOUTMASTER): Do you think he'll see his shadow, Mr. Devon?

SCOUTMASTER (*Squinting at the sky*): Well, from the look of the sun just now, I really couldn't say.

SHERRY: Oh, I hope he doesn't see it. I hate to think of six more weeks of winter.

SCOUTMASTER: My dear child, don't you realize that the groundhog and his shadow have absolutely no effect on the coming of spring? A check of the weather for a period of over twenty years in Chicago showed the groundhog to be a very poor prophet. The state of the weather on February second has no influence whatever on the weather of the next six weeks. There's just one thing we can all be one hundred percent sure about:

> Whether it's cold or whether it's hot,
> Whether it's raining or whether it's not,
> Whether there's sun or whether there's shade,
> Whether the groundhog is brave or afraid,
> There's only one ending to this yearly plot . . .
> We shall have weather, whether or not!

(*There are sudden cries of "Watch out!" "Here he comes!" "Stand back! Give him plenty of room" and a final cry depending on the weather in the locality in which the play is given: "He sees his shadow. In he goes! Six more weeks of winter!" or "The sun's under a cloud! He's out for good! Hooray! Spring is on its way."*)

THE END

Speaking of Speech

(Speech)

Characters

MISS KEEFER, *receptionist*

MR. WATKINS, *manager of the Apex Broadcasting Company*

MISS ELLA MAE PEARSON

MISS ANNE EVANS

MR. TOM STEVENS

SETTING: *The outer office and main office of the Apex Broadcasting Company. A folding screen separates the two offices.*

AT RISE: MISS KEEFER *is at her typewriter and* MR. WATKINS *is at his desk.* ELLA MAE PEARSON *enters. She is a flashily dressed young lady, with poor posture, poor manners and poor speech.*

MISS KEEFER: Good afternoon. What can I do for you?

ELLA MAE: Is this the office of the Apex Broadcasting Company?

MISS KEEFER: Yes, it is.

ELLA MAE: I wanna see Mr. Watkins.

MISS KEEFER: Do you have an appointment?

ELLA MAE: Naw. I just wanna see him about a job.

MISS KEEFER: Just what job did you have in mind? We have several vacancies on our staff right now.

ELLA MAE: I seen in the paper you wanna secretary. I think

I'd like bein' a secretary. (*Looking around*) Nice place you got here! Real neat!

MISS KEEFER: Yes, it is very pleasant. Just a moment, please, and I'll find out if Mr. Watkins can see you. May I have your name?

ELLA MAE: Ella Mae Pearson, but my friends call me Elly. Try and make it snappy, will yuh, 'cause I'd like to catch the next bus.

MISS KEEFER: I'll do my best. (*Presses buzzer, speaks into intercom*) Mr. Watkins, there's a young lady here to see you about the secretarial position . . . a Miss Pearson. Shall I send her in? (*Pause*) Very well, sir. (*To* ELLA MAE) Mr. Watkins will see you. Right this way, please. (MISS KEEFER *ushers her into the next office.* MR. WATKINS *rises.*)

MR. WATKINS: Good afternoon, Miss Pearson. Won't you sit down?

ELLA MAE: Thanks. It feels good to take the load off my feet.

MR. WATKINS: I understand you're interested in becoming a secretary.

ELLA MAE: Yeah, I sure am.

MR. WATKINS: Have you had any previous experience?

ELLA MAE: Naw, I never worked before. But it's never too late to start, I always say.

MR. WATKINS: What training have you had?

ELLA MAE: Training?

MR. WATKINS: Yes, what is your educational background?

ELLA MAE: Well, I took commercial in high school, and I can type pretty good . . . not too fast, but good, understand?

MR. WATKINS: Yes, yes. I think I understand. Have you had any experience in meeting the public?

ELLA MAE: Oh, sure. I love to meet people! The more the merrier!

MR. WATKINS: Well, that wasn't exactly what I meant. You see, a secretary in an office such as this, meets quite a few of our clients. There is also a great deal of telephone work.

ELLA MAE: Oh, I'm good at that. That's where I really shine! Mom says I'm always on the line at home. I can talk a mile a minute when I get started.

MR. WATKINS: I wasn't thinking so much about *your* end of the conversation.

ELLA MAE: I can make myself heard too. Got a good loud voice if I wanna use it.

MR. WATKINS: I'm sure of that. But tell me, Miss Pearson, have you had any training in speech work?

ELLA MAE: You mean public speaking? Nothin' doin'! I'd drop dead if I had to make a speech in public.

MR. WATKINS: I didn't want you to make speeches exactly, Miss Pearson. But you see, in our office, we have to be very careful about matters of speech.

ELLA MAE: Well, I can talk English, if that's what you mean.

MR. WATKINS: Did you take any speech courses in school?

ELLA MAE: Not me! I always went in for the practical stuff.

MR. WATKINS: I see. I tell you what I'd suggest, Miss Pearson. You take one of our application blanks home with you. Fill it in and mail it to us. We'll notify you in a few days. (*He rises. As interview comes to close,* ANNE EVANS *enters receptionist's office, pantomimes conversation with* MISS KEEFER *and sits down to wait.*)

ELLA MAE: Well, gee! er . . . thanks. Is that all?

MR. WATKINS: That's all for the present, Miss Pearson. Thank you for coming.

ELLA MAE: Oh, that's all right. No trouble, I'm sure. (*Exits*)

MISS KEEFER (*Presses buzzer, speaks through intercom*): Another young lady to see you, Mr. Watkins. Shall I show her in?

MR. WATKINS: Very well. I guess I can stand another one. (MISS KEEFER *in pantomime directs* ANNE EVANS *to enter.*)

ANNE: Good afternoon, sir. Are you Mr. Watkins?

MR. WATKINS: Good afternoon, Miss. Yes, I am Mr. Watkins.

ANNE: My name is Anne Evans. I came to inquire about the Poetry Hour your station carries in the afternoon.

MR. WATKINS: Oh, yes, Miss Evans. We've been looking for new readers.

ANNE: I've always been interested in speech work, Mr. Watkins, ever since I started school. I've never had special training, but the choral reading we did in our classes gave me a real feeling for poetry.

MR. WATKINS: Good. Would you like to have an audition?

ANNE: Very much, sir.

MR. WATKINS: Then let me hear what you can do with this script. It's one we're going to use on next week's show. (*Reads suitable poetry selection. As she reads,* TOM STEVENS *enters receptionist's office, pantomimes conversation with* MISS KEEFER *and sits down to wait.*)

MR. WATKINS: Splendid! Splendid! Your voice is clear. Your phrasing is intelligent, and your enunciation is excellent. And you had no special training?

ANNE: I was fortunate in having a fine speech course, and we learned the value of clear, distinct speech.

MR. WATKINS: But poetry is not always easy to read at sight.

ANNE: I guess my liking for poetry is part of the secret. We had the fun of reading poetry aloud in our classes, and the rhyme and the rhythm and the beauty of the words always appealed to me.

MR. WATKINS: Well, Miss Evans, I must say I liked your reading very much. I'd like to hear you in the studio with the proper equipment. Could you see me tomorrow afternoon about four?

ANNE: Indeed, I could, Mr. Watkins. I'll be right on time.

MR. WATKINS: I'm sure you will, and thank you for coming.

ANNE: Thank you, sir, for giving me your time. (*Exit*)

MR. WATKINS (*On intercom*): Miss Keefer, if you have any more young ladies like the last one, send them in.

MISS KEEFER: No more young ladies, Mr. Watkins, but a young man is here to audition for that commentator spot.

MR. WATKINS: Send him in. (TOM STEVENS *is ushered into* MR. WATKINS' *office by* MISS KEEFER.)

TOM: Good afternoon, Mr. Watkins. My name is Tom Stevens.

MR. WATKINS: Glad to see you, Mr. Stevens. Have a chair.

TOM: Thank you. As your receptionist told you, I'd like to audition for you.

MR. WATKINS: We need a young man to do regular newscasts. Here's a piece of copy. Want to try it?

TOM: Right now?

MR. WATKINS: Right now. Take your time and look it over.

TOM (*After scanning copy*): I think I'm ready now, sir.

MR. WATKINS: Very well. Fire away. (TOM *reads typical news column.*)

MR. WATKINS: Good. You have a fine, direct style, and unusually clear enunciation.

TOM: Thank you, Mr. Watkins. That's a real compliment. It might interest to you know that when I was a little boy, I had a very bad speech defect. People could hardly understand a word I said.

MR. WATKINS: Is that so? Well, you'd never suspect it now. How did you overcome it?

TOM: It was quite a struggle, but I had careful guidance, and plenty of good, practical help in school. In my school, speech correction was just as important as any other school subject. I was taken out of classes for special help, and my parents were given suggestions for follow-up help at home. Since there was nothing wrong with me, physically, I learned to overcome my own handicap.

MR. WATKINS: That's a great achievement, Mr. Stevens, and I wish all of the children in America had the same opportunities. Now about this job. Can you come back here tomorrow about two o'clock?

TOM: Yes, indeed, Mr. Watkins. I'll be here promptly. Thank you, sir.

MR. WATKINS: You're very welcome, my boy, and good luck to you. (*Exit* TOM. *He presses buzzer.*)

MISS KEEFER (*At intercom*): Did you ring, Mr. Watkins?

MR. WATKINS: Yes, take a note, please, Miss Keefer. Remind me to check all future applicants on their training in speech, right at the beginning of our interview. It will save us both a lot of time.

MISS KEEFER: Very good, sir. I'll take care of it.

MR. WATKINS: And, Miss Keefer, let's call it a day, shall we? We've done enough work for one afternoon. (*Curtain*)

THE END

Who's Who at the Zoo

(South America)

Characters

ELLEN	PATSY
FAY	TED
MARY	HENRY
BOB	ETHEL
MR. GABLE	JOHN
TOM	FRED
DOROTHY	SARA
RAY	RUTH
ANNE	HARRY

SETTING: *A section of the zoo. There is a row of cages with signs indicating the animals. Where a movie screen and projector are part of the school equipment, slides or colored pictures of the individual animals may be thrown on the screen as they are discussed. Children may make these animal slides as part of their work on the unit.*

BEFORE RISE: *The class is gathering in front of curtains for their trip to the zoo. An arrow points the way:* TO THE ZOO.

ELLEN: Are you sure this is where Mr. Gable said we should meet?

FAY: Yes, this is the place. (*Looking at watch*) He should be here any minute.

MARY: I don't think we should have come to the zoo today.

Bob: For goodness' sake! Why not?

Mary: Because we're having a test tomorrow on South America, and I think we should have stayed at home so we could study. I can never remember all those capitals and exports and imports!

Bob: So what? You can bet your sweet life I'm not going to worry about any old test! I'm going to enjoy myself.

Mary: But don't you want to pass the test?

Bob: Sure I want to pass. But I'll think about that tomorrow.

Mary: Here comes Mr. Gable. I'm going to ask him to postpone the test till Wednesday. (Mr. Gable, *the teacher, enters.*)

Bob: Go ahead and ask him, but I bet he won't do it.

Mr. Gable: Hello, boys and girls. Everybody here? What is it that you're betting I won't do, Bob?

Bob: Aw, Mary's worried about that test on South America, Mr. Gable. She doesn't think we should have it tomorrow.

Mr. Gable: As a matter of fact, I quite agree with her.

Mary: Oh, that's wonderful, Mr. Gable. I'm so glad you're postponing it.

Mr. Gable: Who said anything about postponing it? We're going to have that test today!

All: Today? (*Loud moans*)

Mr. Gable: Yes, today. In fact, we're going to start right now.

Bob: You mean right now, while we're at the zoo?

Mr. Gable: You'll find the zoo is a wonderful place to take a test on South America. You'll find the answers right inside the cages. Come along, let's get started. (*Curtains open and group lines up in front of a cage.*)

Mr. Gable: Here we are, ready for our first question? What is the name of the funny, long-legged animal in this cage? (*If projector is used, flash picture of llama on screen.*) Can you answer that one, Mary?

MARY: Why, that's a llama, Mr. Gable.

MR. GABLE: And what do you know about the llama from our study of South America, Bob?

BOB: The llama is called the South American *camel*.

MR. GABLE: And you can see the reason. He has a long neck and a small head like a camel's.

BOB: It is also called the *sheep of the Andes* because it has wool like a sheep. The llama is a very useful animal and it is the chief beast of burden for the Indians of Bolivia. I guess the people who live in the Andes mountains couldn't get along without the llama.

HARRY: They eat the meat for food, they use the waste material for fuel, and they use the wool for clothing. The llama's really an all-purpose animal.

ELLEN: I wonder what sort of disposition the llama has. Does he bite?

BOB: No, but he spits when he gets in a rage, so maybe we'd better keep a safe distance.

MARY: Look at his tiny feet! No wonder he can move about so gracefully.

MR. GABLE: Tomorrow I'll ask you to write a little story about the llama.

FAY: I have one already written, Mr. Gable. It's not exactly written, but I have it in my head:

MR. GABLE: Then let's hear it, Fay.

FAY:
> The llama's like a camel.
> The llama's like a sheep.
> The llama's like a mountain goat
> Upon the hillsides steep.
> The llama's like a donkey,
> Hauling produce to the shelf.
> But most of all, the llama
> Is exactly like himself! *

* If desired the cast may sing "The Llama," AMERICAN SINGER, Book 5, American Book Company.

TOM: Do you think we'll see an alpaca or a vicuna in the zoo, Mr. Gable? These animals are similar to the llama and also live in the Andes.

MR. GABLE: I'm afraid our zoo doesn't own any of those animals, Tom, but here in the next cage is a little creature I think you can identify. (*Move to next cage. If slides are used, project the chinchilla*)

DOROTHY: It looks like a fluffy gray rabbit.

TOM: I think it looks more like a guinea pig.

MR. GABLE: Do you know what it is?

TOM: I'd say it's a chinchilla. I know they also live in the Andes.

DOROTHY: I wish I had a fur coat like that.

MR. GABLE: You'd pay a big price for it, Dorothy. And it wouldn't wear too well because the fur is very light and soft.

TOM: Don't they raise chinchillas in the United States?

MR. GABLE: Yes, there are chinchilla ranches here in the States, but originally the animals came from the Andes Mountains.

TOM: I read somewhere that a chinchilla will lose all that beautiful fur if it gets in a warm climate.

MR. GABLE: That's right. But in the next cage we have an animal that doesn't need to worry about that because he has no fur to lose. (*If projector is used, flash on slide of armadillo*)

RAY: He looks as if he is wearing a suit of armor.

MR. GABLE: And what is his name?

PEGGY: The sign on his cage says ARMADILLO. Does he come from South America?

MR. GABLE: That's one of your test questions, Peggy.

TED: I know about the armadillo, Mr. Gable. He is found in Brazil and Argentina, in Central America and as far north as Texas. He looks like a pig in armor and he can roll himself into a tight little ball so that nothing can hurt him.

ANNE: The armadillo needs all that armor for protection because he is really a very timid animal with poor eyesight and no teeth.

PATSY: But he's a useful little animal. The natives roast the meat for food and they make baskets out of his shell.

TED: I think he'd make a right nice pet.

MR. GABLE: You do? Why?

TED: Oh, little armadillo,
          I'd love you for a pet.
          I'd play you were a battleship,
          And we'd have fun, you bet!
          Or you could be an armored car,
          A heavy army tank,
          And I would be the fighting man,
          The big, courageous Yank.
          So, Armadillo, stay awhile.
          I think you're fine and dandy.
          For really rough and tumble games,
          Your armor comes in handy! *

MR. GABLE: We'll have to move along to the next cage. Here is a strange looking creature. Where does it come from? (*Flash on ostrich slide*)

MARY: That's an ostrich, and it comes from Argentina. The Gauchos or South American cowboys ride herd on the ostriches the same as they do on their cattle. We know that Argentina is famous for its cattle ranches, but some of the big plantations raise ostriches, too, for their valuable feathers.

TED: An ostrich can really cover the ground with those big strong legs.

BOB: You bet. And it's quite a trick to catch an ostrich. It's almost as bad as roping a steer. The cowboys use long cords

---

* If desired the cast may sing "The Armadillo," AMERICAN SINGER, Book 5, American Book Company.

called bolas. A bolas is made of braided leather loaded with stones at each end. The hunters whirl the cords over their heads and let them fly with such force that they wrap around the legs of the ostrich. The stones cross each other and hold tight so that the bird trips and falls down.

TED: Argentina has lots of animals . . . cows and steers and sheep and horses and goats . . . all because of the wonderful grazing lands.

MR. GABLE: But right now, we're more interested in unusual animals. What do you think of this fellow? (*Flash on slide of a giant turtle*)

ALL: Why, it's a turtle!

HENRY: And it's enormous. It's so big I bet a child could ride on it but it would be slow travel.

ETHEL: That's the way they grow in Venezuela. Some of them weigh hundreds of pounds.

> And now we turn our topics
> To the turtles of the tropics.
> You will find them very old and very tough!
> You can stand right up beside 'em,
> And a little child can ride 'em,
> For a turtle, that is surely big enough!

DOROTHY: I think I'd like to live in Venezuela because the children have all sorts of pets from the jungles . . . parrots, parakeets, and lovebirds and even little tame deer.

MR. GABLE: Maybe you wouldn't enjoy it so much, Dorothy, if you saw the more dangerous side of jungle life.

DOROTHY: Do they have lions and tigers in South American jungles?

MR. GABLE: No, but there are wildcats which are just as savage and just as dangerous. But I was thinking of something else . . . ever so much smaller, but just as deadly.

JOHN: I know . . . ants!

ALL: Ants? How could ants be dangerous?

JOHN: These are tiny black ants that sting you with a deadly
sting. Your whole body swells up and hurts. I've read some
pretty horrible stories about the black ants of Venezuela.
They're not like the kind we have here that get in our sandwiches when we go on a picnic.

MARY: Look . . . Look, Mr. Gable . . . here we are at the
monkey cage! (*Flash on slide of monkeys. Boys and girls
laugh and make sounds of admiration at the monkey cage.*)

MR. GABLE: Monkeys are monkeys the whole world over!

FRED: And these are the little red monkeys from South America. Listen to all that chatter.

> Oh, South American Monkey,
> Interpret your chattering, please.
> Do you talk to your neighbor in Spanish,
> Or jabber in pure Portuguese?
>
> Here, Monkey, come have a peanut.
> The treat is strictly on me,
> For while you are sitting there grinning,
> I'm learning some geography!
>
> I can't understand your palaver,
> I don't get a word that you say!
> But somehow I feel you are friendly
> In the real South American way!

(*Any special song about monkeys or a monkey dance could
be used here*)

MR. GABLE: Well, boys and girls, I think you're doing very
well with your test on South America. Are there any other
animals you'd like to see while we're here?

SARA: I'd like to see the guanay birds of Peru, the birds that
are so valuable no one is allowed to kill them.

MR. GABLE: I'm afraid we don't have any guanays in the zoo,

Sara, but I'm glad you mentioned them as part of our test. Why are those birds so valuable?

SARA: Because they provide guano or fertilizer which the government of Peru sells at a good price.

MR. GABLE: What can you tell us about these birds and their habits?

SARA: Their nests are built so close together, they look like city apartments. The birds fish all day and carry home an extra supply for their babies. Sometimes there are as many as seventy little fish in the craw of a papa bird.

RUTH: They remind me of a pelican . . . "his beak holds more than his belly-can."

MR. GABLE: If you were to visit Peru, you'd find plenty of pelicans, cormorants, gannets and other water birds. But the guanays are the most famous.

RUTH: The guanays, the guanays, the birds of Peru!
They're some of them old and some of them new.
They live on the ledges and fish in the sea,
Protected by law, they're as safe as can be!

FRED: I bet you'd see lots of strange birds and animals if you could take a trip up the Amazon. That's real jungle country.

HARRY: I read a travel book one time about a man who went up the Amazon and I'll never forget all the things he had to eat.

FRED: Like what, for instance?

HARRY: Oh, all sorts of queer things! Roast wild pig, alligator tail, boiled turtle eggs, and fried monkey!

GIRLS: Ugh! Stop it! I don't want to hear any more. *Etc.*

ELLEN: I don't think I'd like to travel in the jungle.

HARRY: I would! It would be exciting.

MR. GABLE: Well, one thing's sure, you'd better read and study a lot more about South America before you decide to go. You know, travel in the jungle can be pretty risky if you don't know your way around.

It doesn't pay to bungle,
When you're walking in the jungle,
And see a harmless vine become a snake!
You must keep your eyes wide open,
And in your heart keep hopin',
That you won't be guilty of a sad mistake!

Wild creatures by the million
Occupy the lands Brazilian
And it would be fun to go there and explore.
But listen well, my buddy,
Be sure you read and study
All the flora and the fauna long before.

For if you wait till later,
You may feed an alligator,
And the alligator's supper might be you!
Before you tour the tropics,
Study all the safety topics,
And rules for healthy living old and new.

Read the jungle's signs of warning,
In the evening and the morning,
And learn about the beasts and birds of prey.
In the jungle there's a medley
Of dangers dark and deadly. . . .
So unless you know the facts, please stay away!

SARA: I think that's pretty good advice, Mr. Gable! I'm not
ready to buy a ticket just yet.

MR. GABLE: Maybe someday, we could all go together! But
right now, it's closing time at the zoo. We'll have to hurry
before we're locked in with the animals. Did you have a
good time?

ALL: You bet! We sure did! *Etc.*

MARY: And we learned a lot too.

Bob: Yes, I think the very best way to study for a test on South America is to go to the Zoo and visit the Animal Fair. (*They sing to the tune of "I Went to the Animal Fair."*)

We saw all the animals gay,
The South American way!
The monkeys still from the land of Brazil and some from
     Paraguay.
You ought to have seen what's new
From way, way off in Peru.
The wild and the tame, we called them by name,
And that's what we learned at the zoo—the zoo—
That's what we learned at the zoo!

CURTAIN

Railroad Rhymes and Rhythms

(Railroads)

Characters

ANNOUNCER
TICKET AGENT
BAGGAGE MASTER
DISPATCHER
CONDUCTOR
ENGINEER
VENDOR
PORTER
STEWARD
PASSENGERS

ANNOUNCER: Today we are giving you a free ticket for a ride on the . . . (*Name of school*) . . . Express. In this day of automobile travel, perhaps it has been some time since many of you have taken a trip by train. Just in case you have forgotten the thrill of going places on the steam cars, we're going to give you a free excursion, and explain to you the special services that are yours when you travel by rail. Our scene opens at the Ticket Window, and here come Mr. and Mrs. John Q. Public to buy their railroad tickets. (TICKET SELLER *enters center in front of closed curtains, and pushes out a small table which he uses for ticket window. Prospective travelers approach stage from audience and form a line*

274

in front of ticket window. Passengers move inside curtain as they purchase tickets.)

GIRL: One way to Chicago with Pullman reservations.

TICKET AGENT: There's a reservation on the Broadway Limited, leaving Harrisburg at 9:27 P.M.

GIRL: That will be fine. Upper or lower birth?

TICKET AGENT: Upper. That will be $48.65.

NEXT PASSENGER: One way to Pittsburgh, please.

TICKET AGENT: $8.96.

NEXT PASSENGER: Round trip to New York City.

NEXT: May I please have a timetable between Baltimore and Washington?

TICKET AGENT: Here you are, ma'am.

NEXT: Can you tell me if the train from Toledo is on time?

TICKET AGENT: The 4:32 is seven minutes late today.

NEXT: One way to Philadelphia, please.

TICKET AGENT: That will be $3.82.

PASSENGER: Thank you.

TICKET AGENT: As you can see, I lead a busy life. I must keep my wits about me, know the routes and prices, wire ahead for reservations, make change, and answer thousands of questions, courteously and accurately. However, selling tickets at a railway station is an interesting job, if you like people, and have a mind for details. The ticket office is open day and night, and someone must be on duty at all times to answer the phone, dispense information, and sell tickets. Oh, well . . . it looks as if this line has thinned out, so I'll just duck inside and check on that Washington train again. (BAGGAGE MASTER *enters from behind curtain.*) In the meantime, the Baggage Master will take my place. (TICKET AGENT *exits.*)

BAGGAGE MASTER (*To* PASSENGER *entering from audience*): Well, sir, what can I do for you?

MAN: I want this suitcase checked through to Chicago.

BAGGAGE MASTER: O.K. Hand her over. Here is your check, sir.

WOMAN (*Carrying dog*): Oh, please, Mr. Baggage Master, can you tell me what to do with Fifi? That hateful conductor says I can't take her on the train with me. He says she'll have to ride in the baggage car.

BAGGAGE MASTER: She could do a lot worse than ride in the baggage car, ma'am. We'll take good care of her.

WOMAN: She's very delicate, poor darling! Must she ride in a crate?

BAGGAGE MASTER: Oh, no! Just put her on a leash. That should keep her out of trouble. And we see that all pets have fresh drinking water, too.

WOMAN: Very well. I'm sure you look like a kind man, and Fifi seems to like you. Usually she is so afraid of strangers. I think it's terrible that dogs cannot ride in passenger cars.

BAGGAGE MASTER: I'm sorry, ma'am, that's the rule, and it applies to all animals except Seeing Eye dogs. A Seeing Eye dog may ride with his master. But don't worry. Your pet will be well cared for.

WOMAN: If you don't mind, I'll just walk her around the platform till the last minute, so she gets plenty of exercise.

BAGGAGE MASTER: Suit yourself, ma'am. (*Exit* WOMAN) So it goes with a Baggage Man. We take care of hundreds of pieces of baggage, large and small. We find lost articles, check suitcases and trunks, and see that all baggage is loaded on the right train. When you ride the railroads, your baggage is safe and arrives when you do. Your claim check is your security. Next time you check a piece of baggage, hold on to that little piece of cardboard. If you lose it, you cost yourself and the poor baggage man a lot of grief and worry.

Well, it's getting close to train time, so I'd better get on the job. (*He exits behind the curtain taking table with him, as the* DISPATCHER *and* CONDUCTOR *enter. A sound effect record of train approaching is played offstage*)

DISPATCHER: Here she comes! (PASSENGERS *emerge from behind curtain and line up*) Train for Harrisburg, Altoona, Johnstown, Pittsburgh, Chicago and Points West. Step lively please. (*Repeats train call*)

CONDUCTOR: All tickets please. Let me see all tickets. Tickets, please. (*Inspects tickets as* PASSENGERS *exit by way of center opening in curtain. As last passenger disappears,* ENGINEER *enters from opposite side of stage.*)

CONDUCTOR: Hiya, Mike.

ENGINEER: Hiya!

CONDUCTOR: Had a good run so far?

ENGINEER: Fine. How about checking our watches? (*Compare timepieces*)

CONDUCTOR (*Addressing audience*): You know, folks, this man is the boss of the outfit, the Engineer. This is the fellow who, with the aid of the first mate, the Fireman, gets you to your destination safely, and on time. If you want to be an engineer, you must start as a brakeman or fireman and work up, taking rigid examinations every six months. The safety of the passengers is in the hands of the engineer, and he feels his responsibility. How about that, Mike?

ENGINEER: That's right. One wreck can ruin the finest engineer on the road.

CONDUCTOR: Would a wreck cost you your job?

ENGINEER: It might cost me my life. Remember, I ride these trains too.

CONDUCTOR: And so do I. But I take the tickets and look after the passengers. You run the engine.

ENGINEER: Carelessness has no place in the life of an engineer.

CONDUCTOR: How long have you had this job, Mike?

ENGINEER: For a good long time, son, and I want to keep my record safe and clean.

CONDUCTOR: Have you ever experienced a wreck on the road, Mike?

ENGINEER: The closest I've ever been to a railroad wreck, Joe, was the time I read the story of Casey Jones.

CONDUCTOR: Was Casey a real person?

ENGINEER: He sure was. In 1932 the *Erie Railroad Magazine* gathered up all the facts of Casey's life, as told by his widow who lived in Jackson, Tennessee, and published them. The song, of course, has become part and parcel of American folklore and is to be found in all sorts of music books and ballad collections. (*At this point "Casey Jones" may be sung by the* CONDUCTOR *and* ENGINEER *or by a chorus. If a chorus is not available, the story can be read in dramatic style*)

ENGINEER: The ballad does not always present the actual facts of the death of Casey. In the song, the wreck was caused by Casey's determination to make up time. However, the inscription on his monument in Cayce, Kentucky, tells a different story. I think I have the clipping here in my pocket. (*Reads from clipping*) "On the morning of April 30th, 1900 while running the Illinois Central fast mail train, Number One, "The Cannon Ball," and by no fault of his, his engine bolted through three freight cars at Vaughn, Mississippi. Casey died with his hand clenched to the brake helve and his was the only life lost. . . . It can be truthfully said of him, 'Greater love hath no man than this . . . that a man lay down his life for his friends.' "

CONDUCTOR: His fireman escaped, didn't he?

ENGINEER: Yes, he did. The fireman was a man named Sim Webb, and according to his story, Casey's last act was to hold down the whistle in a long, piercing scream. The broken whistle cord was still clutched in his hand when Casey's body was found.

CONDUCTOR: It's a grim story, whether it's told or sung, Mike, but thanks for giving us the facts on this great railroad hero of the past. (*They check watches.*) Now, if your watch is the same as mine, it's time to be saying, "All aboard!" (CONDUCTOR *and* ENGINEER *exit behind curtain. Then curtains open revealing inside of train. Chairs are arranged in train pattern with an aisle between them. A* VENDOR *is selling his wares.*)

VENDOR (*Walking down aisle*): Sandwiches, chocolate bars, ice cold milk . . . Sandwiches, chocolate bars, ice cold milk . . . (*Exits*)

PORTER (*Following* VENDOR): Pillows. Nice, soft pillows. Last chance to get your pillows.

PASSENGER: Here, Porter, I'll take one.

MAN: I'm going to take a little nap, Porter. Be sure to wake me up in time to get off at Pittsburgh, will you, please?

PORTER: Yes, sir.

WOMAN: Porter, I have a frightful headache. Could you please get me a box of aspirin?

PORTER: Right here, madam.

WOMAN: Oh, thank you.

PORTER (*To audience*): My! My! My! A porter is asked to do just about everything.

GIRL: Do you like being a porter?

PORTER: Yes, ma'am! I get good money and I sure do see the country.

GIRL: What about your work?

PORTER: Oh, I do a little bit of everything: Take care of the passengers, put 'em to sleep, wake 'em up, brush 'em off! Sometimes I even take care of the babies while their mammas take a little nap.

GIRL: I read in the paper about a porter who lost his life trying to save a passenger in a railway accident. He was a real hero.

PORTER: He did what every railroad employee is expected to do, miss. The passengers always come first. (*Exits*)

STEWARD (*Walking down aisle*): Last call for dinner. Last call for dinner in the dining car. Dining car two cars ahead. Last call for dinner.

GIRL: Ummm! I wonder what they have for dinner.

STEWARD: Here's a menu, miss. I'm sure you'll find something you'll enjoy.

GIRL: You must have some good cooks.

STEWARD: We have a reputation for good food, miss, and we buy the best of supplies.

GIRL: I've always wanted to eat on a train.

STEWARD: This is your opportunity, then. Just go forward two cars. (*As he exits*) I hope you enjoy your dinner.

GIRL: Thank you. (*Exits*)

1ST PASSENGER: I wonder when the Porter will come around to make up the berths.

2ND PASSENGER: I don't know, but we'll ask the Conductor the next time he comes through.

1ST PASSENGER: This is my first trip by Pullman, and I must confess, I'm a bit nervous.

2ND PASSENGER: I think you'll enjoy the experience. Everything is very comfortable.

1ST PASSENGER: I think it's wonderful to be able to go to bed on a train. I wonder who first thought of it.

2ND PASSENGER: If I remember correctly, the idea first came to Mr. George Pullman in 1858 because he had to spend such an uncomfortable night in a day coach. At any rate, it was Mr. Pullman who first invented the sleeping car.

1ST PASSENGER: I guess it was a lot different from modern Pullman cars.

2ND PASSENGER: Yes, indeed. I've seen pictures of those early sleepers. They had wood-burning stoves for heat and candles provided the only light.

1ST PASSENGER: And now we have drawing rooms, and club cars, private compartments, roomettes, complete bedrooms.

2ND PASSENGER: All the comforts of home.

3RD PASSENGER: The history and legends, the tall stories and the folklore of American railroads make interesting reading. Did you ever hear of John Henry?

2ND PASSENGER: Oh yes. John Henry is a tall-story character like Paul Bunyan. He worked on the Big Bend Tunnel of the Chesapeake and Ohio Railroad in West Virginia. They say he could drive steel with two hammers, one in each hand. People came from miles around to see him drive steel with the two hammers, weighing twenty pounds each.

3RD PASSENGER: During the construction of the Big Bend Tunnel, one of the companies introduced a steam drill. John Henry bet that he could sink more steel by hand than the power drill. The contest was arranged and the men put up their money. The ballad version of the story goes like this:

> John Henry said to the Captain,
> "Bring that thirty pound hammer around;
> Thirty pound hammer with a nine foot handle,
> I'll beat your steam drill down."
> John Henry drove fifteen feet,
> The steam drill only made nine,
> But he drove so hard till he broke his poor heart,
> And he laid down his hammer and died.

1ST PASSENGER: There are hundreds of versions of both the words and music of the John Henry song, but he stands out as a great Negro strong man of the railroads.

4TH PASSENGER: The Irish also had their share in building

American railroads. Gangs of Irish workmen put a lot of bone and muscle into the transcontinental railways. It was a rough, tough life, and sometimes fellows like Patrick got the worst end of the deal. "Patrick on the Railroad" is to be found in many collections of American folk songs. Let's sing it. (*They sing "Patrick on the Railroad."*)*

In eighteen hundred and forty one, I put my cord'roy
    breeches on,
I put my cord'roy breeches on to work upon the railway.

Fil-i-me-oo-re-i-re-ay, Fil-i-me-oo-re-i-re-ay,
Fil-i-me-oo-re-i-re-ay, To work upon the railway.

In eighteen hundred and forty two, I left the ould world
    for the new,
Bad cess to the luck that brought me through,
To work upon the railway.
      (*Repeat chorus*)
It's "Pat do this" and "Pat do that!"
Without a stocking or cravat,
Nothing but an old straw hat,
And Pat worked on the railway.
      (*Repeat chorus*)

PASSENGER QUIZ MASTER: Say, gang . . . I mean, fellow passengers, since we're all here together, why not have a little game to pass the time?

BOY: What sort of game?

PASSENGER QUIZ MASTER: How about a Railroad Quiz? And I warn you ahead of time, I know all the answers.

2ND PASSENGER: O.K. Go ahead. Maybe we know more about railroads than you think.

* Music may be found in THE BURL IVES SONG BOOK, Ballantine Books, or A TREASURY OF FOLK SONGS, Bantam.

PASSENGER QUIZ MASTER: Very well. Here's the first question. Who was Peter Cooper?

1ST PASSENGER: Peter Cooper built the first steam locomotive. It was called the Tom Thumb.

PASSENGER QUIZ MASTER: Good for you! And it was the Tom Thumb that took part in the famous race near Baltimore with a car drawn by the fastest stagecoach horses in that part of the country. The Tom Thumb won the race. Now for our next question. What was the Stourbridge Lion?

3RD PASSENGER: The Stourbridge Lion was the first locomotive of any size to be operated on a railroad in America. It was built in England and shipped to this country on a sailing vessel.

PASSENGER QUIZ MASTER: I can see I'll have to try harder questions. What was the golden spike?

1ST PASSENGER: The golden spike was a real railroad spike made of California gold. It was driven in Utah on May 10th, 1869, to symbolize the completion of the first chain of railroads to span the continent.

PASSENGER QUIZ MASTER: I see you know plenty of railroad history. Now I'll bring you up to date. What is a roundhouse?

4TH PASSENGER: A roundhouse is really a gigantic garage in which the locomotives are cleaned, overhauled and serviced after a run.

PASSENGER QUIZ MASTER: What does a train dispatcher do?

5TH PASSENGER: He gives the directions that keep the trains moving according to schedule. The dispatcher knows the movements and location of every train in his district and he keeps them moving. (CONDUCTOR *walks down aisle and stops to listen to quiz.*)

PASSENGER QUIZ MASTER: How many nicknames can you think of for a train or engine?

2ND PASSENGER: Well, there's the Iron Horse, the Steam Wagon . . . the Choo-Choo . . . and some of the old-time engines were called Puffing Billies or Pumper Bellies.

PASSENGER QUIZ MASTER: I can't seem to get ahead of you people on this train.

3RD PASSENGER: How about letting us ask a question.

PASSENGER QUIZ MASTER: Go ahead.

3RD PASSENGER: What railroad songs do you know?

PASSENGER QUIZ MASTER: Well . . . there's "Chattanooga Choo-Choo" . . . "I've Been Workin' on the Railroad" . . . "Atcheson, Topeka and the Santa Fe." . . . Take your choice. (*Group on train sings any one of these songs*)

CONDUCTOR: Nice going, folks, and I think we're having a wonderful train ride. Before our train pulls in to the last stop, I'd like to say a few things about American railroads. The story of railroads is really the story of the growth and development of our country. They carry freight, and mail, and passengers, and raw materials of every description that add to our comfort and welfare. Through the magic of railroads, America has become a strong and united nation. The men and women who work on our railroads are really and truly public servants. Next time you take a train ride or watch the trains go by, or listen to the locomotive whistle in the night . . . remember your friends . . . the stouthearted folks who keep America's railroads running safely and on time.

. *THE END*

The Story of Light

(Light)

Characters

SPEAKER
CHORAL READING GROUP
GIRL NARRATOR
BOY NARRATOR
NAN KIN
TSI ANN
CHINESE FAIRY
CHRISTMAS CAROLERS
HANUKKAH PANTOMIMISTS
CHILD
FLASHLIGHT DRILL TEAM
CHILDREN

AT RISE: *A group of boys and girls dressed in choir gowns stands at center. Each child holds an open Bible with a red bookmark.*

SPEAKER: The story of light has its beginning in the oldest and best loved book in the world.

CHORAL READERS: "In the beginning God created the heaven and the earth.

And the earth was without form, and void; and darkness was upon the face of the deep. And the Spirit of God moved upon the face of the waters.

And God said, Let there be light: and there was light.

And God saw the light, that it was good: and God divided the light from the darkness.

And God called the light Day, and the darkness he called Night. And the evening and the morning were the first day." (*The group then sings a hymn in praise of morning, the music of which should have been played softly as a background for the choral reading.* Then the curtains close and a* Boy *and* Girl *step out on apron of stage.*)

Girl: Yes, the sun is the source of all life, and the natural source of light. But in the days of the cavemen, when the sun went down, and the world was wrapped in darkness, the people were afraid. They needed light, and light came to them in the form of fire. No one knows exactly how fire first came to earth. The ancient Greeks believed that man stole it from the gods and was cruelly punished for his theft. A more natural explanation might be that lightning set fire to a tree and caused some hunter to light a torch. At any rate, man learned to make torches out of branches and twigs and use them for light. The caves became more cheerful and bright and the animals kept their distance.

Boy: People soon learned to love fire. It kept animals at bay; it warmed their homes and cooked their food, and at last, man learned to make a fire when and where he needed it. He learned to rub a stick with a stone or with another stick until it grew hot; and later still, hunters discovered the use of flint. A spark struck from flint could set fire to a pile of dry leaves or twigs.

For many centuries and in many lands, people made light in the same way the hunters did thousands of years ago. In every home was a piece of steel and a box of dry bark which was called a tinder box.

---

* Suggestions: "Now the Shades of Night Are Gone" by Weber, or "Morning" by Henry Baker.

GIRL: People soon began to invent different ways of carrying their precious light from place to place. From the ancient land of China comes the legend of Nan Kin and Tsi Ann who were given two impossible tasks by their honorable father. As we meet these two little girls of long, long ago, they are homeward bound after a visit in the country. (*Curtains open disclosing two girls in Chinese costumes.*)

NAN KIN: The sun is so hot, Tsi Ann! Let us sit here on this wayside bench and rest a while until the noonday heat is passed.

TSI ANN (*As they seat themselves on bench*): How beautiful it is here in the country, and yet I shall be glad to get back to our father's courtyard. Already I can hear the tinkle of the fountains and feel the delicious coolness of the water splashing on my arms.

NAN KIN: Oh, Tsi Ann! (*Jumping up in alarm*) How could we have forgotten our promise!

TSI ANN: You can't be serious! Surely our worthy father was jesting when he asked us to bring wind and fire in a paper.

NAN KIN: Our royal father never jests! It was his condition for our visit and we have not fulfilled it! We dare not go home.

TSI ANN: But it is impossible! How could I catch the wind from the trees and wrap it in a paper?

NAN KIN: And how could I carry fire in a paper? Nevertheless, we promised. Now what are we to do?

TSI ANN: Let us continue on our way and beg our father's pardon for failing to do as he bade us.

NAN KIN: He will turn us out of the palace. He will close the gates before us. His mind was set.

TSI ANN: Then we must go back to the country and stay with our cousins.

NAN KIN (*Starting to cry*): And never see our mother's face again, or see the peacocks on the terrace, or play with tiny Lin-Yin-Yo! That I cannot bear.

TSI ANN (*In tears*): My heart is breaking! Why did we ever make such a foolish promise! Oh, Nan Kin! What are we to do! Wind in a paper! Fire in a paper! It is impossible! (*To tinkling oriental music* FAIRY *enters. In her hand is a folded paper fan*)

FAIRY: What sounds of grief are these, my children? Why do you cry? Perhaps I can help you.

TSI ANN: No one can help us, gracious lady. My sister and I have done a wicked thing.

NAN KIN: We have made a promise we cannot keep. Now we dare not return to our father's house.

FAIRY: Perhaps your promise is not so difficult after all. What vow did you make?

TSI ANN: In return for permission to visit our cousins in the country, I promised our royal father I would return with wind in a paper! How could I have been so foolish?

FAIRY: But you were not so foolish, child. Stop your weeping and see what I have in my hand. (*Unfurls paper fan, waves it about*)

NAN KIN: I feel a breeze . . . a cool, delightful breeze!

TSI ANN (*In great excitement*): It's wind! It's wind in a paper! Gracious lady, how can I ever thank you?

FAIRY: I need no thanks, my child.

NAN KIN: Now you can return to our father's palace, Tsi Ann!

TSI ANN: But what about you? (*To* FAIRY) I cannot go home without my sister, beautiful lady. Her task is even more difficult. She must carry fire in a paper. (FAIRY *moves toward exit.*)

FAIRY: Close your eyes, my children, and count very slowly to three. (*As girls count to three,* FAIRY *skips offstage and re-enters with lighted Chinese lantern.*) Now you may open your eyes!

NAN KIN: How beautiful! Look, look, Tsi Ann! It's fire in a paper!

FAIRY: Now you may both return to your father where I am sure a warm welcome awaits you.

NAN KIN: It's like a dream! Wind in a paper! And fire in a paper!

FAIRY: Only a paper fan, my child, and a Chinese lantern to light you on your way! (*Curtains close and* BOY *and* GIRL *continue their story.*)

GIRL: This fanciful little story from far-off China is one way of explaining the invention of the lantern which has existed in one form or another, in every country of the world. In our own country, during colonial times, our ancestors depended on candles for light, and thrifty housewives saved their fats to make tallow candles. (*Displays candle mold*) Here I have a colonial mold such as you might find at an auction or antique shop today. In New England where bayberries grew in the marshes, women learned to melt the berries and use the fragrant wax for their candles. Even today we burn bayberry candles at Christmas time and enjoy their rich, woodsy smell.

Christmas is a favorite time of year for candles, and the holiday season would not be complete without candles shining from the windows on Christmas Eve. (*The curtains open on a group of Carolers clustered around a small lighted Christmas tree. They hold candles and sing a Christmas song.* As the song is finished, curtains close.*)

BOY: And in the same snowy December when the Christian world celebrates the birth of the Child Jesus, the Jewish world unites in the observance of Hanukkah in memory of the day when the Jewish army drove the Syrians out of Palestine and rededicated the temple of Jerusalem. In this

---

* Suggestions: "Christmas Candles" by Leveen, Breen and Sampson, Leeds Music Corp., or "One Little Candle" by Roach and Mysels, Leeds Music Corp.

eight-day festival, during which the Jewish people renew their faith and rededicate themselves to the God of their fathers, the Menorah, or seven-branched candlestick holds a place of honor. (*Curtains open and the following pantomime is enacted to the words of the speaker.*)

BOY: First, the kindle light is lit, and each evening after sundown, a candle is lighted. The father of the family lights the first candle, the mother the second, and the children and other kinsmen light the rest. The candles are lighted on account of the miracles, the deliverances and the wonders which God worked for the Hebrew people and this is the traditional Hanukkah Prayer:

HANUKKAH PANTOMIMISTS (*Standing by the lighted Menorah*): "Blessed art Thou, O Lord our God, King of the Universe, Who has kept us in life, and has preserved us and enabled us to reach this season." (*Scene closes with HANUKKAH PANTOMIMISTS singing a Hanukkah song.* If music is not available, close scene on prayer with soft musical background. At end of song or prayer, curtains close.*)

GIRL: After the candle, the next improvement in home lighting was the use of oil. At first, fish oil or animal fat was burned in an open bowl called a *Betty Lamp* or *Fat Lamp*. (*Displays one, if possible*) Examples of these early lamps can be seen today in museums and antique shops. With the discovery of petroleum, a new type of lamp was developed, the kerosene lamp. At first, kerosene was burned in lamps similar to the open fat lamps, but finally it was discovered that a glass chimney would make a kerosene lamp burn with a steadier flame and give out more light. (*Child walks across stage carrying a kerosene lamp with chimney*) During the eighteen hundreds, table lamps became more and more decorative as artists turned their hands to painting china shades in all sorts of gay designs. (*CHILDREN carry lamps of this*

---

* Suggestion: "Festival of Lights," from THE AMERICAN SINGER, Book 4, American Book Company.

period across the stage) Many people have kept these pretty
parlor lamps and have had them electrified to add beauty
and a touch of long-ago to their modern homes. The discovery of kerosene as a lighting fuel made street lighting
possible and added to the safety of traveling after dark. A
lamp mounted on a tall post and covered with a little roof
to keep out the rain was the traditional street lamp. Of
course, somebody had to go around each evening at twilight
and light the lamps that would stand guard at the crossings
all night long. The lamplighter was a familiar figure as he
made his rounds each evening and early in the morning,
visiting every street lamp in his territory. The English
poet, Robert Louis Stevenson, wrote a famous poem in
which he tells how he used to wait, as a little boy, for Leerie,
the Lamplighter, to come along his street. (*Curtains open
revealing* CHILD *propped up with pillows in a big chair. He
recites "The Lamplighter" by Robert Louis Stevenson*)

CHILD:

"My tea is nearly ready and the sun has left the sky,
'Tis time to take the window to see Leerie passing by.
For every night at teatime, before I take my seat,
With lantern and with ladder, he comes posting up the
    street.

Now Tom would be a driver, and Maria go to sea,
And my papa's a banker, and as rich as he can be,
But I, when I am stronger, and can choose what I'm to do,
Oh, Leerie, I'll go round at night, and light the lamps with
    you.

For we are very lucky with a lamp before our door,
And Leerie stops to light it as he lights so many more;
And oh, before you hurry by with ladder and with light,
Oh Leerie, see a little child, and nod to him tonight." *

* The recitation of this poem may be followed by chorus singing the
popular song, "The Old Lamplighter" by Tobias and Simon, Shapiro.
Bernstein & Co.

Boy (*As curtains close*): The next lighting fuel was gas. At first, only natural gas was used, but later, man learned to manufacture this important lighting, cooking and heating fuel from coal. Gas was cleaner and more convenient than oil, and it gave a brighter, clearer light. But on February 11th, 1847, the man was born who changed the entire course of lighting. His name was Thomas Alva Edison, and his invention of the incandescent lamp in 1879 was one of the greatest gifts to mankind. Many improvements have been made in the electric light bulb since Edison performed his first successful experiment. The most important is the use of tungsten wires instead of carbon. Tungsten gives a brighter light and does not burn out so quickly. In our world of today, all sorts of bulbs are manufactured, from the powerful searchlights and headlights used by our army, navy and air corps, to the tiny flashlight so useful in the car, at home or on a scout hike. (*Curtains open on a flashlight drill done to the music of "Glow Worm." Curtains close after drill.*)

GIRL: In 1882 New York City built a central station to furnish electric light to the people of the city. Since then, light plants have sprung up all over the country. Dynamos now furnish electric current for millions and millions of lamps in the homes of people all over the world. But it is good to remember, this remarkable advance in modern lighting began with an American scientist, our own Thomas Edison whose birthday we celebrate on February 11th. We take pleasure in concluding our story of light with a poem in his honor:

Boy *and* GIRL: In February comes a day
We all should celebrate,
The birthday of a famous man
Whom we appreciate.

Tom Edison is often called
A *Wizard* and a Whiz!
And when you learn the deeds he did,
You'll say—"You bet he is!"

The phonograph and 'lectric light
We owe this famous man.
He never said, "It can't be done!"
He always said, "It can!"

Tom Edison, from early years,
Put work ahead of play,
And so we thank and honor him
For all he did, today.

So next time you turn on a light,
And see how bright it is,
Remember Thomas Edison,
That scientific whiz!

Today you have no feeble flame,
No smoky lamp to fight,
But Edison's electric bulb
To help preserve your sight.

So "Feb." eleven is the day
To honor Mr. "E.,"
Who gave us better, brighter light
And helped us all to see.

We're proud of Thomas Edison,
The "Whiz" of Menlo Park.
He helped us turn our night to day
By conquering the dark.

THE END

New Shoes

(*Promotion*)

Characters

CUSTOMERS
CLERKS
MANAGER
MASTER COBBLER
MARY
JOHN

SETTING: *A shoe store.*

AT RISE: *A row of boys and girls is seated on benches across the stage being fitted for new shoes. A shoe clerk is kneeling in front of each customer holding an adult-sized shoe of the type described by his customer. There is the usual litter of boxes and papers.*

1ST CUSTOMER: I want a shoe that is long and narrow.

2ND CUSTOMER: I want a toe that's a pointed arrow.

3RD CUSTOMER: I want boots made for any weather.

4TH CUSTOMER: I want shoes that are light as a feather.

5TH CUSTOMER: I need comfort . . . and *white* for nursing.

6TH CUSTOMER: I need slippers for dance rehearsing.

7TH CUSTOMER: Mine must be smart, and with heels like steeples.

8TH CUSTOMER: I want shoes just like other people's.

9TH CUSTOMER: I want boots that will take a polish.

10TH CUSTOMER: I need a pair my corns to abolish.

11TH CUSTOMER: Make mine stylish and right for pleasure.

12TH CUSTOMER: Make mine roomy! Be sure to measure!

13TH CUSTOMER: I'll need heels that will keep me from slipping.

14TH CUSTOMER: I need toes that will keep me from tripping.

ALL: So hurry, please, and get us all suited,
So we will be properly fitted and booted!

CLERKS (*In concert as each one holds up a much-too-large shoe*):
Now here's a bargain—the best of buys!
It's right for price and it's right for size! (CLERKS *try the shoes for size.* CUSTOMERS *hold out their feet and look at them sadly, shaking their heads.*)

CUSTOMERS (*In concert*): They're much too big!

CLERKS (*In concert*): They *are* a bit large! We'll see what we can do. (*Enter* STORE MANAGER.)

MANAGER: What seems to be the trouble here? Can't you find correct shoes for our customers?

CUSTOMERS (*In concert*): They're much too big!

MANAGER: So I see. But you know, sometimes we can be mistaken. Let me call the Master Cobbler.

CUSTOMERS (*In concert*): The Master Cobbler? Who is he?

MANAGER: The Master Cobbler is a very old shoemaker who has been with us for quite some time. I think he will know just what to do about your shoes. I'll go find him. (*Exit* MANAGER. CLERKS *and* CUSTOMERS *sing any Shoemaker or Cobbler song.* After song* MANAGER *enters with* MASTER COBBLER.)

---

* Suggestions: "The Old Cobbler," MUSIC EVERYWHERE, Grade 6, C. C. Birchard & Co., Boston, Mass. "The Happy Cobbler," TUNES AND HARMONIES, Grade 6, Ginn & Co. "The Cobbler and the Crow," OUR LAND OF SONG, Grade 5, C. C. Birchard & Co., Boston, Mass.

MANAGER: I have been telling these young people that you will be able to solve their problem, Master Cobbler.

MASTER COBBLER: And just what is their problem, sir?

CUSTOMERS (*In concert as they extend their feet for the* MASTER COBBLER's *inspection*): It's our new shoes! They're much too big!

MASTER COBBLER: Ummmm! So it would seem! But that's a funny thing about shoes! Young people have a way of growing into them. (*Addressing* 5TH CUSTOMER) You, child, what kind of shoes are you seeking?

5TH CUSTOMER: I want to be a nurse and so I am looking for a pair of comfortable shoes. But they *must* be white. And these are much too big!

MASTER COBBLER (*To* 9TH CUSTOMER): And you, my boy, you seem to be trying on a pair of military boots.

9TH CUSTOMER: Yes, but look at them! They're a mile too big!

MASTER COBBLER (*To* 12TH CUSTOMER): I see you want something sturdy and practical. Where are you planning to wear them?

12TH CUSTOMER: I'm not quite sure. Sometimes, I think I'd like to be a doctor or maybe a lawyer, or even a minister; but whatever I'm doing, I want my shoes to fit.

MASTER COBBLER: You'd do better to say you want to fit your shoes. Mr. Manager, I think the trouble is NOT with the shoes, but with the customers. The shoes are not too big. But the feet are too small!

MANAGER: But, sir, the customer is always right!

MASTER COBBLER: Not in this shop and not in my business. You see, I've been making shoes for a long, long time. As a matter of fact, I've made all the shoes that you boys and girls have been wearing since you were born; and if you will just go down there and sit in the audience where a few rows have been reserved for you, I'll tell you about them. Then perhaps you will understand about these shoes you are trying on today. (CUSTOMERS *and* CLERKS *leave the stage and sit in the first rows of the auditorium. If curtains are used they may close at this point. The benches remain on the stage. The* MASTER COBBLER *moves to the apron of the stage where he talks to one boy and one girl who have remained. He draws from his pocket a pair of baby shoes.*)

MASTER COBBLER: See these pretty little shoes?

MARY: Aren't they sweet!

JOHN: Gee! They're little!

MASTER COBBLER: So little that you can scarcely believe you ever wore them, but you did! And your mother was very careful to see that they fit just right and that they were made of the softest leather for your little feet. (*Curtains open on a tableau of a mother rocking her baby. The children in the audience or an unseen chorus sing Brahm's "Lullaby." Curtains close. If no curtains are used, mother may walk on and offstage.*)

JOHN: I bet I soon grew out of those baby shoes.

MARY: Me too.

MASTER COBBLER: Yes indeed you did. Before long you were running around, and growing so fast that your father was complaining about the bills at the shoe store. Let me see . . . the next pair of shoes I made was a stout pair of play shoes that could stand up under a lot of scuffing and wear and tear. (*Calling to* MANAGER *offstage*) Mr. Manager, how about bringing me a sample of those play shoes I made six or seven years ago. (MANAGER *enters with pair of play shoes.*)

JOHN: Look at those things! The toes are worn out!

MASTER COBBLER: No wonder! You were always climbing trees and kicking stones and playing all sorts of rough and ready games. (*To* MARY) And you were just as bad! Your shoes never lasted more than a few months.

MARY: But I can remember all the fun we had. Dear me, I'd

like to play some of those games right now. (*Curtains open on a group of boys and girls playing any sort of lively game such as London Bridge, Three Deep, etc. Curtains close. If no curtains are used, children may skip on and off.*)

MARY: I bet I can guess what kind of shoes you made next.

JOHN: Sure, so can I. I bet you made us each a pair of school shoes.

MASTER COBBLER: That's exactly right; and you were very very proud of them on your first day of school. You wanted to look just right, and you didn't want a mark or scuff on those brand new shoes.

JOHN: I can remember just as if it were yesterday. My shoes were brown . . . dark brown and very shiny. I could see myself in the toes.

MARY: Mine were brown, too, and they had real silk laces. I thought they were beautiful.

MASTER COBBLER: You thought everything was beautiful on your first day in school. Remember . . . it was something like this— (*Curtains open on group of children sitting on benches. They have books or slates on which they tap with their pencils as they sing "I Can't Do That Sum" by Victor Herbert. Other suggestions for this scene include a pantomime of "Schooldays" or "In the Little Red Schoolhouse." Curtains close. If no curtains are used children may walk on and off stage.*)

MASTER COBBLER: Once you children started to school, it seemed as if I was always making shoes for you. As you began to grow up and take part in more and more activities, you needed all sorts of shoes. For a while, tap dancing was very popular and I had to make tap shoes by the dozen to keep you children happy.

JOHN: I never took tap dancing lessons. I thought that was sissy.

MARY: I loved to tap dance and I got pretty good at it too. I don't know if I'd like to earn my living as a dancer, but I still think it's a lot of fun.

MASTER COBBLER: Well, this is how you looked when you used to tap dance at school entertainments. (*Curtains open either on a solo or group tap dance. Curtains close. If no curtains are used, soloist or group dances on and offstage.*)

JOHN: My Dad never had to buy me any tap dancing shoes, but I remember how I wanted all sorts of gym shoes and heavy football shoes with cleats.

MASTER COBBLER (*As* MANAGER *enters with a pair of heavy gym shoes*): Oh, yes, something like this, I suppose. These were just what you needed for the gym, and you gave them a rough time. Had to have a brand-new pair every year.

JOHN: Yeah, I can remember Mom saying I was growing like a weed, and Dad couldn't understand where I put all the food I ate every night for supper.

MARY: And also for breakfast, lunch and times in between.

MASTER COBBLER: At any rate, those gym shoes really got a good workout. (*Curtains open on sports drill, relay or tumbling stunts . . . one featuring boys, another featuring girls. Curtains close. If no curtains are used, teams may march on and offstage.*)

MARY: Say, Master Cobbler, do you know what? You're really telling us the story of our lives by showing us the shoes you made for us.

MASTER COBBLER: Well, maybe I am. But the shoes themselves have long since been worn out, or out-grown and given away. You've forgotten all about them.

JOHN: Oh no. Since we started talking, I remember quite a lot.

MARY: I never will forget my first pair of party shoes.

JOHN: Neither will I. Oh boy! They pinched my feet something fierce! And besides that, they squeaked! (*Curtains open showing several couples waltzing to music of small orchestra in dancing school style. Scene ends with boys thanking girls for dance. Curtains close. If no curtains are used, couples may waltz on and offstage.*)

JOHN: If we could see all the shoes we've worn in our lifetime, piled together in one heap, it would be quite a sight.

MARY: And we haven't begun to mention all of them. We haven't even spoken of our Sunday shoes.

MASTER COBBLER (*As MANAGER hands him a pair of shoes*): How about these? Here's a pair all new and shiny, just made for Sunday school and church.

JOHN: These are really and truly American shoes, for here in America we can let our Sunday shoes take us to any place of worship we desire.

MARY: And I am glad that all of us here today have had the experience of walking into the house of prayer in our Sunday shoes, and singing together the songs of our faith. (*Curtains open showing a small group of boys and girls singing any hymn or sacred composition. Curtains close. If no curtains are used, boys and girls may walk on and offstage.*)

MASTER COBBLER: Well, my friends, I think your problem is almost solved. It seems to me your shoes have fit you very well for all of these growing years.

MARY: Yes, but what about the future?

JOHN: Where can we find the climbing boots, and doctor's shoes and dancing slippers and working shoes that are needed for the years ahead?

MASTER COBBLER: Have patience, my lad. Have patience. As I told you before, your feet must grow into the shoes that you'll need for next year and the year after that and the year after that. Suppose you call those customers and clerks back on stage and we'll hear what they have to say. (*Original CLERKS and CUSTOMERS return to stage*)

MASTER COBBLER: Come now, my friends, speak up and tell us what's on your mind.

CUSTOMERS: We must have new shoes.

CLERKS: Sorry, there's nothing in your size.

JOHN: See how it is, Master Cobbler.

MARY: That's just how it was before.

MASTER COBBLER: Only now you understand the reason. There are big jobs to do in the world today and America needs big men and strong, intelligent women to do those jobs. Someday you will be filling the shoes of these grownups we see out front. But not right away. Do you understand?

JOHN: I think we understand, Master Cobbler. We must grow up to fit the shoes and the jobs that lie ahead.

MARY: And we must grow in our minds and bodies as well as in our shoe size.

MASTER COBBLER: Exactly. Now you're really catching on. Right now you are leaving your sixth grade at (*Name school*) and going into the new world of junior high school . . . then senior high school . . . then for many of you trade schools and colleges. By that time you'll be ready to fill the shoes that are too big for you today.

JOHN: But before we leave sixth grade and (*Name school*), I'd like to say we've had a lot of fun wearing out our shoes here in the classrooms and on the playgrounds.

MARY: And we've been growing and learning all the time.

MASTER COBBLER: Good for you and good for (*Name school*)! I think that calls for a song. (*Program closes with school song. If the Principal or Guest Speaker is scheduled for a talk to parents and friends, it is suggested that the talk be based on the idea of New Shoes for the New School the children will enter in the Fall.*)

THE END

Production Notes

The Curious Quest

Characters: 6 male; 3 female.
Playing Time: 20 minutes.
Costumes: Modern, everyday dress. Larry and Marie later appear in Uncle Sam and Miss Liberty costumes respectively.
Properties: Two crowns made of newspaper, newspaper scepter, blindfold, scripts, paper, pencil, pair of scales made out of two old pie pans and some chain or wire, books, small Bible, report card, car keys, sample ballot.
Setting: The Bentley living room. It is comfortably furnished with easy chairs and a couch. Two chairs stand together at center, representing thrones. There is a door at right and next to it is a large bookcase. There are some small tables, a few lamps and some straight chairs placed about the room. The properties which are to be used in the citizenship play are placed in their proper positions.
Lighting: No special effects.

The Bar-None Trading Post

Characters: 7 male; 6 female; male and female extras to be additional class members.
Playing Time: 25 minutes.
Costumes: Modern, everyday dress. The custodians of the trading post wear cowboy and cowgirl outfits.
Properties: Toys, comic books, games, puzzles, sign reading "Bar-None Trading Post," baseball glove, mouth organ, tool kit, decorated flatirons, picture, box containing sea shell collection, box containing butterfly collection, stamp album, five-dollar gold piece on chain, music box, alarm clock, pocket watch, Confederate Greenbacks, slip of paper, coin album.
Setting: The Bar-None Trading Post. The center of the stage is occupied by a long counter, well-stocked with items for trade. There are four stools or chairs behind the counter for the custodians. The rest of the stage is empty

but may be decorated by various signs inviting students to do their trading at the Bar-None Trading Post.
Lighting: No special effects.

THE PETRIFIED PRINCE

Characters: 6 male; 8 female.
Playing Time: 25 minutes.
Costumes: Leslie and Carter wear modern, everyday dress. Citizens of the Kingdom of Grammaria may be dressed as elaborately as desired. The King, the Prince and the Princess all wear royal garb. The officials are dressed in court costume with long flowing robes, etc. The girls of the Blue Pencil Brigade are dressed in blue. They carry large blue pencils and wear horn-rimmed spectacles.
Properties: Books, papers, typewriter, handkerchief, small desk bell, elaborate crown for King, summer-weight crown for King, book, piece of paper, six large blue pencils.
Setting: The main throne room of the court of the King of Grammaria. There is a throne upstage center on a raised platform. At left is a large cabinet, similar to a cedar wardrobe, the opening of which is concealed by a draw curtain. At right there is a large table, containing books, papers and typewriter. There is an entrance at right.
Lighting: No special effects.

A TRAVEL GAME

Characters: 15 male; 15 female; Chairman may be male or female.
Playing Time: 15 minutes.
Costumes: Modern, everyday dress for students. Father, Son, Farmer and Men wear blue jeans or overalls and shirts open at the neck. The five Women wear long skirts and peasant blouses. Donkey can wear gray sweater and trousers and should wear a donkey's head made out of a paper bag.
Properties: Model train; model airplanes; model sailing vessel; cardboard letters: R, D, Y, L, A, E, T, N, H, W; toy truck.
Setting: A classroom. There is a long table running the length of the stage with enough chairs around it to seat all children playing the game.
Lighting: No special effects.

THE POLKA DOT PUP

Characters: 10 male; 6 female; or there may be any number of pupils, both male and female, and the speaking parts may be redistributed among them.

Playing Time: 20 minutes.

Costumes: Everyday dress for Miss Doyle and the children. The Fire Chief and the Fire Driver wear dark blue uniforms.

Properties: Fire Prevention posters, chart, Fire Hazard Exhibit (including old electric light cord, glass jar, paper streamer, cardboard jack-o'-lantern, oily rag, candle, piece of curtain, cigarette, matches, newspaper clippings), ten lettered cards for the story of Prometheus, a real Dalmatian (or toy dog or an enclosed box to fake the scene with Polka.)

Setting: A classroom decorated with Fire Prevention exhibits and posters. There can be desks or chairs for Miss Doyle and the children.

Lighting: No special effects.

GIRLS IN BOOKS

Characters: 12 female; as many female extras as desired to be the Guest Panel.

Playing Time: 20 minutes.

Costumes: Modern everyday dress for everyone except the book characters, who are dressed as indicated in the text. For further suggestions about the costumes of book characters, consult illustrated editions of the books.

Properties: Pencils and paper for

Guest Panel; basket with rolls for Heidi; lock of hair for Jo March; books, lunch pails and slates for Becky and Amy.

Setting: A school stage. A semicircle of chairs for the Guest Panel is placed on one side of the stage. For the various scenes, the Stagehand brings in and then removes a chair, a sign "Jarley's Waxworks," and a bench.

Lighting: No special effects.

BOYS IN BOOKS

Characters: 15 male; male extras.

Playing Time: 20 minutes.

Costumes: The Chairman, the Student Reader, the Guest Panel, Mr. Williams and Sam wear modern everyday dress. Suggestions for the costumes of the other book characters are indicated in the text. Consult illustrated editions of the various books for further details on costumes.

Properties: Ball and chain for Convict; board, chalk, pin and needle for Tom and Huck; ladder and fishing rod for Tom Brown; small bundle of clothing tied on the end of a stick for Oliver Twist; pencils and pieces of paper for the Guest Panel (these should be distributed before the start of the program so that the Guests can note down the names of the various book characters as they identify them).

Setting: A school stage. Chairs for the Guest Panel are placed in a semicircle on one side of the stage. The other half of the stage should be cleared so that it can be used as the playing area.

Lighting: No special effects.

NOT FOR GIRLS

Characters: 4 male; 5 female.

Playing Time: 25 minutes.

Costumes: Modern, everyday dress. Larry and Mr. Finch are dressed up for their appearance on television. They wear suits and ties. Mr. Wizard wears a black gown and a tall, peaked hat. Both hat and gown are decorated with white plus, minus, multiplication, and equal signs. Annie wears a dark-colored dress and an apron. Mrs. Finch and the girls wear bright-colored dresses.

Properties: Tablecloth, breakfast dishes and silverware, newspaper, book, report card, score card, pencil, measuring cup, recipe book, construction paper. Needed for sound effects: door bell, telephone bell, alarm clock, cake timer, striking clock.

Setting: The Finch dining room. There is a table and four chairs at center. It is set for breakfast. There is a door at left leading to the front hall, and a door at right leading to kitchen. There are several windows upstage center and there is a low bookcase underneath them. A telephone is placed on a small table near door at left. Additional chairs, a buffet or china closet complete the furnishings of the room.

Lighting: No special effects

PILGRIM PARTING

Characters: 9 male; 5 female; male and female extras.

Playing Time: 20 minutes.

Costumes: All wear typical Pilgrim dress except Sailor Humphrey and Master Jones, who are dressed for sailing.

Properties: Small sea chest, two cloaks, covered basket, parcel, letter.

Setting: A beach. There may be some boxes and trunks to one side and perhaps some driftwood. Otherwise the stage is bare. If possible, there should be a backdrop representing the sea and sky.

Lighting: No special effects.

THE BREAD AND BUTTER SHOP

Characters: 12 male; 10 female.

Playing Time: 20 minutes.

Costumes: Modern everyday dress. Granny should wear a

gay apron; her hair is in a pony tail. Officer Durgin wears a policeman's uniform, and the Scouts wear Cub Scout uniforms.

Properties: Dough, bowls, bread pans, muffin pans, spoons, slip of paper, packages, doughnuts, pastry, bags, plate covered with napkin, recipe, book.

Setting: Granny Grayson's shop resembles a country kitchen with an old-fashioned stove upstage center. Down center is a work table. A counter at left holds several loaves of bread and the baked goods described in the script. A table with four chairs is at right. Down right is the door with a bell.

Lighting: No special effects.

Paul Revere Rides Again

Characters: 22 male; 9 female. (Since many members of the cast may play more than one part each, this play can be put on with a minimum cast of about 15.)

Playing Time: 20 minutes.

Costumes: Modern, everyday dress. Editor, Reporter and Copy Boy wear trousers and white shirts open at the throat. Radio announcer and Mr. Cabot wear business suits, as do TV announcer and Farmer Pyncheon. The TV Cameramen, mike operator and at-

tendant are dressed similarly to the newspaper men. Mail carrier wears a blue uniform and carries a leather mail bag. Telegraph boy wears Western Union uniform, if possible.

Properties: Book, three-cornered hat, sign saying "News Editor," two telephones, pencil, pad, typewriter, newspapers and newspaper bag for newsboy, microphone, bulletins, two cardboard TV cameras, boom microphone made from a tin can suspended on a pole, earphones, flip board containing appropriate signs (see script), wooden rifle, bag of mail for mailman, earphones and mouthpiece for telephone operator, hand microphone.

Setting: Scene 1: City Room of the Boston *Star.* The Editor's desk and chair are at right. There is a telephone on the desk. At left is a telephone booth. A folding screen could be used to divide the stage in half, so that it is clear to the audience the phone booth is not in the newspaper office. Scene 2: Studio at Radio Station WBTZ. A table and two chairs are the only necessary furnishings. There is a microphone on the table. Scene 3: A Boston TV Studio. There are a desk and two chairs at left. There is a flip board at right. Upstage center there are two cameras and a boom microphone.

Lighting: A light should go on in the phone booth when the Reporter is speaking to the Editor in Scene 1.

STAR CADETS

Characters: 11 male; 3 female; as many male and female extras as desired to be Stargazers.

Playing Time: 20 minutes.

Costumes: The overnight campers wear jeans and sweaters. The campers in the dream sequence wear space outfits. These may be as elaborate as desired. Chief Deega-Moris should look as weird and horrible as possible. A papier-mâché mask would add to his fantastic appearance. The Stargazers wear everyday clothes.

Properties: Three sleeping bags or cots, three pillows, comic books, flashlight, three space helmets, long silver spear, traffic whistle, large star map, small star maps, field glasses, camera, pointer.

Setting: An open field. A few cardboard trees and bushes will give the effect of being outdoors. The boys' sleeping bags are placed at extreme right. The dream sequence takes place at left.

Lighting: The stage is darkened and a spotlight is used during the dream sequence.

THE CASE OF THE BALKY BIKE

Characters: 10 male; 5 female.

Playing Time: 25 minutes.

Costumes: Modern, everyday dress. Officer Clark is in uniform and the Reporter and Photographer wear business suits.

Properties: A boy's bicycle, register, pencil, camera, paper bag containing pair of coon tails and fake TV aerial, notebook, tool kit, handle grips, reflecting tape.

Setting: Room in local police station. There is a platform upstage center on which is placed the Balky Bike. The platform is enclosed by a decorated rope railing. Above it there is a sign reading, "If You Can Ride It, You May Have It!" At left is a table or desk and a chair.

Lighting: No special effects.

RIGHT OF ADOPTION

Characters: 2 male; 10 female.

Playing Time: 20 minutes.

Costumes: Modern, everyday dress. Mr. Guthrie wears a business suit. Mrs. Hawkins and Lena are dressed in dark-colored uniforms and wear white aprons. The Tree

Troopers wear jeans and blouses.

Properties: Dust cloth, dust mop, piece of toast, notebooks, field glasses.

Setting: The Guthrie living room. The furnishings may be as elaborate as desired. A few chairs and a table are all that are necessary. There is a door at left and a telephone on a small table near door. Upstage center is a large window.

Lighting: No special effects.

IT's A PROBLEM

Characters: 7 male; 8 female.

Playing Time: 20 minutes.

Costumes: Everyday dress. Problem Pete may be dressed in dirty play clothes.

Properties: A list of health rules compiled by the class.

Setting: The Board of Experts sit at a large table. There are a small table and chair for the Problem Pupils. A microscope is on the large table.

Lighting: No special effects.

A FEBRUARY FAILURE

Characters: 1 male; 1 female; as many male and female members of the class as desired.

Playing Time: 15 minutes.

Costumes: Modern, everyday dress.

Properties: Paper, pencil, picture of Lincoln, package containing framed list of "Lincoln's Failures."

Setting: A classroom. There is a large desk for Teacher upstage center. There are additional chairs or desks for pupils. There is an entrance at left. The room is decorated with appropriate Lincoln display material.

Lighting: No special effects.

A LINCOLN MUSEUM

Characters: 4 male; 6 female; Curator and the ten Student Commentators may be male or female.

Playing Time: 20 minutes.

Costumes: Everyday dress.

Properties: Old-fashioned silk hat, piece of wood, Lincoln and Liberty banner, sheet music, large Bible, placard, flattened dime, theatre program, letter, empty picture frame.

Setting: A bare stage with a flag-draped table downstage center to receive the Lincoln exhibits.

Lighting: No special effects.

VISITOR TO MOUNT VERNON

Characters: 12 male; 7 female; or there can be any number of pupils, both male and female and the speaking parts may be redistributed among them.

Playing Time: 25 minutes.

Costumes: Everyday dress. The Teddy Bear wears a red coat, white shirt, blue pants and, if possible, a white vest. He wears a bear mask. The painter wears work clothes and the photographer a business suit. He has a press card in his hat band and carries a large camera.

Properties: Prologue, Epilogue and Scene 1: No special properties needed. Scene 2: Post cards, souvenir booklets, pennants, coats, lunch boxes, cameras, toy teddy bear painted red, white and blue.

Setting: Prologue and Epilogue take place in front of the curtain. Scene 1: A classroom. There can be desks or chairs arranged for the children and Miss Shelby. Scene 2: Bus Stop. This can be indicated on a bare stage by a typical bus stop sign.

Lighting: No special effects.

THE PATRIOTIC TEDDY BEAR AND THE UN

Characters: 7 male; 3 female.

Playing Time: 10 minutes.

Costumes: Everyday dress for the children. The toys wear appropriate costumes: uniforms for the Soldier and the Policeman, brightly colored suits for the Jack-in-the-Box and the Clown, a frilly dress for the French Doll. The

Teddy Bear should wear a red coat, blue pants and white gloves.

Properties: Book for Freddy.

Setting: A playroom. The only necessary furnishings are two chairs. Tables, lamps, shelves and wall decorations may be added.

Lighting: No special effects.

HELLO, MR. GROUNDHOG

Characters: 17 male; 13 female. The cast may be reduced in number by eliminating some of the Lodge members, or increased by adding others.

Playing Time: 25 minutes.

Costumes: The members of the Royal Order of Slumbering Groundhogs are dressed in long white gowns, wear high silk hats and carry lanterns. Scoutmaster wears uniform. Photographers wear modern, everyday dress and carry photographic equipment. The girls who are not masquerading as Lodge members wear jeans and sweaters or jackets.

Properties: Sign saying, "Groundhog Hole" on one side and "No Trespassing" on the other, set of weather flags (white flag, black triangle, white flag with black square in center, blue flag, red triangle, red square with black center), large covered box, membership cards.

Setting: The woods. There is a groundhog hole at left. This can be made of papier-mâché or cardboard. Cardboard trees and bushes or greens will give a woodsy effect. Large logs may be used as seats for members of the Lodge.
Lighting: No special effects.

SPEAKING OF SPEECH

Characters: 2 male; 3 female.
Playing Time: 10 minutes.
Costumes: Modern, everyday dress. Miss Keefer and Anne Evans wear smart-looking suits. Mr. Watkins and Tom Stevens wear business suits. Ella Mae Pearson is very gaudily dressed. She wears too much make-up and her fingernails are painted a bright red. She wears a hat with a very large brim, and has on high heels with thin ankle straps.
Properties: Typewriter, telephone, buzzer, intercom, book containing poetry selection, copy of typical news column.
Setting: Offices of Apex Broadcasting Company. The receptionist's office is at left and Mr. Watkin's office is at right. The two are separated by a folding screen. In each office there is a desk at left. In Miss Keefer's office there is a line of chairs upstage and a magazine rack close by. There is a chair placed close to Mr. Watkin's desk in which the interviewee sits.
Lighting: No special effects.

WHO'S WHO AT THE ZOO

Characters: 9 male; 9 female.
Playing Time: 15 minutes.
Costumes: Modern, everyday dress.
Properties: Cages with signs indicating the type of animal which each contains or slides of animals, watch.
Setting: The Zoo. There is a row of cages with signs indicating the animals which each contains. If play is staged in a classroom, the signs alone may be used to indicate the animals, or pictures of the animals may be drawn on the blackboard. Where a movie screen and a slide projector are part of the school equipment, slides or colored pictures of the individual animals may be thrown on the screen as they are discussed. Children may make these animal slides as part of their work on the unit.
Lighting: No special effects.

RAILROAD RHYMES AND RHYTHMS

Characters: 9 male; large number of male and female actors to take the parts of passengers.

Playing Time: 20 minutes.

Costumes: Railroad employees wear typical uniforms, or an approximation thereof. Passengers wear modern, everyday dress. Passengers wear hats and coats. They carry suitcases.

Properties: Railroad tickets; baggage check; dog; sound effect record of train approaching; two pocket watches; newspaper clipping; box for Vendor containing sandwiches, chocolate bars, milk; pillows for Porter.

Setting: Half of this play takes place on the apron of the stage which represents a railroad station. A small table at center representing a ticket window is the only furnishing necessary. The second half of the play takes place on a train. Chairs for passengers should be arranged in train fashion with an aisle down the middle. No other furnishings are necessary, though the train interior may be as elaborate as desired.

Lighting: No special effects.

THE STORY OF LIGHT

Characters: 2 male; 4 female; as many male and female as desired to be Choral Readers, Christmas Carolers, Hanukkah Pantomimists, Flashlight Drill Team, Children.

Playing Time: 15 minutes.

Costumes: Choral readers wear choir gowns. Boy and Girl Narrators wear everyday dress. Nan Kin, Tsi Ann, and Fairy wear Chinese costume. Christmas Carolers may wear outdoor clothes or modern everyday dress. Hanukkah Pantomimists wear modern, everyday dress. Child wears pajamas. Flashlight Drill Team wears dark clothing.

Properties: Bible with red bookmarks for each Choral Reader, paper fan, Chinese lantern, candle mold, small lighted Christmas tree, candles (battery lighted, if possible), the Menorah (seven-branched candlestick), Betty Lamp, kerosene lamp with chimney, painted china lamp, pillows, flashlights for Drill Team.

Setting: A bare stage. For the scene in China a bench should be placed on stage. For the Christmas scene, a small lighted Christmas tree should be placed on a table on stage. For the Hanukkah Pantomime, the Menorah should replace the Christmas tree. For the recitation of The Lamplighter, a large easy chair should be placed on stage. The stage should be

bare for the flashlight drill.
Lighting: No special effects.

New Shoes

Characters: 3 male; 2 female; 13 clerks and 13 customers, male and female; plus as many male and female extras as desired to be children, students, tap dancers, athletes, dancers, and choir members.

Playing Time: 25 minutes.

Costumes: Everyday dress. Master Cobbler wears a cobbler's apron. Manager and Clerks wear suits. Costumes for the tap dance and the waltz may be as elaborate as desired. Gym suits are worn for the sports drill and choir robes for the hymn singing.

Properties: Fourteen pairs of adult shoes conforming to the description given in the play, shoe boxes and papers, baby shoes, play shoes, gym shoes, Sunday shoes.

Setting: A bare stage across which are placed several benches.

Lighting: No special effects.